ELEMENTARY
NUCLEAR
THEORY

ELEMENTARY NUCLEAR THEORY

Second Edition

HANS A. BETHE

John Wendell Anderson Professor of Physics
Cornell University

and

PHILIP MORRISON

Professor of Physics and Nuclear Studies
Cornell University

NEW YORK · JOHN WILEY & SONS, INC.
LONDON · CHAPMAN & HALL, LIMITED

PREFACE TO THE SECOND EDITION

The purpose and emphasis of this book have not changed essentially in eight years. But knowledge of nuclei has grown greatly. The present edition has been revised and expanded throughout to take into account the many increases in our understanding both on the side of theory and on the side of experimental information, especially the extension of experiment to higher energies.

Although the problem of the nuclear forces is still the central theme, more space has been devoted to the structure and the reactions of heavier nuclei. This attention is again demanded by the elegance and successes of scattering theory and of the shell model.

Some space has been given to the great growth in experimental meson physics and meson field theory in the intervening time. The field theory is still no sure guide to correct results in nuclear physics.

A more complete textbook *has* been written, and for an advanced treatment of many topics the reader may consult the fine work *Theoretical Nuclear Physics*, Blatt and Weisskopf, John Wiley & Sons, New York 1952.

H. A. BETHE
P. MORRISON

April, 1956

v

PREFACE TO THE FIRST EDITION

This book is not meant to be a textbook of the theory of atomic nuclei. It is merely a selection of certain topics in the theory, and even these topics are treated in only an elementary way. Until a more complete textbook is written, the reader who wishes to obtain a thorough knowledge of nuclear theory will have to consult the original literature, or for certain topics the articles of the present author in *Reviews of Modern Physics* (Vol. 8, p. 83, 1936; Vol. 9, pp. 69 and 245, 1937).

The emphasis in this book is placed on the problem of *nuclear forces*. This problem is the central problem of nuclear physics. The problem is treated entirely from the empirical point of view, and I have made an effort to present the evidence available on nuclear forces from the behavior of the simplest nuclear systems. Purely theoretical considerations about nuclear forces, particularly the meson theory of these forces, are treated with the greatest brevity, because they are not yet in a form in which they would permit useful predictions.

As a second field of nuclear physics which is sufficiently well developed and fundamental, I have chosen the theory of beta disintegration.

The theory of the compound nucleus and its consequences for the prediction of the probabilities of nuclear reactions I have treated only very briefly. The reason for this was partly a matter of time: the lecture on which these chapters are based contained only twenty lectures, and it seemed more profitable to treat part of the theory thoroughly than to treat all of it superficially. Partly, however, the brevity of treatment of the more complicated nuclei was purposeful; in the last ten years the workers in this field have shown an inclination to devote a large proportion of their effort to the study of the complicated nuclei, and the danger exists that the right perspective may be forgotten.   The wartime research in the atomic energy project tended further to emphasize the usefulness of the predictions from the theory of the compound nucleus.   To correct this tendency, it seemed even more important to put special emphasis on the fundamental theory of nuclear forces and off the theory of the complicated nuclei.

The theory of the fission process has been left out entirely for the same reason: this process is, after all, only a very special phenomenon in nuclear physics.

The theory of alpha radioactivity could be left out with a good conscience because it is given in many elementary textbooks on wave mechanics.   With some regrets I also had to leave out the theory of nuclear systems containing from 3 to 60 nuclear particles, especially the successful calculations of binding energies on the basis of group theory by Wigner.

H. A. BETHE

CORNELL UNIVERSITY
July, 1947

CONTENTS

A.

DESCRIPTIVE THEORY
OF NUCLEI

I. BASIC FACTS ABOUT NUCLEI

Each atomic nucleus has a charge Ze, a mass M, and a mass number A. Ze is an integral multiple of the charge e of the proton. M is very close to an integral multiple of the proton mass. The integer A which gives the multiple closest to M is the mass number.

The nuclear charge Z determines all the chemical properties associated with an element. It has values from $Z = 0$ (neutron) to $Z = 101$ for observed nuclei. Some of these do not occur in nature: $Z = 0, 43, 61, 85, 87$ (87 occurs in very small abundance as a member of a branch of the radioactive family of Ac), 93 through 101.

The mass number A ranges from $A = 1$ (proton or neutron) to $A = 255$. Nearly every mass number in this range is found in nature. There are good reasons why the notable exceptions $A = 5$ and $A = 8$ are not stable long enough to be observed even in the laboratory. The mass numbers of form $4n + 1$ beyond 209 (Bi) are not found in nature, but many of them have been produced in the laboratory. These nuclei belong to a radioactive series which does not contain any long-lived members and, therefore, could not have survived on earth.

Isotopes. Nuclei of the same Z but different A are called isotopes. On the average there are about three stable isotopes for each Z. To distinguish isotopes A is usually written as a right superscript, and for convenience Z is sometimes written as a left superscript. To illustrate: Si^{28}, Si^{29}, and Si^{30} are the stable isotopes of Si. In addition to the stable isotopes, most elements also possess radioactive isotopes; e.g., Si has the known isotopes Si^{27} and Si^{31}. Of these, Si^{27} is β^{+}-radioactive (having too little mass for its charge) and decays with a half-life of 4 seconds to Al^{27} and a positron

$$Si^{27} = \beta^+ + Al^{27}$$

Si^{31} (having too little charge for its mass) decays with a half-life of 170 minutes to P^{31} and an electron

$$Si^{31} = \beta^- + P^{31}$$

Isobars. For a given A, there may well be several possible values of Z (isobars). There are many instances of stable isobaric pairs, e.g., $^{16}S^{36}$ and $^{18}A^{36}$, or $^{44}Ru^{104}$ and $^{46}Pd^{104}$, and some stable isobaric triples, e.g., $^{40}Zr^{96}$, $^{42}Mo^{96}$, and $^{44}Ru^{96}$, as well as numerous radio-active isobars.

Regularities. There are several striking regularities in a table of the stable nuclei. Nuclei of even Z are much more numerous than those of odd Z. Nuclei of even A are more numerous than those of odd A. Nearly all nuclei with even A have even Z; the exceptions are $^1H^2$, $^3Li^6$, $^5B^{10}$, and $^7N^{14}$. (There are also $^{19}K^{40}$ and $^{71}Lu^{176}$, but these are not properly stable, being β-radioactive with very long lifetimes.) The fact that nuclei with odd Z cannot have even A with the listed exceptions is what makes stable nuclei with even Z more numerous than those with odd Z, for a nucleus with even Z may

Table IA.   Sample of Isotope Statistics

Z	Number of Stable Isotopes	Number with Odd A	Number with Even A
48	8	2	6
49	2	2	0
50	10	3	7
51	2	2	0

have A either odd or even. Table IA illustrates all three rules. For odd A, there is apparently no preference between even Z and odd Z.

Energy. In considerations involving the energy of nuclei the mass M is important. According to Einstein's relation, the energy equivalent of a change in mass ΔM is

$$\Delta E = \Delta M c^2$$

Such changes in mass occur when protons and neutrons are changed from one configuration to another in which they are bound more or less strongly.

Modern mass spectrographic techniques permit the determination of M to better than 1 part in 10^6 which just makes possible the determination of the decrease in the atomic weight of a heavy atom due to the binding of the electrons in the field of the nucleus).   From such data the binding energies of nuclei can be calculated.   For example, from the atomic weight scale based on O^{16}

$$M(O^{16}) = 16.00000$$

nuclear reaction data give $M(^{1}H^{1}) = 1.008142$, $M(^{0}n^{1}) = 1.008982$. On the supposition that the O^{16} nucleus is made up of 8 protons and 8 neutrons, the binding energy is $8M(H^{1}) + 8M(n) - 16.00000 = 0.13699$ mass unit.   It is to be noted that the masses of the neutral atoms O^{16} and H^{1} are used here (and will be used throughout the book).   The justification for this is that the masses of 8 electrons of the O^{16} are canceled in the calculation by the masses of the 8 electrons of the hydrogen.   (The change in the mass of the 8 electrons, due to their stronger binding around the O^{16} nucleus, is beyond the experimental error in the mass determinations.)   Two quantities sometimes useful in describing the binding energy of nuclei are:

Mass defect $= \Delta = A - M(A)$; mass excess $= -\Delta$

Packing fraction $= f = -\Delta/A$

Consider now a nuclear reaction

$$^{3}Li^{7} + {}^{1}H^{1} \rightarrow {}^{2}He^{4} + {}^{2}He^{4}$$

Both the mass number and charge balance.   In addition, mass-energy conservation must hold.   The balance sheet is as follows:

Initial mass:
$$M(^{3}Li^{7}) \quad = 7 \text{ mass units} + 16.97 \text{ Mev}$$
$$M(^{1}H^{1}) \quad = \underline{1 \text{ mass unit} \; + \; \underline{7.58 \text{ Mev}}}$$
$$\text{Total} \quad = 8 \text{ mass units} + 24.55 \text{ Mev}$$

Final mass:
$$2M(^{2}He^{4}) = 8 \text{ mass units} + 2 \times 3.61 \text{ Mev}$$
Mass decrease $=$ energy release $= 17.33$ Mev

We have used the mass defect in energy units, from the Appendix. The relation $E = Mc^{2}$ gives the conversion factor from mass units to electron volts of energy

1 millimass unit $= 0.93114$ Mev

The mass decrease here is then 0.01862 mass units.   If the Li and H had little velocity, the α-particles would fly off in nearly opposite directions,   each   carrying   8.67-Mev   kinetic   energy.   Systematic observations of reactions such as this have verified the Einstein relation very accurately over a great range of nuclear phenomena and are one of the strongest bulwarks of the special theory of relativity. In all nuclear reactions involving heavy particles only, energy has been found to be strictly conserved.

Stability. For a nucleus to be stable it must have a mass which is less than the combined masses of any pair of nuclei made by subdividing it. For example, $^3\text{Li}^7$ is stable against the subdivision

$$^3\text{Li}^7 \rightarrow {}^2\text{He}^4 + {}^1\text{H}^3$$

because $M(^3\text{Li}^7) = 7.01822$ and $M(^2\text{He}^4) + M(^1\text{H}^3) = 4.00387 + 3.01700 = 7.02087$. $^2\text{He}^5$ is unstable because the decomposition

$$\text{He}^5 \rightarrow \text{He}^4 + n^0$$

is energetically possible. The mass of He^5 can be found by studying the reaction

$$\text{Li}^7 + \text{H}^2 \rightarrow \text{He}^4 + \text{He}^5$$

Knowing the masses $M(\text{Li}^7)$, $M(\text{H}^2)$, and $M(\text{He}^4)$, and measuring the kinetic energy and momentum of Li^7, H^2, and He^4, we can determine the mass of He^5. It is 5.0137 mass units. This is 0.9 millimass unit greater than $M(\text{He}^4) + M(n^0)$. (There is the possibility that the measured mass of He^5 might not be for the ground state, but in all known nuclear reactions involving heavy particles, whenever a reaction yields an excited state, it also yields the ground state. Since the experiment gives a unique mass, it is presumed to correspond to the ground state.) Li^5 is unstable to the decomposition $\text{Li}^5 \rightarrow {}^2\text{He}^4 + \text{H}^1$, and Be^8 to the decomposition $\text{Be}^8 \rightarrow \text{He}^4 + \text{He}^4$. This explains the absence of nuclei of mass numbers 5 and 8 which was mentioned above.

Fundamental particles in nuclei. The word *nucleon* is often used to refer to either a proton or a neutron. Present ideas are that a nucleus is composed of nucleons: Z protons and $A - Z$ neutrons. This replaces older conceptions of a nucleus made up of protons and electrons. Thus the binding energy of any nucleus will be

$$\text{B.E.} = (Z)M(^1\text{H}^1) + (A - Z)M(^0n^1) - M(A, Z)$$

Figure 1 is a graph of the binding energy per nucleon for the whole range of stable nuclei.

It is fairly certain now that the nucleons within nuclear matter are in a state made rather different from their free condition by the proximity of other nucleons. The exchange of transient mesons, for

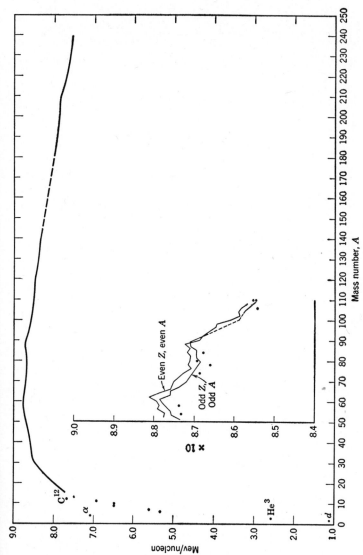

Fig. 1. Binding energy per nucleon as a function of mass number. The values for some of the lighter nuclei are entered as individual points; the solid curve represents average values for the several isobars for each of the larger values of A. The various humps and dips in this averaged curve are real (though the dotted section is interpolated). The inset shows the course of the experimental values, from A about 50 to A = 110, on a ten-times-magnified vertical scale. The curves connect two classes of nuclei as marked. The points in the inset mark values which lie off the course of the general curve, and also a few nuclei with other odd-even properties. Most of the structure even of the magnified curve is safely beyond experimental error.

example, is a typical picture of the mode of interaction of nearby nucleons.   Such processes cannot affect over-all energy relationships if initial and final states are precisely defined.   The binding energy is just the energy difference between the assembled nucleus and a collection of stationary, well-separated nucleons having Z protons and $A - Z$ neutrons.

II. THE SIZE OF NUCLEI

A. METHODS OF DETERMINING SIZE

The methods of determining the size of nuclei fall into two classes: those that indicate the presence of nuclear matter even if it is electrically neutral, and those that are purely electromagnetic and are influenced only by the electric charge distribution within the nucleus.

1. NUCLEAR METHODS

(a) *Cross section for fast neutrons.* The cross section presented by a nucleus to a fast neutron should, under certain conditions, approach the geometrical cross section of the nucleus. The first condition is that the neutron wavelength be small compared to the nuclear radius, $\lambda/2\pi = \lambda \ll R$, because only in this case is a geometrical point of view permissible. The second condition is that every neutron hitting the nucleus strongly interacts with it, and this condition is satisfied as long as the neutron energy is not too high, let us say below 50 Mev. An energy around 20 Mev is considered to satisfy both conditions best.

The geometrical cross section is πR^2, thus permitting a calculation of the nuclear radius from the observed cross sections for not too light nuclei and neutron energies in the 20-Mev region. ("Shadow scattering" at small angles must be excluded.) (See Chapter XX, Section A.)

Heavy elements Pb, U, etc., are found to have cross sections of about 3×10^{-24} cm^2 so that their radius is 10^{-12} cm. Middle elements such as Fe are found to have cross sections a little above 10^{-24} cm^2, corresponding to radii of about 6×10^{-13} cm.

At higher energies similar results are found after correction is made for the partial transparency of the nucleus to fast-enough nucleons.

(b) *Lifetimes for α radioactivity.* Nuclei with a mass number A greater than 208 are found to emit helium nuclei (α-particles) spontaneously according to the equation

$$Z^A \to (Z - 2)^{A-4} + {}^2\text{He}^4$$

The lifetimes of such radioactive nuclei are found to vary over a wide

7

range and to depend strongly on the amount of energy available for the reaction.   This is illustrated by the tabulation:

Element	Lifetime	Energy	Radius
Th^{232}	1.4×10^{10} years	4.05 Mev	8.6×10^{-13} cm
Po^{214}(RaC′)	1.6×10^{-4} second	7.83 Mev	8.1×10^{-13} cm

A factor of 2 in energy is thus seen to be equivalent to a factor of the order of 10^{20} in lifetime.   This strong energy dependence was explained by Gamow, and simultaneously by Gurney and Condon, to result from the necessity of the α-particle to penetrate a potential barrier before escaping.

At large distances, the potential is that due to Coulomb repulsion between a nucleus of charge $Z - 2$ and one of charge 2.   At some very short distance, attractive nuclear forces predominate.

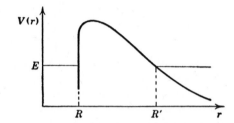

Fig. 2.   Nuclear potential barrier for α-particles.

The potential as a function of separation r between α-particle and residual nucleus is shown in Fig. 2.

The inner radius R at which nuclear forces come into play is defined as the nuclear radius.   The probability of an α-particle of energy E penetrating the barrier is given by the Wentzel-Brillouin-Kramers method to be proportional to

$$\exp\left[-\frac{2}{\hbar} \int_R^{R'} \sqrt{2M[V(r) - E]} \, dr \right] \qquad (2.1)$$

This is called the transmission coefficient of the barrier.

Comparison of this formula with experimental lifetimes shows that the enormous variation of lifetime with energy is indeed explained by the theory, with very nearly the same radius used for all radioactive nuclei.   Moreover, the formula permits a determination of nuclear radii.   With a few exceptions, all of these lie between 8.4 and 9.8 $\times 10^{-13}$ cm.   The wide success of this first application of quantum mechanics to nuclear phenomena gives us confidence in the general use of quantum mechanics for the description of the motion of heavy particles in nuclei.

The radius R given by equation 2.1 must be corrected for the radius of the α-particle before the radius of the isolated nucleus can be obtained. Since the nuclear matter is distorted at α-emission, it is not possible to define the nuclear radius with great accuracy by this method.

(c) *Cross sections for nuclear reactions involving charged particles.* These reactions also involve the penetration of a barrier. The cross sections, in comparison with neutron cross sections, give the transmission of the barrier. Nuclear radii can be computed from these transmissions, thus extending the "α-activity method" down to non-radioactive nuclei.

All these results depend on the distance over which nuclear forces, and not purely electromagnetic ones, can be felt. A satisfactory fit to these observed radii can be given by the empirical formula

$$R = 1.4 \times 10^{-13} A^{1/3} \text{ cm} \tag{2.2}$$

This is a very reasonable, if approximate, result. It implies that there is roughly a constant volume for each nuclear particle.

2. ELECTROMAGNETIC METHODS

(a) *Electrostatic interaction of protons in the nucleus.* If the binding energies of a pair of nuclei which differ only in the interchange of neutrons and protons are compared, a difference in binding energy which increases with the charge of the nuclei is found. Examples of such "mirror" nuclei are:

$$^1\text{H}^3 \ ^2\text{He}^3; \ ^3\text{Li}^7 \ ^4\text{Be}^7; \ ^5\text{B}^{11} \ ^6\text{C}^{11};$$
$$^6\text{C}^{13} \ ^7\text{N}^{13}; \ ^7\text{N}^{15} \ ^8\text{O}^{15};$$
$$^8\text{O}^{17} \ ^9\text{F}^{17}; \ ^{14}\text{Si}^{20} \ ^{15}\text{P}^{20}$$

If neutrons and protons are assumed to be the same as far as nuclear forces alone are concerned, this difference in binding energy is the result of the additional Coulomb repulsion of the extra proton in the field of the original Z protons. To calculate this, all protons are assumed to be uniformly distributed over a sphere of radius R. Then the extra Coulomb repulsion energy due to the replacement of a neutron by a proton is

$$C = \tfrac{6}{5} Z e^2 / R \tag{2.3}$$

Using this formula and the observed differences in binding energy to determine nuclear radii leads to the empirical formula

$$R = 1.5 \times 10^{-13} A^{\frac{1}{3}} \text{ cm} \qquad (2.4)$$

For many years this was taken to indicate good agreement with equation 2.2 above. It is now generally realized that especially for this method, which depends on the charge distribution of only one nucleon, the uniform sphere model is too rough. If a charge distribution wave function believed more appropriate for this outermost nucleon is used, and the effect of quantum-mechanical exchange integrals is included, the result tends to give a smaller value: $R = 1.3 \times 10^{-13} A^{\frac{1}{3}}$ cm.

(b) *Electron scattering.* The electron is known to interact very little with nuclear matter by specifically nuclear forces and to feel therefore only the electric charge distribution of the nucleus. Direct-scattering experiments with electrons can be interpreted to give the radius of the equivalent sphere of electric charge and indicate a value

$$R = 1.2 \pm 0.1 \times 10^{-13} A^{\frac{1}{3}} \text{ cm} \qquad (2.5)$$

At electron energies of over a hundred Mev, the electron wavelength is short enough so that some details of the charge distribution can be noticed, and the tentative conclusion is drawn that the nuclear charge density falls from some roughly uniform central value rather rapidly, but continuously, toward zero at the edge.

(c) *μ-Mesonic atomic x-ray energies.* Another particle known to have negligible specifically nuclear interaction is the μ-meson. Negative μ-mesons can be captured in orbits in the Coulomb field of nuclei, forming the so-called μ-mesonic atoms. Now the Bohr radius of the lowest (1s) orbit in a pure Coulomb field is given by the formula

$$r_B = 2.82 \times 10^{-13} (137)^2 m_e / mZ \text{ cm}$$

where m_e is the electron mass, and m is the mass of the particle moving in the orbit around the point charge Ze. The radius of the electron 1s orbit in Pb is then about one hundred times the radius of the Pb nucleus itself, so that the point-charge model for the atomic electron orbits is an excellent one. But the μ-meson is 210 times as heavy as the electron, and its 1s orbit radius lies well inside the lead nucleus. Evidently the nucleus will not appear as a point charge but as a volume distribution of charge whose shape and size will determine the actual energy levels of the μ-meson in the nuclear Coulomb field. The radiation emitted by such captured mesons has energies of a few Mev for heavy nuclei, compared to the tens of kev of the analogous ordinary x-ray transitions. The precise energies observed form a sensitive means of determining the nuclear charge distribution. The measurements so far conducted give only a single parameter of this distribution, the mean square radius of electric charge. When this is interpreted for a uniform distribution, the value becomes

$$R = 1.2 \times 10^{-13} A^{1/3} \text{ cm} \tag{2.6}$$

with a variation of only a few per cent over the range of Z from Al to Pb.

(d) *Electron energy levels.* Similar measurements have been made with ordinary electronic x-rays. Here the effect of the nuclear size is very much smaller, and corrections for small shifts and broadening of the x-ray levels which arise from the finite lifetimes of the levels are so important as to make the result uncertain. At face value it would give R 50 per cent larger than the other electromagnetic methods described.

The binding energy of any s electron is very slightly decreased from what it would be in a pure Coulomb field by the finite radius of the nuclear charge distribution. This is true not only in the x-ray lines arising from the innermost K electrons but even for the outer electrons giving spectral transitions in the visible. Here very high resolution must be used, and the magnetic hyperfine structure effects carefully separated from the charge volume effects. Slightly displaced lines from the several isotopes of a given element can often be seen. The observed shifts can be somewhat indirectly interpreted to yield an electromagnetic radius in rough agreement with the two more accurate methods.

(e) *General trend of nuclear Coulomb energies.* The general trend of nuclear masses can be fitted by a rather simple semi-empirical formula (see Chapter XVIII). Individual nuclei may occasionally fit poorly, but the over-all behavior is given fairly well over the whole range of A. In this formula, a term is introduced which represents the electrostatic energy of a uniformly charged sphere of charge Ze and radius R, just $\frac{3}{5} e^2 Z^2 / R$. From the best empirical fit, R can be evaluated as $1.23 \times 10^{-13} A^{1/3}$ cm.

It seems almost certain that the nuclear force radius is somewhat greater than the radius of the proton charge distribution in nuclei. This may in part be due to the range of nuclear forces, and in part to an actual fringe of neutrons on the nuclear surface, extending further than the protons do. A picture of the nucleus not as a uniform drop but rather like a uniform central core with a tapering outward extension (cf. Fig. 3) allows one to represent the data for all A to better than 10 per cent by the formula

$$R = (0.7 + A^{1/3})1.2 \times 10^{-13} \text{ cm} \qquad (2.7)$$

where the first term represents a low-density fringe roughly similar for every nucleus, and the second term a charged core of uniform density. Special nuclei may differ somewhat; and the correct radius for any calculation will plainly depend on how sensitive is the calculated process to the presence of the low-density nuclear fringe.

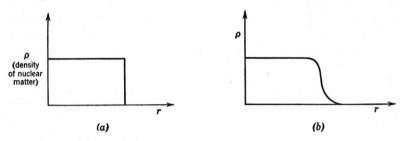

(a)   (b)

FIG. 3.   Nuclear density in two models: (a) for uniform sphere; (b) more realistic model with fringe of lower-density matter.

Formula 2.7 gives over-all radii for nuclear interaction; formula 2.6 gives radii of the electric charge only.

B. CONCLUSIONS REGARDING THE CONSTITUENTS OF NUCLEI

The size of nuclei is a strong argument for the presence of protons and neutrons in the nucleus rather than protons and electrons. The de Broglie wavelength of a neutron or a proton in the nucleus can be estimated to be

$$\lambda = \hbar/p = \hbar/\sqrt{2ME} \sim 1.5 \times 10^{-13} \text{ cm} \qquad (2.8)$$

if we use a kinetic energy E of 8 Mev, in other words of the same order of magnitude as the binding energy per nucleon.

On the other hand, for electrons at this relativistic energy, we would have

$$\lambda = \hbar/p \approx \hbar c/E \sim 2.5 \times 10^{-12} \text{ cm} \qquad (2.9)$$

Thus the neutron or proton wavelength is of the right order of magnitude for the space available in the nucleus, whereas the electron wavelength is much too large.

Another argument against the presence of electrons is the long lifetime found for β-emitting nuclei. The long lifetime is not explainable by a potential barrier, because the low electron mass would result in a high transmission coefficient in any barrier the width of which is reasonable considering the nuclear size. Moreover, no barrier at all should be expected for electrons, because they are attracted by the Coulomb field of the nucleus. Finally, great difficulties would be encountered in any relativistic theory of the electron if barriers of height greater than $2mc^2$ (m = electron mass) were assumed.

These objections to electrons do not apply to particles of mass a few tenths of the nucleon mass, like the observed π-mesons, though their status in the nucleus is not simple. The best current picture of nuclear matter is that of a collection of nucleons, continually emitting and reabsorbing π-mesons, which act to transfer charge, current, momentum, and angular momentum among the moving nucleons.

III. β-DISINTEGRATION

(DESCRIPTIVE)

Nuclei are found in nature (and more can be produced artificially) that emit electrons spontaneously according to the reaction scheme

$$Z^A \rightarrow (Z + 1)^A + \beta^-$$

The energy available for such a reaction is given by

$$E = M_n(Z^A) - M_n(Z + 1)^A - m(e)$$
$$= M_a(Z^A) - Zm(e) - M_a(Z + 1)^A + (Z + 1)m(e) - m(e)$$
$$= M_a(Z^A) - M_a(Z + 1)^A \tag{3.1}$$

where the subscript n denotes nuclear mass and the subscript a atomic mass.

Artificially radioactive substances are found which emit positrons:

$$Z^A \rightarrow (Z - 1)^A + \beta^+$$

Writing out the mass-energy equation as before, we now find that the energy available is

$$E = M_a(Z^A) - M_a(Z - 1)^A - 2m(e) \tag{3.2}$$

Whenever positron emission occurs, electron capture (usually from the K shell) can also occur, according to the scheme

$$Z^A + \beta_K^- \rightarrow (Z - 1)^A$$

leading to the same nucleus. Clearly, the energy available for electron capture is

$$E = M_a(Z^A) - M_a(Z - 1)^A \tag{3.3}$$

or greater than that available for positron emission by 2 electron masses.

Whenever energy is available for a disintegration process, i.e., $E > 0$, this process can be expected to occur—although in some cases the probability will be small, owing to nuclear selection rules.

It should be noted that the energies just computed neglect the binding energies of the electrons in the atom, since these are usually small compared with nuclear binding energies. This assumption, of course, is not completely valid for K-electron capture in the heavier elements but becomes increasingly valid for electrons from the outer shells of the atom.

A. STABILITY OF ISOBARS

The criteria for β-decay account for the rules for existence of isobars in nature: of two nuclei Z^A and $(Z-1)^A$, the one with greater atomic mass is unstable against β-decay to the other. This makes the existence in nature of isobars of neighboring Z unlikely. There are, however, many (about fifty) isobar pairs in nature of the type Z^A and $(Z-2)^A$, with both Z and A even. The intermediate nucleus, $(Z-1)^A$, of odd charge, decays to both its even-even neighbors; usually one of these decays dominates.

Table IIIA.   Properties of Some Neighboring "Stable" Isobars

Mass No.	Product (spin, parity)		Parent lifetime (spin, parity)		Product (spin, parity)
40			^{19}K		
	^{18}A		1.3×10^9 yr		^{20}Ca
	(2^+)	$(9\% \text{ EC})$	(4^-)	$(91\% \ \beta^-)$	(0^+)
50			^{23}V		
	^{22}Ti		Stable?		^{24}Cr
	(0^+)		(6)		(0^+)
87			^{37}Rb		
			6.2×10^{10} yr		^{38}Sr
			$(\tfrac{3}{2}^-)$	$(100\% \ \beta^-)$	$(\tfrac{9}{2}^+)$
115			^{49}In		
			6×10^{14} yr		^{50}Sn
			$(\tfrac{9}{2}^+)$	$(100\% \ \beta^-)$	$(\tfrac{1}{2}^+)$
138			^{57}La		
	^{56}Ba		7×10^{10} yr		^{58}Ce
	$(?)$	$(94\% \text{ EC})$	$(4^+ \text{ or } 5^{\pm})$	$(6\% \ \beta^-)$	(0^+)
176			^{71}Lu		
	^{70}Yb		2.2×10^{10} yr		^{72}Hf
	(0^+)	$(1\% \text{ EC})$	(≥ 9)	$(99\% \ \beta^-)$	(6^+)
187			^{75}Re		
			5×10^{10} yr		^{76}Os
			$(\tfrac{5}{2}^+)$	$(100\% \ \beta^-)$	$(1\tfrac{1}{2} \text{ or} 1\tfrac{3}{2}^+)$

The natural occurrence of the exceptional pairs Z^A and $(Z-1)^A$ is accounted for by a very long half-life of the unstable partner against

β^--decay, so long that not all the unstable species has had time to decay since the time when the nuclei were formed. These pairs (or triads) are described in Table IIIA. The first of these, with mass 40, is of considerable geophysical importance. The argon of the atmosphere owes its origin to the decay of K^{40} by K-electron capture, forming A^{40} in an excited state about 1.5 Mev above ground. The probability of K capture is about one-twentieth that of β^--decay to Ca^{40}, which has a partial lifetime about 1.4×10^9 years. The energy release from this naturally radioactive element in rock is still far from negligible compared to that from the heavy elements, and, because of its comparatively short lifetime and relatively high abundance, potassium must have contributed much heat in the early stages of the earth's history. No other radioactivity is presently giving appreciable energy on the earth, except those of Th and U. β-decay theory can account very well for the long half-life and the competition between K capture and electron decay. Even the high values of the spin are reasonable from the shell model of the nucleus (see Chapter XVIII).

B. APPLICATION TO NUCLEAR ABUNDANCE

In Chapter I it was stated that (1) with very few exceptions the stable nuclei with even A had even Z, and (2) the number of species with even A is larger than with odd A. These facts can now be interpreted. It need only be assumed that for even A the energy (atomic mass) is generally smaller for even Z than for odd Z, whereas for odd A there is no such alternation. Then, a nucleus with even A and odd Z will have an atomic mass greater than one or both of its neighbors and may decay to one or both by β-emission and K capture. This explains rule 1. Both neighbors of the above-mentioned nucleus, however, may be stable, giving the possibility of isobars differing by *two* units of nuclear charge: for even A there are therefore many pairs of isobars. For any given odd A, on the other hand, there is usually only *one* possible nucleus—either of even Z or of odd Z. This explains rule 2.

Moreover, for a given even Z, the isotopes with even A are more stable and therefore generally extend farther away from the mean value of the mass number. For instance, xenon has the stable isotopes

$A = 124$ 126   128   130   132   134   136

                                129   131

IV. FURTHER FACTS ON
NUCLEAR DISINTEGRATIONS

A. γ-RAYS

Nuclei emit not only particles (heavy particles and electrons) but also γ-radiation (light quanta). Such emission is possible only when a nucleus goes from an excited energy state to a lower energy state. The half-lives for dipole radiation (nuclear spin change $\Delta I = 0$, or ± 1) are generally of the order of 10^{-17} second to about 10^{-13} second. Quadrupole radiation ($\Delta I = \pm 2$) also often gives lifetimes of the order of 10^{-13} second, in contrast to the situation in atomic spectra where the lifetimes are much longer for quadrupole than for dipole radiation. However, for lower frequency ($h\nu \approx 20$ to 200 kev) the lifetime for quadrupole radiation is much longer (10^{-10} to 10^{-3} second). For octopole radiation ($\Delta I = \pm 3$) of similarly low energy the half-life may be from 10^{-5} second to several hours, and for $\Delta I = \pm 4$ from 1 second to many years.

When the lowest excited state of a nucleus has a sufficiently different spin from the ground state that the half-life is very long, the excited state is called metastable, or an *isomer* of the nucleus. The excited isomer is usually denoted by an asterisk; In* was the first observed.

B. SUMMARY OF DECAY PROCESSES

Consider a nucleus Z^A in some quantum state.

1. It may be unstable to the emission of heavy particles.

Neutrons. The lifetime will be 10^{-21} to 10^{-18} second, except if the energy available to the neutron is exceedingly small (a few electron volts), when it may be as long as 10^{-12} second. A lower limit can be calculated roughly by finding the time for a neutron of average velocity to travel the nuclear radius, i.e., 10^{-12} cm/(10^9 cm per second) $= 10^{-21}$ second; thus a nucleus unstable to neutron emission is scarcely observable.

Protons. If the protons have enough energy to go over the Coulomb barrier, the lifetimes are about equal to the lifetimes for neutrons. If the protons must penetrate the Coulomb barrier because their kinetic energies are low, then the Gamow penetration factor leads to much longer lifetimes.

α-Particles. In general, the same rule applies as for protons except that for a given energy longer half-lives are to be expected because of the larger mass and charge of the α-particle. In particular, to get observable half-lives (as short as 10^{14} years), the energy of the α-particle in the nucleus must be greater than 3.5 Mev for $Z = 92$, greater than 1 kev for $Z = 4$.

2. It may be unstable to the emission of light quanta. Half-lives are in general from 10^{-17} second to 10^{-10} second, but occasionally (in isomers, for instance) run from seconds to years.

3. Emission of β-rays or K-electron capture. Half-lives are 0.02 second to 10^{11} years, and more.

Thus the unstable nuclei can be put into three groups:

Group I. Lives unobservably short:

First, from 10^{-21} to 10^{-18} second: The very unstable nuclei He^5 and Li^5 in their ground states, or any nucleus in an excited state of high-enough energy so that a fast neutron, fast proton, or α-particle can be emitted.

Second, from 10^{-17} to about 10^{-8} second: Nearly all excited states of nuclei not contained in the group just described. These nuclei will in general lose their energy by γ-emission, or sometimes by emission of slow neutrons, protons, etc. By the use of special techniques, not applicable in all cases, lifetimes in the range from about 10^{-14} to 10^{-8} second can occasionally be directly observed.

Group II. Lives observable (10^{-8} second to 10^{12} years): Nearly all β-radioactive nuclei, many α-radioactive ones, and many "nuclear isomers" emitting γ-rays.

Group III. Lives unobservably long: If a radioactive nucleus has a half-life greater than about 10^{14} years, its activity will generally be unobservable. For α-radioactivity, this sets a lower limit on the energy of the α-particles which will make the activity observable for a given nuclear charge Z as follows:

$$Z \quad = \quad 10 \quad\quad 30 \quad\quad 50 \quad\quad 70 \quad\quad 90$$

$$E_{min.} \, (\alpha) = 0.13 \quad\quad 0.8 \quad\quad 1.7 \quad\quad 2.7 \quad\quad 3.7 \quad \text{Mev}$$

In general all the known "stable" nuclei with mass numbers above about 60 are members of group III; they are actually α-radioactive but with lifetimes unobservably long, and of course so much longer than geologic time that their activity has no influence on their abundance. Here, too, special techniques sometimes permit observation of decay with lifetimes as great as 10^{18} years.

V. SPIN AND STATISTICS

A. SPIN AND ITS MEASUREMENT

Each nucleus has an intrinsic angular momentum which interacts with angular momenta of electrons or other nuclei. It is measured in units of $\hbar$ and, according to quantum mechanics, can take on only integral or half-integral values. Three methods of determining nuclear spin are:

1. *Hyperfine structure of spectra.* The interaction of the magnetic moments of the electrons and the nucleus may separate in energy the states of the atom corresponding to various relative orientations of these two magnetic moments. Such energy differences can be observed in optical spectra as the splitting (hyperfine structure) of single atomic transitions into components of very slightly different frequency, or even more accurately in the microwave region by the direct absorption of quanta corresponding to the actual energy separation of the hyperfine levels. (In some microwave spectra molecular transitions occur simultaneously with hyperfine transitions.)

2. *Zeeman spectra.* The magnetic moment associated with nuclear spin can interact with an external magnetic field. This is an exact analog of the Zeeman splitting of the energies of atomic electrons in a magnetic field. If the electrons of a particular atom or molecule have no net magnetic moment (singlet state), then the interaction energy is proportional to the nuclear magnetic moment. The frequency associated with radiative transitions between levels corresponding to different spatial orientation of the magnetic moment gives the nuclear magnetic moment if the magnetic field is known; the number of levels fixes the spin. The first measurements of this sort (Stern, Rabi, and co-workers) depended on a Stern-Gerlach experiment, in which the atoms in an atomic beam were deflected in different directions by an inhomogeneous magnetic field, according to the value of the component of the nuclear magnetic moment in the direction of the field. An external radio-frequency field can induce radiative transitions between states of different orientation and therefore modify the beam intensity for various states. A measurement of frequency, possible with extremely high precision, and of

19

magnetic field, then fixes the nuclear moment. Such measurements are among the most accurate of results in physics; the limitation in precision is set by the definition of magnetic field strength.

Related methods for observing the Zeeman resonance frequencies are: (*a*) direct observation of the absorption of energy from consequent loading of the external oscillator (Purcell); (*b*) detection in an external circuit of a radio-frequency signal induced by the precession of the nuclear moment during transition between states (Bloch, Hansen). All measured nuclear spins are listed in the Appendix; magnetic moment values are compiled, for example, by Klinkenberg in *Revs. Mod. Phys.* **23**, 63 (1952).

3. *Band spectra.* Intensity variations of alternate lines in the band spectra of diatomic molecules with identical nuclei yield nuclear spins. The rotational degeneracy of the nuclear spin vector, in the absence of any external field, determines the statistical weight of the molecular state. (See Section C of this chapter, Nuclei of Nonzero Spin.)

Nuclear constituents. These observed spin values are another reason for rejecting a nuclear model composed of electrons and protons. Such a model for the nucleus Z^A has A protons and $A - Z$ electrons or $2A - Z$ particles. On this basis, nuclei with odd Z (and therefore an odd total number of particles) should have half-integer spin; and nuclei with even Z, integer or zero spin. $^7N^{14}$ with spin 1 was the first contradiction found, but there are many more, e.g.,

$$\bullet \quad {}^1H^2, \, {}^3Li^6 \qquad \text{have spin 1}$$

$$^{48}Cd^{111}, \, {}^{48}Cd^{113} \text{ have spin } \tfrac{1}{2}$$

On the other hand, the model $Z^A = (A - Z)$ neutrons $+ Z$ protons gives A particles in all, and with half-integer spin assumed for the neutron, the rule becomes: even A, integer or zero spin; odd A, half-integer spin. This agrees with all measured spins.

B. STATISTICS

Identical particles obey either Fermi statistics or Bose statistics; that is, a wave function $\psi(P_1, P_2)$, depending on the space and spin coordinates P_1 and P_2 of particles 1 and 2, will be either symmetrical or antisymmetrical under exchange of P_1 and P_2:

$$\psi(P_2, P_1) = \begin{cases} +\psi(P_1 P_2) & \text{Bose} \\ -\psi(P_1 P_2) & \text{Fermi} \end{cases} \qquad (5.1)$$

Electrons obey Fermi statistics. To determine the statistics of nuclei, we shall investigate how an exchange of identical nuclei will affect the sign of the wave function for a molecule.

Consider a diatomic molecule with identical nuclei. Its wave function may be written

$$\psi = \psi_{\text{elec.}} \varphi_{\text{vibration}} \rho_{\text{rotation}} \sigma_{\text{nucl. spin}} \qquad (5.2)$$

Let the operation of exchanging nuclear coordinates and spins be denoted by P. Then

$$P\psi_{\text{elec.}} = \pm\psi_{\text{elec.}}$$

The sign may be plus or minus; it is known from molecular spectroscopy and is usually plus for the ground state. Further,

$$P\varphi_{\text{vibration}} = +\varphi_{\text{vibration}}$$

because φ depends on R (the distance of the nuclei) alone, and $PR = R$.

Now

$$\rho = P_l{}^m(\cos \theta)e^{im\phi}$$

$P_l{}^m(x)$ is an associated Legendre polynomial, and θ and ϕ are the polar coordinates of the two nuclei. P means replacing the direction θ, ϕ by the opposite direction, i.e.,

$$\theta \to \pi - \theta$$

$$\phi \to \pi + \phi$$

Now

$$P_l{}^m(\pi - \theta) = (-1)^{l+m}P_l{}^m(\theta)$$

Further,

$$e^{im(\phi+\pi)} = (-1)^m e^{im\phi}$$

so that

$$P\rho = (-1)^{l+m}P_l{}^m(\cos \theta)(-1)^m e^{im\phi} = (-1)^l \rho \qquad (5.3)$$

Thus ρ is symmetrical for even l and antisymmetrical for odd l.

The analysis of $P\sigma_{\text{nucl. spin}}$ can be carried out for arbitrary spin but is particularly simple for spin zero, in which case $P\sigma_{\text{nucl. spin}} = +\sigma_{\text{nucl. spin}}$. Thus for spin zero (and symmetrical $\psi_{\text{elec.}}$) the total wave function ψ is antisymmetrical for odd l and symmetrical for even l. Now the nuclei must certainly obey either Bose or Fermi statistics. Therefore, either only the states with even l or only those with odd l can exist. Evidence for this conclusion is obtained from the band spectra. These show that if the nuclei have spin zero, every second rotational state of the molecule is absent. Indeed, it is found in every instance that only the *even* rotational states exist, indicating that all the nuclei of zero spin (which have been found previously to have even A) obey Bose statistics. Similarly, it has been found that *all* nuclei of even A (including those with a spin that is not zero) obey Bose statistics, and all those of odd A obey Fermi statistics.

This result throws light on the nature and *statistics of the elementary particles* in the nucleus. Suppose that each elementary particle obeys Fermi statistics; then ψ must be antisymmetrical to interchange of a pair of elementary particles. Therefore, if each of the two identical nuclei contains an even number of particles, the exchange of the nuclei is equivalent to an even number of changes of sign, and ψ must be symmetrical to an interchange of nuclei (Bose statistics); if each nucleus contains an odd number of particles, then exchange of the nuclei is equivalent to an odd number of changes of sign—i.e., ψ is antisymmetrical to nuclear interchange (Fermi statistics).

Now it was found experimentally that nuclei with even A obey Bose statistics, those with odd A Fermi statistics. This can be explained if the total number of elementary particles in a nucleus is A—as is the case if neutrons and protons are considered the fundamental particles—and if, further, each of the elementary particles obeys Fermi statistics. This proves that the neutron must obey Fermi statistics, just as the proton for which this fact is known experimentally. The electron-proton hypothesis fails again because, in this case, the number of elementary particles is $2A - Z$, so that nuclei with even/odd Z would have to obey Bose/Fermi statistics, whereas A rather than Z was found to be the actual criterion. Additional Bose particles, or even pairs of Fermi particles, cannot be excluded on these grounds.

C. NUCLEI OF NON-ZERO SPIN

A nucleus of total angular momentum I can have a component M in any prescribed direction, taking any of the values $I, I - 1,$ $\cdots , -I$ a total of $2I + 1$ states. For two identical nuclei $(2I + 1)^2$ wave functions of the form $\psi_{M_1}(A)\psi_{M_2}(B)$ can be constructed. If the two nuclei are identical, these simple products must be replaced by linear combinations of these products which are symmetric or antisymmetric for interchange of the nuclei.

If $M_1 = M_2$, the products themselves are $(2I + 1)$ symmetric wave functions. The remaining $(2I + 1)(2I)$ functions where M_1 and M_2 are unequal have the form $\psi_{M_1}(A)\psi_{M_2}(B)$ and $\psi_{M_2}(A)$ $\psi_{M_1}(B)$. Each such pair is to be replaced by one symmetric and one antisymmetric wave function of the form

$$\psi_{M_1}(A)\psi_{M_2}(B) \pm \psi_{M_2}(A)\psi_{M_1}(B) \qquad (5.4)$$

Thus half of the $2I(2I + 1)$ functions are antisymmetric, giving $I(2I + 1)$ antisymmetric functions. A similar number of symmetric functions exist, to which the $(2I + 1)$ symmetric functions with $M_1 = M_2$ must be added. Thus the ratio of the number of symmetric to antisymmetric functions is

$$\frac{(I + 1)(2I + 1)}{I(2I + 1)} = \frac{I + 1}{I} \qquad (5.5)$$

If the electronic wave function for the molecule is symmetric, it was shown (equation 5.3) that interchange of nuclei produces a factor $(-1)^l$ in the total molecular wave function, where l is the rotational quantum number. Thus, if the nuclei obey Bose statistics,

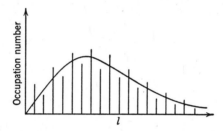

Fig. 4.   Intensity alternation in band spectra.

symmetric nuclear spin functions must be combined with even l rotational states, and antisymmetric spins with odd l. Because of the statistical weights attached to the spin states, the intensity of even rotational lines will be $(I + 1)/I$ as great as that of neighboring odd rotational lines.

For Fermi statistics of the nuclei, the spin and the rotational states combine in a manner opposite to that previously stated, and the *odd* rotational lines are more intense in the ratio $(I + 1)/I$.

Thus, by determining which lines are more intense, even or odd, the nuclear statistics is determined, and by measuring the ratio of intensities of adjacent lines the nuclear spin is obtained.

The reason why adjacent lines must be compared is that the rotational lines vary in intensity with l (neglecting nuclear spin), according to the occupation numbers of the rotational states; in other words, according to a Boltzmann distribution

$$(2l + 1) \exp [-E(l)/(kT)] \qquad (5.6)$$

where $E(l) = Bl(l + 1)$, and B is a constant (about 0.01 ev in H_2).

This Boltzmann distribution provides a smooth intensity variation about which the even and the odd states alternate in intensity (Fig. 4).

The experimental results of band spectra measurements, as already pointed out, are that nuclei of even A obey Bose statistics and nuclei of odd A obey Fermi statistics. Experimental determinations of nuclear spin are tabulated in the Appendix. One empirical rule from these data is that, with no known exceptions, all nuclei of even Z and even A have total nuclear spin zero.

VI. β-DISINTEGRATION

AND THE NEUTRINO

Negative β-disintegration consists in the conversion of a neutron into a proton and an electron. Since all three particles are assumed to have spin $\frac{1}{2}$ and Fermi statistics, this reaction will not conserve spin and statistics unless it is assumed that an additional particle of spin $\frac{1}{2}$ and Fermi statistics is emitted. To conserve charge this particle must be neutral. It is also clear that its mass must be small, and it is therefore called the *neutrino* (Italian for "the small neutral one").

A. DISTRIBUTION OF ELECTRON ENERGIES

The emitted β-particles are found to have a continuous distribution of energies, up to a certain maximum E_0, rather than a single

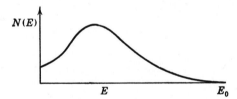

FIG. 5.   Energy distribution in β-spectrum.

energy (Fig. 5). The neutrino is therefore also needed to conserve energy; it is assumed to take the remaining energy, $E_0 - E$, where E is the electron energy. This hypothesis is strongly supported by the fact that the maximum electron energy is found within experimental error to be equal to the energy available for the reaction, as determined from mass data. This shows also that the neutrino mass must be assumed negligible.

Experimental data directly supporting this assertion may be found, for instance, in the β-disintegration of H^3 into He^3 with the low and well-measured maximum electron kinetic energy of only 18.5 ± 0.5 kev.

Careful measurements have been made of the threshold energy of the reaction $H^3(p, n)He^3$. [See, e.g., Taschek et al., *Phys. Rev.* 76, 325 (1949).] The incident proton energy for threshold was measured and corrected to center-of-mass coordinates by the factor $\frac{3}{4}$. The mass-energy equation becomes

$$763.7 \pm 1 \text{ kev} + H^3 + H^1 = He^3 + n$$

or

$$He^3 - H^3 = 763.7 - (n - H^1) \text{ kev} = -19.3 \pm 1.3 \text{ kev} \quad \text{(measured)}$$

where the neutron-proton mass difference is obtained from other reactions not involving neutrinos and from mass-spectrographic data and is 783 ± 1.5 kev.

The energy available for β-emission is just the mass difference $H^3 - He^3$, so that

$$E_{\text{available}} = +19.3 \pm 1.3 \text{ kev}$$

This checks with the observed maximum electron energy, and the energy balance proves directly that the neutrino mass must be less than 1 or 2 kev, a range fixed by the uncertainties of measurement. By use of the formalism of β-decay theory and the observed shape of the H^3 β-spectrum, an even closer limit on the neutrino mass can be obtained; viz., it is certainly less than $\frac{1}{2}$ kev.

B. EXPERIMENTAL EVIDENCE FOR THE NEUTRINO

The only process which a free neutrino can be expected to cause *with certainty* is the inverse β-process which is fundamentally (letting ν indicate the neutrino) of the form

$$n + \nu \rightarrow H^1 + \beta^-$$

Actually, to observe this process, it is necessary, of course, to use neutrons bound in some nucleus, for instance:

$$Li^7 + \nu \rightarrow Be^7 + \beta^-$$

This process can occur only if the incident neutrinos have sufficient energy to supply the mass difference between Be^7 and Li^7.

In any case the cross section for such a reaction would be extremely small; its order of magnitude is given by the cross section for striking the nucleus (about 10^{-24} cm^2) and the probability of β-decay within a nucleus (about 10^{-20}), so that the cross section would be of the order of 10^{-44} cm^2, implying a mean free path in solid matter about one hundred light years long. Yet it seems probable that the inverse β-process has been observed.   The reaction used is the positron ejection,

$$\nu + {}_1H^1 \rightarrow \beta^+ + {}_0n^1 \tag{6.1}$$

which requires a neutrino energy of at least 1.80 Mev.   The experimenters [Cowan and Reines, *Phys. Rev.* **92**, 830 (1953)] employ a counting volume of some 10 cubic feet, filled with a scintillating liquid.   Ninety photomultipliers can receive light quanta from every part of this large volume.   They look for pairs of pulses separated in time by some hundred microseconds.   The reaction (6.1) gives rise to such pulse coincidence, for the emitted positron (and its annihilation γ-rays) gives a first ionization pulse within 10^{-9} second after the event, and the delayed pulse arises much later from the γ-ray emitted on capture of the neutron after it has been slowed down to thermal energies.   The liquid, already rich in hydrogen, is usually loaded with a capturing element like Cd to make the second pulse more sure.   For neutrino source they depended on the β-disintegrations occurring within a large chain reactor in operation.   Heavily shielding the detector, they reduced the background for such specific pulses so far that they were able to report an effect probably significant statistically.   Improved counters should make the result unambiguous in the near future.

Recoil.   An easier way of learning something about the neutrino is to obtain further evidence as to how it participates in β-emission. For example, the neutrino energy can be determined in two ways: first, by measuring the electron energy and subtracting it from the total energy available, and second, by measuring the electron and nuclear *momentum* and using conservation of momentum to obtain the neutrino momentum and energy:

$$E(\nu) = E \text{ (available)} - E(e)$$

$$-p(\nu) = p \text{ (nucleus)} + p(e) \tag{6.2}$$

$$E(\nu) = cp(\nu)$$

where c is the velocity of light (and of the neutrino).

This method, unfortunately, requires measurement of both the nuclear recoil energy and its direction with respect to the electron momentum.   Both of these are very difficult measurements to make because of the small recoil energy.

A more satisfactory method has been employed [J. Allen, *Phys. Rev.* **86**, 446 (1952)], in which the recoil nucleus from K-electron capture is observed.   Use of a very light nucleus would be advantageous, because the recoil energy is greater for a given neutrino energy. But the recoil has only some electron volts of energy in any case, and it is very important to avoid all surface forces and chemical binding effects. A noble-gas atom is thus chosen for the experiment. Its energy was measured by a direct measurement of its time of flight across a known path in vacuum. The reaction employed was

$$A^{37} + \beta_K{}^- \to Cl^{37} + \nu \qquad (6.3)$$

Since the K electron has negligible momentum, the momentum of the recoil nucleus will be equal to that of the neutrino. Further, the emitted neutrinos are monochromatic, having an energy equal to the difference in mass available. The recoil energy can thus be easily computed (p = neutrino momentum):

$$E \text{ (recoil)} = \frac{p^2}{2M} = \frac{[E(\nu)/c]^2}{2M}$$

The measured recoil energies had an isolated peak around 9.7 ev. The observation of such recoils does not "prove" the actual emission of a neutrino, but it adds the very encouraging information that the momentum which disappears in the process is that associated with a single relativistic particle moving in a definite direction with the neutrino energy.

Further evidence for the existence of the neutrino comes from the detailed theory of β-disintegration described in Chapter XVI.

VII. π-MESONS AND OTHERS

The emission, absorption, and scattering by nuclei of other nuclei, of protons, neutrons, electrons, and γ-rays (photons), are of course phenomena of long standing. The simplest of the nuclei, the particles neutron and proton, are regarded as the building blocks for all the more complex systems. The photons are created in the act of transition between states of the nuclear system and are not thought of as independently present constituents. It is clear that the fundamental particles are not wholly independent; the neutron is observed to change spontaneously into a proton, an electron, and a neutrino. This process is so rare that we can often ignore it. Neutron decay takes on the average some thousand seconds for a free neutron, whereas within a nucleus the characteristic time between nucleon-nucleon collisions is only 10^{-21} second. For a satisfactory picture it is often enough to think of the nucleus as a grouping of protons and neutrons in interaction, with the appearance or disappearance of photons, and even more infrequently of electrons and neutrinos, as events marking transitions between stationary states of the system of nucleons.

But since 1947 it has been known that there is another class of particles, called π-mesons, which are capable of strong interaction with nucleons and nuclei. They can be emitted, absorbed, scattered. When free, they have an independent existence, long compared to the nuclear collision time, and their intrinsic properties are open to measurement. Their role as transient constituents of nuclei has been theoretically indicated for a long time; it is still by no means clear. In Chapter XVII we shall sketch the theories which connect these particles to the nuclear forces and the properties of the nucleons themselves. For the present, we shall describe them as independent particles, which may appear in nuclear reactions when adequate energy is available. Three varieties of π-meson are known, classified by their electric charge as positive, negative, and neutral. Some measured properties follow.

A. CHARGED π-MESONS

Charge: $+e$, $-e$ (both easily observable in cloud chambers and in photographic emulsion).

Mass: π^+: 273.4 $\pm$ 0.2.

π^-: 272.5 $\pm$ 0.3 electron masses, or 139.5 $\pm$ 0.1 Mev. The difference in mass between π^+ and π^- is probably not significant.

Decay: $\pi^{\pm} \rightarrow \begin{cases} \mu^{\pm} + \text{neutrino} & 100\%. \\ \beta^{\pm} + \text{neutrino} \leq \frac{1}{2} \times 10^{-4}. \end{cases}$

The mean lifetime for this decay is equal for π^+ and π^- to within the experimental uncertainty ($\sim 10\%$); the best measured value is

$$\tau(\pi^+) = 2.55 \pm 0.1 \times 10^{-8} \text{ seconds}$$

Spin: Zero. This is definitely known from cross-section measurements and the use of detailed balancing to fix the statistical weight of free meson states (see Chapter IX). Measurements are on π^+ only; it can be shown that π^+ and π^- must have spins differing by zero or an integer. Since they have otherwise very similar properties, we assume that π^+ and π^- have identical spin.

Intrinsic parity: Odd. This quantum-mechanical property, which determines the course of certain reactions involving emission or absorption of mesons, is known. See Chapter IX for an account of its meaning.

B. NEUTRAL π-MESONS

Charge: Zero.

Mass: 263.7 $\pm$ 0.5 electron masses, or 135.0 $\pm$ 0.3 Mev.

Decay: $\pi^0 \rightarrow \begin{cases} 2\gamma \sim 99\%. \\ \gamma + \beta^+ + \beta^- \sim 0.8 \pm 0.2\%. \quad \text{The decay into two} \\ \beta^+ + \beta^-?. \end{cases}$

γ's has been observed by direct coincidence methods. The lifetime is about $10^{-14.5}$ second.

Spin: The decay into two γ's proves that the spin is integer rather than half-integer, and also that it cannot be 1. This makes 0 the most likely value; the agreement with the known value for π^+ is very satisfactory.

Intrinsic parity: Odd, like π^+.

C. μ-MESONS

We have already used the symbol $\mu^{\pm}$ to indicate a decay product of the $\pi^{\pm}$-meson decay. This particle is called a μ-meson and was the first-known particle of mass intermediate between electron and nucleon. It is most familiar in its role as the main ionizing constituent of cosmic rays at sea level, and it is practically the only remaining cosmic ray particle at any depth more than a few meters underground.

Charge: $+e$, $-e$.

Mass: 207 ± 0.4 electron masses, or 105.8 ± 0.2 Mev.

Decay: $\mu^{\pm} \rightarrow \beta^{\pm} + 2$ neutrinos. The mean lifetime is accurately known for μ^+ only; $\tau(\mu^+) = 2.22 \pm 0.02 \times 10^{-6}$ seconds. It is very likely that both types decay at the same rate.

Spin: Half-integer certainly, and very probably $\frac{1}{2}$.

The characteristic property of μ-mesons is their very weak interaction with nuclei. In consequence their range-energy relationship is determined by ionization almost entirely, and very-high-energy μ-mesons will penetrate literally kilometers of solid rock. The π-mesons, on the contrary, interact strongly with nuclei and in consequence have a mean free path in matter determined by approximately the geometrical cross section of the nuclei, which appear more or less opaque to the π-mesons. Their penetration is then limited to some meters of solid matter at any energy; sometimes spontaneous decay ends the flight.

D. OTHER MESONS

Other mesons have been discovered, or at least indicated, almost in dozens. They may or may not play an important role in the unraveling of the nature of the nuclear forces. The π-mesons seem certainly connected with nuclear forces in an intimate way; we shall not discuss any others in the course of this book. The other mesons belong still to the field of high-energy physics.

One class of these new particles, called hyperons, is intimately related to the nucleons. They are heavier in mass than the nucleons, and include nucleons among their decay products, either in primary or later steps of decay. Thus the general rule which says that nucleons can neither be created nor destroyed must be amended to include hyperons in the conserved class of nucleon-like particles. Moreover, a number of unusual and highly unstable nuclei have been observed, chiefly in photographic emulsions, which can be interpreted as ordinary nuclei; for one or more of whose nucleons, however, a hyperon has been substituted. Such "hyper-fragments," as they are called, appear to bind the hyperons with forces similar to, but not precisely like, the nuclear forces themselves.

The total annihilation of nucleons (protons) has been recently observed. This can occur when an "anti-proton" ($Z = -1$,

$A = +1$) meets a proton ($Z = +1, A = +1$). "Anti-neutrons" (particles with $Z = 0, A = +1$, but capable of combining with and annihilating an ordinary neutron, of the same Z and A) presumably also exist, but have not yet been observed. The total annihilation of electrons by combination with positrons to emit two light quanta has long been known. The nucleon analogue differs only in that π-mesons are more likely products than are photons. Processes which change the number of nucleons and hyperons thus can occur, but only with a simultaneous and balancing change in the number of "anti-particles." The general conservation law of nucleon number can be kept intact by counting anti-particles with negative sign.

The word *neutrino* has been used to represent any assumed product of decay which has half-integer spin, no charge, and negligible mass. Whether these particles are all identical with the neutrino of β-decay is so far conjecture.

B.

QUANTITATIVE THEORY
OF NUCLEAR FORCES

VIII. PHYSICAL PROPERTIES
OF PROTON, NEUTRON, AND DEUTERON

The theory of nuclei is to be contrasted with the theory of atoms. In the latter, the principal force between the constituent particles, electrons and nuclei, was known when the theory got under way, and the problem was to find the proper mechanics to describe the motion of those particles under the given force; quantum mechanics is the answer to this problem.   In nuclei, there are good reasons to believe that quantum mechanics is correct (the success of the Gamow theory of α-particle decay is one example), but the forces are unknown.

In investigating these forces, the crucial test of any theory is the deuteron, which is the simplest stable combination of the heavy particles (neutrons and protons) which compose nuclei.   The position of the deuteron problem in nuclear theory is similar to that of the problem of the hydrogen atom in atomic theory.   It tests the theory without aggravating the computational situation which is already complicated enough in the theory of the simplest nuclei.

There are two ways of going about the study of these forces.   The simplest way is by analogy to the ordinary Schrödinger wave-equation scheme for studying atoms: We assume that there is some more or less complicated potential energy of the two given particles, neutron and proton.   These have properties—mass, magnetic moment, etc.—as though they were free.   A more difficult but deeper way is to employ the quantum theory of particle fields, in which the number of particles present is by no means fixed, and the properties of the system emerge as a result of possible transient as well as permanent constituents.   It is in such a treatment that mesons play

33

their role. We shall follow mainly the first path, often called the phenomenological theory. It is in any case an essential beginning. The formal scheme for the second approach is not yet fully clear.

First, a tabulation of existing information concerning the proton, the neutron, and the deuteron may be helpful.

A. PROTON

Charge: $+e$ (makes it easily observable by its ionization in matter).
Mass: 1.008142 (includes mass of 1 electron) atomic mass units.
    938.72 Mev (including the electron).
Range-kinetic energy relationship. Protons of a given energy have a definite range in matter of given density and atomic number. For example, 10-Mev protons have a range of about 1 mm of water. (For quantitative information, including many curves, see Segrè, *Experimental Nuclear Physics*, Vol. I, Part II, John Wiley & Sons, New York, 1953).
Spin: $\frac{1}{2}$.
Statistics: Fermi.
Magnetic moment: $+2.79275$ nuclear magnetons. The present value [after Hipple, Sommer, and Thomas, *Phys. Rev. 82*, 697 (1951), and Collington et al., *Phys. Rev. 99*, 1623, (1955), with correction for diamagnetic influence of atomic electron] is known to 2 parts in 100,000. It is obtained directly by measuring the ratio between the resonant frequency ω_r for flipping over the proton magnetic moment in a given uniform magnetic field B and the cyclotron frequency ω_c for the revolution of the proton in a circular orbit in the same field. At the resonant frequency $\hbar\omega_r = \mu_p B - (-\mu_p B) = 2\mu_p B$, and in a circular orbit we have $M_p v = eB\rho/c$; $\omega_c = v/\rho = eB/M_p c$ (e in esu). Form the ratio $\omega_r/\omega_c = \mu_p/(e\hbar/2M_p c)$, and the right-hand member is evidently the proton magnetic moment in units of nuclear magnetons.

The Dirac theory of the electron predicts that the magnetic moment of an electron is exactly 1 Bohr (electron) magneton, $-|e|\hbar/2mc$. This quantity can be measured with high precision and turns out not to be exactly unity but actually $1 + 1/137 \cdot 2\pi$. Even this small discrepancy from the simple Dirac theory can be calculated with high accuracy from the quantum theory of radiation, agreeing with the experimental value to within the small error, a few parts per hundred thousand. If the proton, a spin $\frac{1}{2}$ particle with unit charge, obeyed the Dirac equation as precisely as does the electron, it should have a magnetic moment very near 1 nuclear magneton. This wide disagreement with the facts is demonstration that the simplified notion of a structureless and well-defined individual particle does not apply to nucleons so well as it does to the electron.   Meson theory in its simplest form accounts for the additional moment as the effect of the current of transient mesons near the proton, and of the motion of the proton which the meson emission and reabsorption causes, but this idea is at best only qualitative.   The small correction to the Dirac moment for the electron is calculated on the very same basis; the transient presence of photons, rather than mesons, causes a fluctuating recoil and spin reorientation of the electron, and hence a small additional moment.   The agreement is excellent for the electron, where the whole correction effect is only a part in one thousand. But no analogous theory has been found which can account quantitatively for the dominating effect in the case of the proton.

The positive sign of a magnetic moment indicates conventionally that the magnetic dipole is pointing in the same direction as the spin or mechanical moment vector, which is what would be classically expected from a rotating positive distribution of charge.   The sign of the proton moment has been shown to be positive, and that of the neutron negative, by a rather elaborate variant of the magnetic moment measuring experiments, which makes use of a rotating radio-frequency field of known direction of rotation. [See Rogers and Staub, *Phys. Rev.* **76**, 980 (1949).]

B. NEUTRON

Charge: 0.

Mass: 1.008982 atomic mass units; 939.50 Mev.

Decay: $_0n^1 \rightarrow {_1}H^1 + \beta^- + \nu$.

$T_{\frac{1}{2}} = 770 \pm 140$ seconds.

Spin: $\frac{1}{2}$.   The spin of the free neutron has been measured by a somewhat indirect method by means of coherent reflection from magnetized mirrors [Hammermesh, *Phys. Rev.* **75**, 1281 (1949)]. This fully confirms the value suggested by many nuclear results.

Statistics: Fermi.

Magnetic moment: -1.9128 nuclear magnetons.   The measurement is carried out by a variant of the molecular beam resonance method so useful for the other nuclei.   A beam of neutrons was passed through a block of iron saturated by a magnetic field.   This polarized the neutrons with magnetic moments parallel to the field.   Then, still in a constant steady field but now out of the iron, it was acted on by a radio-frequency field perpendicular to the steady field.   Finally it passed through another iron block, the analyzer, with its saturated magnetic field parallel to the former one, and into a neutron detector.

If the radio frequency were close to the Larmor precession frequency of the neutron, the beam would be strongly depolarized in the radio-frequency field and strongly scattered in the analyzer block. Thus the Larmor precession frequency was the radio frequency at which fewest neutrons were transmitted. The Larmor frequency divided by H, the steady magnetic field, is proportional to the gyromagnetic ratio of the neutron, i.e.,

$$\frac{\nu}{H} \sim \frac{\text{(magnetic moment)}}{\text{(angular momentum)}}$$

In the very accurate recent determinations of the neutron moment, direct measurement of the magnetic field is replaced by a determination of the proton magnetic moment in the same field, by one of the radio-frequency methods. This gives the neutron moment in units of the nuclear magnetons directly, as a ratio of resonance frequencies (see Chapter XVII).

C. DEUTERON

Charge: $+e$.

Mass: 2.014735 atomic mass units; $M - A = 13.72$ Mev (includes 1 electron).

Spin: 1.

Statistics: Bose.

Magnetic moment: 0.85735 nuclear magneton. The value given here is a comparison of radio-frequency resonances for flipping the spin in a given field, made between a sample of ordinary hydrogen and one of deuterium. This measures the nuclear moment (after corrections for molecular effects) in a very uniform field.

The method of atomic hyperfine splitting has also been carried out with extraordinary accuracy, giving a result different by about two parts in 10^4. This discrepancy far exceeds the experimental uncertainties of the two measurements.* It is a consequence of the relative motion of the electron and the nucleons of the deuteron. The hyperfine splitting measures the interaction of nuclear moment with the electron current, not with an external uniform field. When the electron is close to the nucleus in its motion, its probability density distribution centers not on the nuclear center of mass but on the charge center at the proton. Then the rapid and nearly spherically symmetric motion of the neutron about the proton tends to

---

* For theory, see A. Bohr, *Phys. Rev. 73*, 1109 (1948); for experiments, Prodell and Kusch, *Phys. Rev. 79*, 1009 (1950), and Smaller, *Phys. Rev. 83*, 812 (1951).

cancel out any magnetic effect of the neutron when the electron is within the neutron "orbit." Consequently the negative neutron magnetic moment does not make its full contribution, and the apparent deuteron moment in electron-deuteron interaction is increased. Precise measures of such very small effects provide a means for getting information about nuclear structure without any use of specifically nuclear techniques or of high energies.

In the quantum-mechanical description of the deuteron, it is reasonable to assume the ground state to be an S state, i.e., a state of no orbital angular momentum, $L = 0$. This means that the wave function has no angular nodes. (With plausible assumptions on the forces it can be proved theoretically that the ground-state wave function has no nodes whatever.) With $L = 0$, ψ is spherically symmetrical and the angular momentum of the nucleus is entirely attributable to spin. Assuming that the neutron has spin $\frac{1}{2}$, the deuteron spin of 1 implies that the proton and the neutron spins are parallel. In such a case the magnetic moments should also add:

$$\text{Proton moment} = 2.7925 \pm 0.0001$$

$$\text{Neutron moment} = -1.9128 \pm 0.0001$$

$$\text{Sum of the two moments} = 0.8797 \pm 0.00015$$

$$\text{Deuteron moment} = 0.85735$$

$$\text{Difference} = 0.0223 \pm 0.0002$$

It is seen that the deuteron moment almost but not quite agrees with the sum of the moments of proton and neutron. The reason for the small difference will be indicated below.

The approximate agreement can be achieved only by assuming, as has been done here, that the neutron spin is $\frac{1}{2}$ and the orbital angular moment of the deuteron is 0. This is shown by Table VIIIA, in which the magnetic moment of the deuteron is calculated for a number of different assumptions on the neutron spin and the value of L, the orbital momentum in the deuteron ground state (see equation 19.8).

It is seen that only $S = 1$, $L = 0$ leads to a result that is not very far from the measured one; all other combinations, especially those for $S = \frac{3}{2}$ (or for positive neutron moment), are completely different from the measured moment of the deuteron.

Thus the magnetic moment measurements, even taken alone, are good evidence for the following:

1. In the ground state of the deuteron the spins of proton and neutron are parallel (triplet state).

2. The neutron spin is $\frac{1}{2}$.

3. In the ground state of the deuteron the orbital angular momentum is zero (S state).

Direct measurements confirm the spin and the sign of the magnetic moment of the neutron, as was stated above.

Table VIIIA.   Calculated Magnetic Moment of the Deuteron

$S_n =$	$\frac{1}{2}$		$\frac{3}{2}$	
$S\ =$	0	1	1	2
L				
0	—	0.854	−6.232	—
1	0.500	0.677	−2.866	−2.512
2	—	0.323	3.866	−0.504

$S_n =$ assumed spin of the neutron.
$S =$ resultant spin of the deuteron.
$L =$ orbital momentum of the deuteron.
$I =$ total angular momentum $= 1$. A dash (—) indicates that these combinations cannot lead to $I = 1$.

Quadrupole moment.   Rabi and his co-workers have shown that the deuteron also possesses an electric quadrupole moment such that it appears as a spheroid prolate along the spin axis,

$$\frac{\overline{z^2}}{\overline{r^2}} = \frac{\text{average } z^2 \text{ for proton}}{\text{average } r^2 \text{ for proton}} = \frac{1}{3} \cdot (1.14) \qquad (8.1)$$

instead of $\frac{1}{3}$ as it would be for a spherically symmetrical charge distribution: $(\overline{r^2} = \overline{x^2} + \overline{y^2} + \overline{z^2})$. Thus the wave function ψ cannot be independent of the angle θ between the total spin and the line joining the nuclei. If ψ be expanded in spherical harmonics, a dependence such as

$$\psi = u + wP_2(\cos \theta) \qquad (8.2)$$

must be assumed, where P_2 is a normalized Legendre polynomial. (No P_1 term appears because the electric dipole moment is zero.) In order to obtain the functions u and w, the deuteron problem must be solved with an explicit assumption about the nuclear forces. This was done by Rarita and Schwinger (see Chapter XIV).   The most important result of their calculations is the fraction of the time during which the deuteron has orbital moment 2, viz.,

$$p_D = \frac{\int w^2\, dr}{\int u^2\, dr + \int w^2\, dr} = 3.9 \text{ per cent} \qquad (8.3)$$

Since the deuteron now is no longer perfectly symmetric, its magnetic moment should not be exactly the sum of the moments of proton and neutron.   There will be a contribution from the orbital motion in the D state, just as in some of the entries of Table VIIIA.   Indeed, the measured deuteron moment is smaller than the sum of the moments of the individual particles by 0.0223 nuclear magneton. From this figure it is possible to calculate the percentage of time during which the deuteron is in the D state ($L = 2$).   If this state were pure, Landé's formula would give for the deuteron moment the value 0.3111 from the measured moments of neutron and proton. If the fraction of time in the D state is p_D, the moment should be

$$\mu_d = \mu_n + \mu_p - \tfrac{3}{2}(\mu_n + \mu_p - \tfrac{1}{2})p_D = 0.8797 - 0.5696 p_D$$

With this set equal to the measured moment,

$$p_D = 3.93 \text{ per cent}$$

is obtained with apparently great accuracy.

Unfortunately, this argument is unreliable, because the nucleons need not have the same magnetic moments when they are in the nucleus as in the free state, as explained in the next subsection.   It is very difficult to calculate the correction for the non-additivity of the moments; even its sign is unknown; only its order of magnitude can be estimated to be about 2 per cent.   Thus the fraction of time the deuteron spends in the D state can be said only to be between 2 and 6 per cent.

D. NON-ADDITIVITY OF THE NUCLEON MOMENTS

The whole discussion of magnetic moments has assumed that the moments measured for the free nucleons are entirely unchanged for the nucleons interacting in the deuteron.   Relativistic effects of nucleon motion and the picture of the possible transient presence of other particles with different charges and magnetic polarization densities makes perfect additivity and absence of deviations from the free nucleon values seem rather unrealistic assumptions.   Clear evidence for other contributions to the magnetic moment comes from the very accurate measurements on the next heavier nuclei beyond the deuteron, H^3 and He^3. The measured values are:

	Spin	Magnetic Moment in Nuclear Magnetons
H^3	½	$+2.9786$
He^3	½	-2.1274

The wave functions for these three-body systems are by no means as well understood as that for the deuteron, but the simplest procedure is to assume that these nuclei also are almost spherically symmetric, and that any orbital angular momentum states except zero are present only as corrections. With a general procedure like that used for the deuteron, it can be shown* that the sum of the two moments should satisfy the relation

$$\mu(H^3) + \mu(He^3) = \mu_p + \mu_n - 2(\mu_p + \mu_n - \tfrac{1}{2})(p_D)$$
$$+ \text{ other corrections} \cdot \cdot \cdot$$

Now if we use $p_D \sim 3$ to 4 per cent as for the deuteron, we get

$$\mu(H^3) + \mu(He^3) = 0.8512 \cong 0.8797 - 2 \cdot 0.38 \times 0.04$$
$$= 0.849 \text{ nuclear magneton}$$

This is in excellent agreement. But the individual moments do *not* agree. Indeed, we get

$$\mu(H^3) \cong 2.83; \qquad \mu(He^3) \cong -1.97$$

The experiments give

$$\mu(H^3) = \mu_{\text{calc.}} + 0.15 \quad \text{and} \quad \mu(He^3) = \mu_{\text{calc.}} - 0.16$$

all in nuclear magnetons. It is hard to doubt that ± 0.15 is a contribution to the moment over and above that of the free nucleons and their orbital motion. That it is equal and opposite for the two mirror nuclei (which differ from each other only by changing all neutrons into protons, protons into neutrons) is a very general consequence of any theory which considers that other currents than those of the nucleon motion may be present in nuclei. This new term may be thought of as arising from the exchange of mesons in the interaction of the nucleons and is called an exchange or interaction moment. Details of its origin are lacking, but its modification of the free-nucleon moments seems hard to doubt. It is striking that symmetry arguments of a very general kind show that such contributions must be negligible in a two-body system like the deuteron, where the spin and parity are uniquely related.

* Avery and Sachs, *Phys. Rev.* *74*, 1320 (1948).

However, relativistic corrections should occur also in the deuteron. Normally, the magnetic moment of a moving particle is less than that of a particle at rest.   Theoretical calculations have shown, however, that the correction is very sensitive to the details of the interaction between the nucleons, and of the meson field responsible for this interaction.   Neither the magnitude nor even the sign of the correction is known.

Even heavier nuclei show surprisingly close agreement with the Landé formula.   The reasons for and implications of this fact are discussed in the Section *C Model* of Chapter XIX.

IX. GROUND STATE OF THE DEUTERON

A. BINDING ENERGY

The most important experimental basis for the theory of the deuteron is its binding energy. This can be obtained by using the photodisintegration of deuterons,

$$H^2 + h\nu \to H^1 + {}^0n^1 \tag{9.1}$$

This reaction takes place when $h\nu$ is greater than the binding energy of the deuteron; the difference between $h\nu$ and the binding energy appears as kinetic energy of the neutron and the proton. Because the momentum of the γ-ray is so small, the momenta of proton and neutron are very nearly equal and opposite, and, since their masses are almost exactly equal, they share the excess energy, $h\nu$ minus binding energy, very nearly equally. The energy E of the proton can be determined by measuring the total ionization it produces or by measuring its range. The binding energy is then $h\nu - 2E$.

The first measurements, by Chadwick and Goldhaber in 1934, were made with the 2.62-Mev γ-rays from ThC'', and measuring E. This gave the first value: binding energy = 2.14 Mev. Range measurements, however, cannot be very accurate.

Two other rather direct methods have been used. In the experiment of Bell and Elliot [*Phys. Rev. 79*, 282 (1950)], the inverse reaction $H^1 + n \to H^2 + h\nu$ was studied. Neutrons from the chain-reacting pile were captured in hydrogen and the outgoing γ-rays allowed to make electron-positron pairs whose energy was measured by deflection in a magnetic field. They obtained a binding energy of 2.230 ± 0.007 Mev. Another very accurate determination was made by Mobley and Laubenstein [*Phys. Rev. 80*, 309 (1950)], who studied the neutrons emitted from deuterium excited by artificially produced γ-rays. The γ's were made by allowing high-energy electrons from a Van de Graaff machine of carefully and simultaneously calibrated potential to fall on a heavy target. The authors observed the yield of neutrons as a function of electron energy and found a relation which, extrapolated only very little, gave a threshold at 2.226 ± 0.003 Mev.

42

An entirely independent method is to take the difference in mass between the deuteron and the free constituent nucleons. The masses of deuteron and proton are known from mass spectrographic data, and the neutron-proton mass difference may be found, for example, from direct observation of the end-point energy of the electrons emitted in the β-disintegration of the free neutron. The equation

$$\text{Binding energy} = 2M(\text{H}^1) + M(n) - M(\text{H}^1) - M(\text{H}^2)$$

gives the result 2.225 ± 0.015 Mev with these data. A consistent value which we will adopt is 2.225 ± 0.002 Mev, from all sources of data.

Nature of forces. In order to discuss the deuteron quantum mechanically, we must know or guess something about the nature of the "nuclear" force holding neutron and proton together. This force cannot be electrical, as the neutron is uncharged; nor can it be magnetic, for the bar-magnet forces between proton and neutron free magnetic moments are too small by a factor of about 100. Assuming a gravitational force gives an interaction potential too small by about a factor 10^{38}! So we must accept the nuclear force as a new type of force and try to find out more about it.

We shall first of all assume a central force, i.e., that the interaction potential of neutron and proton is some function $V(r)$, where r is the distance between the particles. This is only in slight disagreement with known facts, for a central force would yield a ground state with angular momentum zero, whereas it was shown in Chapter VIII that the deuteron ground state has a small fraction of the state $l = 2$ in addition to the predominant state $l = 0$.

Second, it was shown by Wigner that the nuclear force has a short range. This assumption must be made to explain the low binding energy (2.22 Mev; about 1 Mev per particle) of the deuteron compared to that of H^3 (8.5 Mev; about 3 Mev per particle) and of He^4 (28 Mev; about 7 Mev per particle) which cannot be explained by a long-range force (e.g., $V(r) \sim -1/r$). Wigner's argument was essentially that the nuclei with more particles have more nuclear bonds per particle (D^2 has $\frac{1}{2}$, H^3 has $\frac{3}{3}$, He^4 has $\frac{6}{4}$ bonds per particle). This in itself is not sufficient to explain the ratios of binding energy per particle; however, the larger number of bonds per particle in the heavier nuclei causes these particles to be pulled within the (short) range of the nuclear forces a greater percentage of the time, increasing the binding energy by a large amount. Thomas has shown by a rigorous mathematical proof that it is possible to get as large a ratio of the binding energy of H^3 to that of H^2 as desired by choosing the range of forces small enough (and simultaneously adjusting the depth of the hole to yield the correct binding energy). From this argument, one would expect that the binding energy of the deuteron is small compared to the total depth of the potential hole and that the particles in the deuteron spend a great part of the time outside the range of the nuclear forces—i.e., the "radius" of the deuteron is considerably greater than the range of nuclear forces.

B. WAVE EQUATION

If the potential $V(r)$ is known, the binding energy is determined by the Schrödinger equation

$$\nabla^2 \psi(r, \theta, \phi) + (2m/\hbar^2)[E - V(r)]\psi(r, \theta, \phi) = 0 \qquad (9.2)$$

where r is the distance between neutron and proton and m is the reduced mass:

$$m = \frac{M_n M_p}{M_n + M_p} \approx \frac{1}{2} M \text{ (of proton or neutron)}$$

E is negative and numerically equal to the binding energy. Conversely, if E is known, equation 9.2 determines, in principle, *one* parameter relating to $V(r)$.

Since $l = 0$ is being taken for the ground state, ψ must be spherically symmetrical. When $\psi = u(r)/r$ is substituted, equation 9.2 takes on the simpler form

$$\frac{d^2u}{dr^2} + \frac{M}{\hbar^2} [E - V(r)]u = 0 \qquad (9.3)$$

We must now assume a shape for the potential function $V(r)$. One shape which certainly represents a short-range force and also makes for easy solution of the differential equation is the rectangular

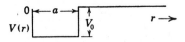

FIG. 6. Potential "well" of deuteron: square-well model.

potential well shown in Fig. 6. (There is of course no implication at all that the real potential function has this "square-well" shape; it is used as a simple tool for investigating relationships.) Here there are two parameters, width and depth of the well; since the Schrödinger equation with a given E will determine only one parameter, we expect only to find a relation between V_0 and a, not definite values for them.

With $E = -W$, where W is positive, equation 9.3 becomes for the potential well

$$\frac{d^2u}{dr^2} + \frac{M}{\hbar^2}(V_0 - W)u = 0 \qquad \text{for } r < a \qquad (9.4a)$$

$$\frac{d^2u}{dr^2} - \frac{M}{\hbar^2}Wu = 0 \qquad \text{for } r > a \qquad (9.4b)$$

Now ψ must be continuous and bounded and have a continuous derivative everywhere. Therefore, $u = r\psi$ must have the same continuity condition, must go to zero at $r = 0$, and must not diverge faster than r as $r \to \infty$. To satisfy the conditions at zero and infinity the solution of equations 9.4 must be

$$u = A \sin kr \qquad \text{for } r < a \qquad (9.5a)$$

$$u = Be^{-\gamma r} \qquad \text{for } r > a \qquad (9.5b)$$

where

$$k = \sqrt{M(V_0 - W)}/\hbar \qquad (9.6a)$$

$$\gamma = \sqrt{MW}/\hbar \qquad (9.6b)$$

Relation between range and depth of potential. Now, if u and its derivative are continuous, then the derivative of $\ln u$ must also be continuous; applying this at $r = a$ gives

$$k \cot ka = -\gamma \qquad (9.7)$$

which conveniently does not involve A and B, but only the two unknown a and V_0, W being known to be 2.22 Mev. V_0 and a are not restricted further. Thus equation 9.7 is the relation anticipated between a and V_0.

Equation 9.7 can be put in a simpler but approximate form. As seen above, W is small compared to V_0 and can be neglected in equations 9.6. Thus

$$\cot ka = -\gamma/k \approx -\sqrt{W/V_0} \qquad (9.8)$$

Thus $\cot ka$ is negative and small in absolute value. Therefore, ka is only slightly larger than $\pi/2$. (ka slightly larger than $3\pi/2$ is not the correct solution, for then there would be a radial node in the wave function ψ at $kr = \pi$, indicating that this ψ is not the lowest energy level, which contradicts our hypothesis.) Using $ka \approx \pi/2$ and again neglecting W in the expression for k gives

$$V_0 a^2 \approx \pi^2 \hbar^2/4M \qquad (9.9)$$

Actually $V_0 a^2$ is slightly greater than the quantity on the right; but we can be virtually certain that

$$V_0 a^2 < \pi^2 \hbar^2 / M \qquad \text{or} \qquad ka < \pi \qquad (9.10)$$

a result which will be needed later. The expression $V_0 a^2$ frequently occurs in nuclear calculations, it often being not necessary to know V_0 and a separately.

Other types of short-range potential function give about the same results as the rectangular well. Potentials of the form e^{-r} and e^{-r^2} have been treated by Bethe and Bacher [*Revs. Mod. Phys. 8*, 83 (1936)], and the function e^{-r}/r, the so-called Yukawa potential, which arises in the simplest and most fundamental form of meson theory,

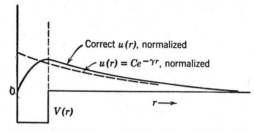

FIG. 7. Exact and approximate wave functions of deuteron ground state.

has also been discussed. A very useful approximation to the wave functions for Yukawa potential is considered in detail by Hulthén, for example in *Revs. Mod. Phys. 23*, 1 (1951).

Discussion of wave function. Another result which does not depend on the form of the potential (as long as it has a short range) is the exponential decrease of $u(r)$ for r greater than the range of nuclear forces. In fact, the function

$$u = Ce^{-\gamma r} \qquad (9.11)$$

is close enough to the true $u(r)$ over the whole region to be useful in many calculations. This is seen clearly by considering Fig. 7. The quantity $1/\gamma$ can be taken as a measure of the size of the deuteron. It was shown above that the "radius" of the deuteron is considerably larger than the range of nuclear forces, i.e.,

$$1/\gamma \gg a \qquad (9.12)$$

Thus most of the area under $u(r)$ occurs for $r > a$. Using another form for the potential function changes $u(r)$ appreciably only for $r < a$. Therefore, independent of the shape of the potential, $Ce^{-\gamma r}$ is close to the true wave function over most of space. This approximation does not give a bounded ψ at $r = 0$; however, ψ is normalizable, and fortunately the main contribution to the normalization integral comes from $r > a$, so the infinity introduces little error.

$$\int \psi^2 \, dr = 4\pi \int_0^\infty u^2 \, dr = 4\pi C^2 \int_0^\infty e^{-2\gamma r} \, dr = \frac{2\pi C^2}{\gamma} = 1$$

or
$$C = \sqrt{\gamma/2\pi}$$

Therefore
$$u(r) = \sqrt{\gamma/2\pi} \, e^{-\gamma r} \tag{9.13}$$

is the normalized approximate form of $u(r)$.

If definite values are assigned to a and V_0, then A and B of the true $u(r)$ given by equations 9.5 can be found from the continuity

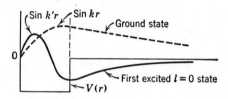

FIG. 8.   Wave function of the excited state of the deuteron (if it existed).

condition and normalization. B is a little greater than C of the approximate $u(r)$. In fact,

$$B = \sqrt{\gamma/2\pi} \, (1 + \tfrac{1}{2}\gamma a) \tag{9.14}$$

is a good approximation.

C. EXCITED STATES OF THE DEUTERON

On the basis of the preceding theory the possibility of other bound states of the deuteron may be investigated.   For $l = 0$ there are no other bound states.   For in the extreme case, binding energy $W \simeq 0$, ka is still only slightly greater than $\pi/2$, since W of the ground state was already negligible compared to V_0 in equations 9.4.   But for the first excited state ka would have to be greater than $3\pi/2$, since the wave function ψ would have to have a radial node (Fig. 8).   But from equation 9.10 ka is certainly less than π for all positive binding energies.   Therefore, there is no bound excited state for $l = 0$.   There are, of course, free states.

We shall now prove that the deuteron has no bound excited states for states of higher l.   It will be assumed in this proof that the force between neutron and proton is the same for higher l as it was in the case $l = 0$. (The possibility of excited states with other total spins, especially $S = 0$, and with a different neutron-proton force will turn out to be of importance in our future discussions of neutron-proton scattering.)

To prove that no bound state exists for $l \neq 0$ we shall compute the minimum well depth V just required to produce a bound state, i.e., one for which the binding energy W is just zero. This required well depth will be found to be considerably larger than the actual well depth as determined above from the binding energy in the ground state. Since the actual depth is less than the minimum required for binding for states of angular momentum $l \neq 0$, no such bound states exist.

The differential equation 9.3, generalized to angular momenta $l \neq 0$, becomes

$$\frac{d^2u}{dr^2} + \frac{M}{\hbar^2}(E - V)u - \frac{l(l+1)}{r^2}u = 0 \qquad (9.15)$$

The procedure to be followed in a general proof is as follows: Assume a square well of depth $V = -V_0$ and radius $r = a$. Find the solutions to differential equation 9.15 inside and outside the well. Match these solutions at $r = a$. This will give a relation between well depth V_0 and binding energy $W = -E$. Setting $W = 0$ will give the minimum well depth.

Only the proof for the case $l = 1$ will be carried out here, as an illustration. For this case, the solutions to differential equation 9.15 are found to be:

$$u = (\sin kr)/kr - \cos kr \qquad r < a \qquad (9.16a)$$

$$u = e^{-\gamma r}[(1/\gamma r) + 1] \qquad r > a \qquad (9.16b)$$

where

$$k^2 = M(V_0 - W)/\hbar^2 \qquad (9.17a)$$

$$\gamma^2 = MW/\hbar^2 \qquad (9.17b)$$

It will be simpler to set $W = 0$ before satisfying the boundary conditions. As $\gamma \to 0$, the outside solution (equation 9.16b) becomes (except for a multiplying factor)

$$u = 1/r \qquad r \geq a \qquad (9.18)$$

This outside solution satisfies

$$(d/dr)(ru) = 0 \qquad r \geq a \qquad (9.19)$$

The inside solution, in order to match, must satisfy the same condition at $r = a$:

$$\frac{d}{d(kr)} (kru) = kr \sin kr \Big|_{r=a}$$

$$= ka \sin ka = 0 \tag{9.20}$$

or

$$ka = \pi \tag{9.21}$$

Using the definition of k with $W = 0$ from equation 9.7:

$$MV_0 a^2/\hbar^2 = \pi^2 \tag{9.22}$$

This required well depth V_0 is almost four times as large as the actual well depth in the ground state (equation 9.9). The latter satisfied an equation like 9.21, in which ka was slightly greater than $\pi/2$ but definitely less than π (equation 9.10).

Similar proofs with larger values of l would lead to even larger required values of ka.

X. SCATTERING OF NEUTRONS

BY FREE PROTONS

The theory of scattering is presented, for example, by Mott and Massey, *Theory of Atomic Collisions* (2nd ed., Oxford, 1949). A major result of the theory (Rayleigh, Faxen and Holtsmark)—often called the method of partial waves—is the cross section for pure elastic scattering in the center-of-mass coordinates:

$$d\sigma/d\Omega = \left| (2ik)^{-1} \sum_l (2l + 1)P_l(\cos\theta)(e^{2i\delta_l} - 1) \right|^2 \quad (10.1)$$

The cross section $d\sigma$ is defined as the number of neutrons scattered per unit time by one proton through an angle between θ and $\theta + d\theta$, if there is a primary beam intensity of one neutron per unit area and per unit time. $d\Omega = 2\pi \sin\theta\, d\theta$ is the solid angle in center-of-mass coordinates, $l\hbar$ is the angular momentum of the system around its center of mass. The de Broglie wave number in these coordinates is given by

$$k = 2\pi/\lambda = 1/\lambda = p/\hbar = \sqrt{2mE}/\hbar \quad (10.2)$$

The relations between center-of-mass coordinates (c.m.) and laboratory coordinates (lab.) for two particles of equal mass are given by

$$m = \frac{M_p M_n}{M_p + M_n} \simeq \frac{M}{2} \quad (10.3a)$$

$$\theta_{\text{c.m.}} = 2\theta_{\text{lab.}} \quad (10.3b)$$

$$E_{\text{c.m.}} = \tfrac{1}{2}E_{\text{lab.}} \quad (10.3c)$$

Equation (10.3a) merely gives the reduced mass of the system in center-of-mass coordinates. Equation (10.3c) states that only half of the neutron energy in the laboratory system is available in the center-of-mass system, the other half representing the kinetic energy of the center of mass.   Equation (10.3b) can be obtained from simple geometrical considerations.

The phase shifts δ_l are measured in radians, and their physical significance may be seen as follows: At large distances beyond the range of nuclear forces $V(r)$, equation 9.15 for the radial function $u_l(r)$ associated with angular momentum l and angular distribution P_l (cos θ) reduces to the equation of a free wave.   The asymptotic solution $u_l(r)$ of equation 9.15 will therefore behave in the same manner, except for a possible shift in phase, as $v_l(r)$, the radial wave function of a *free* particle which has angular momentum l:

$$v_l(r) \sim \sin (kr - \tfrac{1}{2}l\pi) \qquad \text{(large } r) \qquad (10.4a)$$

$$u_l(r) \sim \sin (kr - \tfrac{1}{2}l\pi + \delta_l) \qquad \text{(large } r) \qquad (10.4b)$$

If all the phase shifts δ_l were zero, the total wave u obtained by adding up all the components of angular momentum l would appear at large distances to add up to the incident plane wave with no waves traveling in other directions.   The result is verified if we set $\delta_l = 0$ in equation 10.1 for the scattering cross section.

It should be also noted that if the two waves u_l and v_l differ in phase by $\delta_l = \pi$ they are again indistinguishable, and the cross section (10.1) vanishes.

A. PHASE SHIFTS AS A FUNCTION OF ANGULAR MOMENTUM

Classical argument.   If p is the momentum and b the impact parameter (classical distance of closest approach), then the angular momentum is given by

$$|\mathbf{r} \times \mathbf{p}| = bp = l\hbar \qquad (10.5)$$

or

$$l = b(p/\hbar) = b/\lambda$$

An interaction will take place only if this closest approach distance b is smaller than the range of nuclear forces a, i.e., if

$$l < a/\lambda \qquad (10.6)$$

Thus for a given energy and definite wavelength, only a finite number of l's contribute to the cross section for collision.   The corresponding *quantum-mechanical statement* is that for any integral value of l greater than a/λ the phase shift δ_l will be negligibly small.

According to equation 10.6, $\lambda = a$ corresponds to the energy below which only the $l = 0$ term is of importance; this energy is

$$E_{\text{lab.}} = 2E_{\text{c.m.}} = 2\hbar^2/M\lambda^2 = 2\hbar^2/Ma^2$$

$$\cong \frac{2 \times 10^{-54}}{(1.6 \times 10^{-14})(2.8 \times 10^{-13})^2}$$

$$= 1.6 \times 10^{-5} \text{ erg} = 10 \text{ Mev} \qquad (10.7)$$

B. SPHERICAL SYMMETRY OF SCATTERING

The result of these arguments is that δ_0 is the only important phase shift for energies up to 10 Mev. If all higher terms in equation 10.1 are dropped, the cross section becomes

$$d\sigma = d\Omega\lambda^2 \sin^2 \delta_0 \qquad (10.8)$$

where

$$d\Omega = 2\pi \sin \theta \, d\theta = \text{the solid angle} \qquad (10.8a)$$

Thus the cross section (10.8) is found to be independent of direction, or spherically symmetric for neutrons below 10 Mev. This conclusion is based chiefly on the short-range nature of the forces. Thus, if spherical symmetry is found experimentally, this will verify that the forces are short range and test the applicability of quantum mechanics to such scattering problems.

The best experimental determination of the angular distribution of scattered neutrons is based on measurement of the energy distribution of the recoil protons. An elementary consideration shows that uniform angular distribution corresponds to uniform distribution in energy of the recoil protons from zero to the incident neutron energy (in the laboratory system).

Early cloud-chamber measurements of the angular distribution showed preferential neutron scattering in the forward direction; i.e., most of the recoil protons were at large angles to the beam. The energy of the protons is smaller if they are emitted at large angles. Now, it could be shown that high-energy tracks were often missed in the experiments because they were long enough to leave the chamber except when they were almost in the plane of the chamber. A check on the azimuthal distribution, for which there can be no asymmetry, verified this by revealing that most of the measured long tracks were in the plane of the chamber. Careful cloud-chamber experiments by Dee and Gilbert produced an exactly spherical symmetry.

Measurements of proton recoil energy by ionization chamber methods by Ladenburg and his co-workers gave an almost uniform distribution in energy. Experiments at Los Alamos by Staub and others indicate uniformity even more accurately to within an experimental error of about 1 per cent.

Major experimental effort centers now on the deviations from spherical symmetry at higher energies. These will be discussed in Chapter XV. The present chapter is limited to the spherically symmetric results below some 10 Mev, that is, to the single partial wave of $l = 0$, with angular dependence like P_0 (cos θ), the so-called S wave.

C. TOTAL CROSS SECTION

The total cross section for scattering of neutrons by protons follows from integration of equation 10.8:

$$\sigma = 4\pi \lambda^2 \sin^2 \delta_0 \qquad (10.9)$$

for energies of the incident neutrons less than 10 Mev, where $2\pi\lambda$ is the de Broglie wavelength of the neutron in the center-of-mass system, and δ_0 is the phase shift of the scattered wave function for $l = 0$. Outside the range of the nuclear forces, the wave function u (a solution of equation 9.15 with $l = 0$ and E positive) will be proportional to sin $(kr + \delta_0)$, where $k = \sqrt{ME/\hbar}$ ($E =$ neutron energy in the center-of-mass system $= \frac{1}{2}E_{\text{lab.}}$; $M =$ mass of neutron).

The phase shift δ_0 is of course determined by the exact wave function, which depends on the assumed shape of the nuclear potential. In the case of the rectangular well, the condition that the logarithmic derivative of the wave function be continuous at the boundary of the well is enough to fix δ_0.

Such a calculation is, for instance, given by Bohm (*Quantum Mechanics*, Chapter 21 Prentice-Hall, New York, (1951). However, when the scattering was calculated for various shapes of the potential, the resulting cross section as a function of energy turned out to be essentially independent of the potential shape. It is therefore valuable to analyze the scattering in such a way that the shape of the potential is unimportant, rather than to choose a potential entirely for its analytical convenience. For this purpose a special method of calculation has been developed for treating the scattering process in the deuteron problem. (For the small influence of shape, see below.)

D. SCATTERING LENGTH

We can write the total cross section as in equation 10.9, using the wave number k; $\sigma = 4\pi \sin^2 \delta_0/k^2$. Now at very low energies, $k \to 0$. We need to assume only that the cross section for low energies remains finite, going neither to zero nor to infinity. (Actually, those values become special cases for the theory to be developed.)

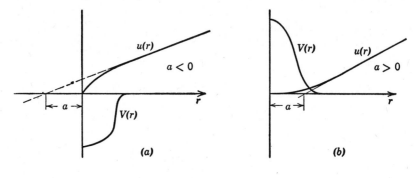

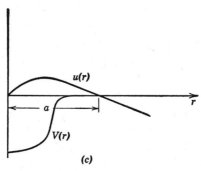

Fig. 9. Geometrical interpretation of a, the Fermi scattering length: (a) an attractive potential, with a negative Fermi length; (b) a repulsive potential, with a positive Fermi length; (c) an attractive potential, but a positive Fermi length, implying the existence of a bound state.

Then $\sin^2 \delta_0/k^2 \to (\delta_0/k)^2 \to a^2$, where we have introduced the quantity a with dimensions of a length. This length a, defined so far for the limit of zero energy only, is called the Fermi scattering length. Its sign has still to be fixed.

A geometrical interpretation of a is shown in Fig. 9. At very low k, the asymptotic wave function outside the region of the nuclear forces is just proportional to $\sin (kr + \delta_0) \to kr + \delta_0$. This is linear in r and extrapolates to zero at the radius $-\delta_0/k$. The node may lie on either side of the axis $r = 0$. We choose the sign of the scattering length so that $a = -\delta_0/k$. A positive phase shift then implies a negative scattering length, and the low-energy wave function looks like $k(r - a)$. This convention is the usual one and implies that an impenetrable sphere of radius a has a scattering length $+a$.

The Fermi scattering length is evidently fixed by experiment; the low-energy cross section determines its magnitude, and its sign relative to a conventional standard can come from any interference experiment capable of measuring the sign of the phase shift in the scattered wave. Any wholly repulsive potential (e.g., Coulomb force between like charged particles) has by our convention a positive scattering length. Although any entirely repulsive potential implies a positive scattering length, an attractive potential may give either a negative or a positive value for $a(0)$, depending on the features of the potential. (See Chapter XI for further details.)

We may generalize the Fermi scattering length to define a quantity $a(k)$ for all k, if we keep the limiting relation $\delta_0 \to -ka$. Writing $\tan \delta_0 = -ka(k)$ we clearly allow $a(k)$ to take on arbitrarily large values even though the phase shift has a limited range of variation. The cross section can be rewritten:

$$\sigma = 4\pi \sin^2 \delta_0/k^2 = \frac{4\pi}{k^2}\left(\frac{1}{1 + \cot^2 \delta_0}\right) = \frac{4\pi}{[k^2 + 1/a^2(k)]} \quad (10.10)$$

Now we have the relation $k \cot \delta_0 = -1/a(k)$, and a complete knowledge of the single length $a(k)$ as a function of energy determines the entire S-wave scattering. Call $a(k)$ the general scattering length, which at zero energy approaches the Fermi scattering length,
$$a(k) \xrightarrow[k \to 0]{} a.$$

E. EFFECTIVE RANGE

We now show that, independently of the shape and depth of the potential, the general scattering length $a(k)$ is simply a linear function of the energy, with an intercept which is of course the Fermi scattering length $a(0) = a$, and a slope given by another parameter with the dimensions of a length, called the effective range r_0. This statement is not exact; higher terms in k^2 do occur, but they are almost negligible in the region where the dominant scattering is still S wave. Thus measurements of scattering in the S-wave domain can fix only two parameters, a and r_0, and any effect of the detailed shape of the potential depends on high accuracy and demands consideration of the corrections due to higher l values.

To obtain the linear relation for $-1/a(k)$ we first write the wave equation for two states of energy E_1 and E_2 (always S states):

$$d^2u_1/dr^2 + (M/\hbar^2)[-E_1 - V(r)]u_1 = 0 \qquad (10.11a)$$

and

$$d^2u_2/dr^2 + (M/\hbar^2)[-E_2 - V(r)]u_2 = 0 \qquad (10.11b)$$

Multiply equation 10.11a by u_2 and equation 10.11b by u_1, subtract and integrate, getting

$$u_2u_1' - u_1u_2' \Big|_0^R = (k_2{}^2 - k_1{}^2) \int_0^R u_1u_2 \, dr \qquad (10.12)$$

where the integral is extended from 0 to an arbitrary radius R. With R infinite, this is just the orthogonality relation for two eigenfunctions.

Now we perform the same operations, using not the exact wave functions u which solve the Schrödinger equation but comparison functions ψ which behave exactly like $u(r)$ at distances large compared to the range of the forces. These are the free-particle functions with shifted phase:

$$\psi_1 = c_1 \sin (k_1r + \delta_1) = \sin (k_1r + \delta_1)/\sin \delta_1 \qquad (10.13)$$

We have chosen the normalizing constant so that ψ approaches 1 at the origin. Then the normalization of u is fixed, since ψ must approach u asymptotically.

We get a relation like equation 10.12 for the ψ's as well:

$$(\psi_2\psi_1 - \psi_1\psi_2') \Big|_0^R = (k_2{}^2 - k_1{}^2) \int_0^R \psi_1\psi_2 \, dr \qquad (10.14)$$

and we may now subtract equation 10.14 from equation 10.12. On the left-hand side there will be no contribution from the upper limit if we make R safely larger than the range of the forces, for there $\psi \to u$. On the right, we can extend the integration to infinity for the same reason. Since $u(0) = 0$, there results from the given form of ψ_1 and ψ_1' for all real k

$$\psi_2'(0) - \psi_1'(0) = k_2 \cot \delta_2 - k_1 \cot \delta_1 = 1/a(k_1) - 1/a(k_2)$$
$$= (k_2{}^2 - k_1{}^2) \int_0^\infty (\psi_1\psi_2 - u_1u_2) \, dr \qquad (10.15)$$

This equation is exact for any potential shape of finite range.

Now we can use relation 10.15 for the case of $k_1 \to 0$ and arbitrary

$k_2 = k$.   Since the Fermi scattering length a is just $a(0)$, we obtain

$$-k \cot \delta = 1/a(k) = 1/a - \tfrac{1}{2}k^2\rho(0, E) \qquad (10.16)$$

with

$$\tfrac{1}{2}\rho(0, E) = \int_0^\infty (\psi_0\psi - u_0u)\, dr \qquad (10.17a)$$

The integral ρ can be defined for two arbitrary energies E_1 and E_2:

$$\tfrac{1}{2}\rho(E_1, E_2) = \int_0^\infty (\psi_1\psi_2 - u_1u_2)\, dr \qquad (10.17b)$$

The point is that the functions ψ and u differ only *inside* the range of the forces.   But just in that region their dependence on energy is slight, because the potential energy is much larger than k^2 through the whole low-energy region, up to some 10 Mev.

Therefore, it is an approximation good throughout this whole energy region to replace ψ and u in equation 10.17a by the corresponding functions for zero energy.   Then equation 10.17a becomes equal to a constant, $\tfrac{1}{2}r_0$, thus:

$$\tfrac{1}{2}\rho(0, E) \cong \tfrac{1}{2}\rho(0, 0) \equiv \tfrac{1}{2}r_0 = \int_0^\infty (\psi_0{}^2 - u_0{}^2)\, dr \qquad (10.18)$$

We call the constant defined by equation 10.18 the "effective range."

To investigate the accuracy of the approximation (10.18), we expand ψ, equation 10.13, up to second order in k, using immediately expression 10.16 with 10.18 for $k \cot \delta$; this yields

$$\psi = 1 - r/a + \tfrac{1}{2}k^2r(r_0 - r) + \tfrac{1}{6}k^2r^2 \cdot r/a + \cdots \qquad (10.19)$$

The energy-dependent part of ψ, $\tfrac{1}{2}k^2r(r_0 - r + r^2/3a)$, vanishes at $r = 0$ and again at approximately $r_0(1 + r_0/3a)$, which is not far from r_0.   Thus it is small compared to $k^2r_0{}^2$ just where it is of interest.   Making a similar expansion for u, we finally obtain

$$1/a(k) = 1/a - \tfrac{1}{2}k^2r_0 + Pk^4r_0{}^3 + \cdots \qquad (10.20)$$

where P is a small numerical coefficient which has been shown by direct calculation to vary between -0.04 and $+0.15$, depending on the potential shape and range, for typical cases.   Whatever the shape of the potential, the scattering can then be described by the two parameters, a and r_0.   In very good approximation, the plot of $1/a(k)$ vs. k^2 (which is proportional to the energy) will give a straight line.   Such a plot can be made, using experimental results for the cross section at several energies, and computing $a(k)$ in each case from equation 10.10.   The slope of this plot determines the effective range r_0; the intercept at $k^2 = 0$ gives the Fermi scattering length a.

Only the small correction term P depends on the actual shape of the potential, making the plot of $1/a(k)$ vs. k^2 deviate from a straight line. For a concentrated potential, like that of a square well, the curve would be bent below the straight line; for a potential with a long tail, the deviation is upward.

It is useful to apply formula 10.15 to the case of the ground state, with accurately known binding energy, so that $E_2 = -W$. Then we have $\psi_2 = e^{-\gamma r}$ with $\gamma^2 = MW/\hbar^2$; and if we take $k_1 \to 0$, we get

$$\gamma = 1/a + \tfrac{1}{2}\gamma^2 \rho(0, -W) \tag{10.21}$$

If we now make the effective range approximation $\rho(0, -W) = r_0$, there follows

$$r_0 = (2/\gamma)(1 - 1/\gamma a) \tag{10.22}$$

The use of equation 10.21 represents an extension of the effective range theory to negative energies (bound states), or of the function $a(k)$ to imaginary k. Equation 10.22 gives the most accurate determination of the effective range because the binding energy, and hence γ, is very accurately known.

Using the simplest possible shape, a nuclear well of zero range, we would get from the binding energy alone $1/a = \gamma$, and

$$\sigma = \frac{4\pi}{k^2 + \gamma^2} = \frac{4\pi\hbar^2}{M} \cdot \frac{1}{E + W} \tag{10.23}$$

Corrections to this can be made for any assumed shape and finite range. Taking r of the order of 2 to 3×10^{-13} cm leads to corrections to the zero-range theory which can hardly exceed a factor of 2 for any well whatever.

F. EXPERIMENTAL RESULTS
ON NEUTRON-PROTON SCATTERING

The first experiments on neutron-proton scattering used 2.5-Mev d-d neutrons. The cross section measured was within 20 to 30 per cent of the theoretical value which was then within experimental error. However, the cross section was then also measured for *thermal neutrons* (very slow) for which equation 10.23 gives

$$\sigma \simeq 2.4 \text{ barns}* \tag{10.24}$$

The experimental result was ~50 barns.

Two reasons for this discrepancy are:

1. Corrections to the simple formula (10.23), for the finite range of the forces.

* 1 barn $= 10^{-24}$ cm^2.

2. Fermi showed that protons bound in molecules should have a σ larger than that for free protons by a factor of about 2.5. This second correction brings the experimental value for free protons down to ~ 20 barns. This was checked by measuring the scattering at neutron energies between 1 and 10 ev, where the molecular binding would presumably have no effect. The measured value which is so far most accurate is $\sigma_{\text{free}} = 20.4 \pm 0.1$ barns, still a long way from the expected 3 barns or so.

G. SINGLET STATE OF THE DEUTERON

In 1935 Wigner made a suggestion which closed the gap. He pointed out that the ground state of the deuteron gives information about the interaction of neutrons and protons only if their spins are parallel, and that there must also be a state of the deuteron in which the spins of neutron and proton are antiparallel (singlet state). We are still free to make assumptions about this singlet state, and a small energy W for this state would lead to a large scattering cross section at low neutron energy E, since σ is proportional to $1/(W + E)$. Since W is not known, it must be deduced from the observed cross section. Writing

σ_s = scattering cross section due to singlet state; spins antiparallel

σ_t = scattering cross section due to triplet state; spins parallel

σ = total scattering cross section

we get

$$\sigma = \tfrac{1}{4}\sigma_s + \tfrac{3}{4}\sigma_t \qquad (10.25)$$

The $\frac{1}{4}$ and $\frac{3}{4}$ are the statistical weights of the singlet state and the triplet state, respectively.

To prove that these are the correct statistical weights, it is necessary only to construct the sets of wave functions of the two particles, 1 and 2, corresponding to the two situations. Let α be the eigenstate of spin $+\frac{1}{2}$ and β of spin $-\frac{1}{2}$ along some fixed z axis for a single particle. Then for two particles, 1 and 2,

$$\alpha(1)\alpha(2) \text{ has } M = +1$$

($M = z$ component of total spin)

$$\beta(1)\beta(2) \text{ has } M = -1$$

$$[\alpha(1)\beta(2) + \alpha(2)\beta(1)]/\sqrt{2} \text{ has } M = 0$$

$$[\alpha(1)\beta(2) - \alpha(2)\beta(1)]/\sqrt{2} \text{ has } M = 0$$

The first three functions have total spin 1; the last has total spin 0; there are no more linearly independent functions. Therefore, the statistical weights 3 and 1 are justified.

Using then the zero-range approximation of equation 10.24, inserting the weights from equation 10.25, and denoting the energies of triplet and singlet state by W_t and W_s, respectively, we obtain the cross section

$$\sigma = \frac{\pi\hbar^2}{M}\left(\frac{3}{E + W_t} + \frac{1}{E + |W_s|}\right) \qquad (10.26)$$

Inserting the measured low-energy cross section and the known $W_t = 2.23$ Mev, we infer that W_s must be about 60 kev, much smaller than W_t. The binding in the singlet state is far weaker than in the triplet.

Using our more general theory of effective range with the extension to include both triplet and singlet states, we can write an expression for the S-wave part of the cross section which must hold for any potential and fit experiment up to some 10 Mev, using four parameters:

$$\sigma = \frac{3\pi}{k^2 + (1/a_t - \frac{1}{2}k^2 r_{0t})^2} + \frac{\pi}{k^2 + (1/a_s - \frac{1}{2}k^2 r_{0s})^2} \qquad (10.27)$$

Here a_t, r_{0t} are the Fermi scattering length and effective range for the triplet state, and a_s and r_{0s} the same quantities for the singlet state.

Evidence for neutron spin. These experiments are also strong evidence that the neutron spin is exactly ½. If it were ⅜, there would be two states of the deuteron contributing to the scattering: a quintet, $S = 2$, with statistical weight 5, and a triplet, $S = 1$, with statistical weight 3. This would give

$$\sigma = \frac{\pi\hbar^2}{2M}\left(\frac{3}{E + W_t} + \frac{5}{E + W_q}\right) \qquad (10.28)$$

If this is made to agree with the measured σ at low energies by a choice of W_q, then it gives results for $2E \sim 400$ to 800 kev, which are too large by a factor greater than 1.5, far outside the experimental error. For spin of the neutron greater than ⅜, one must use $l \neq 0$ in order to get the right total spin for the ground state of the deuteron. As was pointed out in Chapter IX, $l \neq 0$ is very unlikely on general principles.

Sign of energy in singlet state. From equation 10.10 or 10.23 it is clear that the square of $a(k)$ is what enters the cross-section formula; the magnitude, but not the sign of $a(k)$ (and hence of $\gamma^2 = MW/\hbar^2$), is fixed by such measurements of total cross section. To determine the sign of the phase shift in the scattered wave, and from it $a(k)$, some measurement involving coherent scattering is necessary. The scattered wave must be allowed to interfere with some other scattered wave, and from the consequences the relative sign may be inferred. It turns out that the sign of a_s is negative, opposite to that of a_t. Now only if a is positive does equation 10.21 have a solution with real γ, corresponding to a bound state. Hence the singlet state of the neutron-proton system is not a real bound state but what is often called a virtual one. The energy W_s has no direct significance; i.e., nothing special happens when the incident neutrons have kinetic energy W_s. The only meaning of W_s is that it describes the scattering through equation 10.26.

For neutrons of zero energy, the triplet state will have a phase shift δ_0 such that

$$k \cot \delta_0 \rightarrow -1/a_t = -1/|a_t|$$

This phase shift is nearly π. For singlet-state scattering we have

$$k \cot \delta_0 \rightarrow -1/a_s = +1/|a_s|$$

so that the shift in phase approaches zero. The amplitudes of the scattered waves in the two cases have opposite sign. It is this fact which leads to the possibility of sensitive interference experiments using various cases of coherent scattering. (See Chapter XI.)

XI. EFFECTS OF MOLECULAR BINDING;
COHERENT SCATTERING

In the preceding chapter the scattering of neutrons was discussed only in the case when the forces acting on the proton before the collision were neglected. It is now worth while to investigate the effects of binding of the proton in molecules.

A. EFFECTS OF BINDING
OF PROTON IN MOLECULES

1. *Chemical bond effect.* If it is assumed that the scattering may be treated in Born's approximation, then the differential cross section is

$$d\sigma = \text{constant} \times m^2 \times |\int \psi_1{}^* \, V \, \psi_2|^2 \, d\Omega \qquad (11.1)$$

where m is the reduced mass of scattered particle and scatterer, and V is their interaction potential. The quantity within the absolute value signs is the matrix element of V between the initial and the final states. Equation 11.1 comes from treating as a perturbation the term $(2m/\hbar^2)V$ in the Schrödinger equation

$$\nabla^2 \psi + (2m/\hbar^2)(E - V)\psi = 0 \qquad (11.2)$$

Solution of the problem gives the cross section proportional to the square of the matrix element of the perturbation which leads to equation 11.1.

Now the reduced mass m depends on whether the proton is free or fixed. (The integral in equation 11.1 does not.) The two limiting cases are:

1. Proton free: $m = \frac{1}{2}M$.
2. Proton bound to *heavy* molecule (e.g., paraffin): $m = M$. We therefore expect

$$\sigma \text{ (bound)} = 4\sigma \text{ (free)} \qquad (11.3)$$

In order to use this argument it is necessary to (1) be able to say when a proton is free and when bound, and (2) justify the use of Born's approximation. Fermi [as reported by Bethe, *Revs. Mod.*

Phys. 9, 122 (1937)] examined the first of these problems and showed that essentially the proton is bound if

$$E_n \ll h\nu \qquad (\approx 0.4 \text{ ev for CH bond in paraffin})$$

where E_n is the neutron energy and ν is the frequency of vibration of the proton in the subgroup of the molecule. Figure 10 shows the ratio of the actual to the free cross section as a function of E_n.

For $E_n < h\nu$, the neutron can-not lose energy to the vibration; at $E_n = h\nu$ the abrupt rise in the cross section comes from a con-tribution due to the possibility of losing one quantum of energy to the vibration. Similar breaks oc-cur at $E_n = 2h\nu$, etc. For E_n much larger than the vibration energy of the proton in the mole-cule, the proton is easily dislodged from its position and acts as a free proton: $\sigma \rightarrow \sigma$ (free).

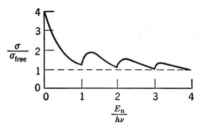

FIG. 10. Cross section for scattering of neutrons by elastically bound protons.

Neutrons with $E_n < h\nu$ will be more difficult to slow down than those with $E_n > h\nu$, because they cannot lose energy to the vibration of the *proton* in the subgroup of the molecule. They can, however, lose energy to vibrations of whole CH_2 subgroups, which have smaller quantum energies. Speaking practically, it can be said that neutrons are easily "cooled" to room temperature ($\frac{1}{40}$ ev), but are with difficulty "cooled" to 20° K or lower.

Of course, Born's approximation is not directly justifiable for neutrons with E_n of the order of 1 ev, as the perturbation (which is considered "small") is of the order of 10 Mev (interaction potential of neutron and proton). However, many theoretical studies, espe-cially by Breit, have shown its validity for the present problem. Placzek and Wick have obtained accurate and useful approximations for the molecular binding effects in many important cases [see *Phys. Rev. 94*, 1228 (1954)].

For heavier nuclei, say mass A, the reduced-mass relation of equa-tion 11.3 becomes instead

$$\sigma \text{ (bound)} = \left(\frac{A+1}{A}\right)^2 \sigma \text{ (free)} \qquad (11.4)$$

2. *Molecular velocity effect.* When the neutron energy is of the order of thermal energies or smaller, it is certainly not permissible to

neglect the thermal motion of the proton. Consider a neutron with velocity v which passes through a thickness L of scattering material, and consider collisions with protons which are moving with velocity $\mathbf{u}$. Then the cross section σ_1 is a function of $|\mathbf{v} - \mathbf{u}|$, and the number of collisions per second is proportional to $\sigma_1 \times |\mathbf{v} - \mathbf{u}|$. The number of collisions in the scatterer will then be proportional to $(L/v)\sigma_1 \times |\mathbf{v} - \mathbf{u}|$, since L/v is the time spent in the scatterer. The effective scattering cross section, defined as proportional to the number of collisions per unit thickness of the scatterer, is

$$\sigma_{\text{eff.}}(\mathbf{u}) = [\sigma_1(|\mathbf{v} - \mathbf{u}|)] \times |\mathbf{v} - \mathbf{u}|/v \qquad (11.5)$$

To obtain the actual effective cross section this expression must be averaged over the distribution in $\mathbf{u}$ [for the case when σ_1 is independent of the magnitude and the direction of $(\mathbf{v} - \mathbf{u})$, see Schwinger, *Phys. Rev. 58*, 1004 (1940)].

B. COHERENT SCATTERING AND ITS MEASUREMENT

Three methods have been employed for the measurement of the coherent neutron-proton scattering at low energies. It is of interest to consider each of these in turn. We present them in order of increasing theoretical complexity.

1. *Neutron diffraction by crystals.* The most direct reliable method for measuring the coherent scattering of neutrons by protons is the study of the diffraction of slow neutrons by crystals containing hydrogen.

The experiment is done in close analogy to similar work with x-rays. A monochromatic beam of neutrons, with wavelength about 1.06 angstroms, is obtained by using the strong Bragg reflection peak from a single crystal of rock salt in a beam of thermal neutrons from a chain-reacting pile. These monochromatic neutrons are in turn scattered from a hydrogenous crystalline powder, and the powder diffraction pattern intensities and positions are carefully measured.

For a given specimen and instrument geometry, the intensity in a given diffraction peak is proportional to the square of the Bragg scattering amplitude, say to $F_{ijk}{}^2$. Here the indices ijk designate the crystal plane responsible for the scattering peak, and when the crystal has a known unit cell structure and dimensions F_{ijk} is just the sum with proper phases of the nuclear scattering amplitudes f for all the atoms of the unit cell.

All this assumes complete coherent Bragg scattering. The random distribution of nuclear spins through the unit cell, the similar random distribution of isotopic nuclei, and the thermal lattice vibrations are all sources of incoherence. The effect of chemical binding must be considered; the coherent Bragg scattering of crystals always means complete binding effects, since the momentum is transferred to the lattice as a whole. Then equation 11.1 gives σ (bound) $= [(A + 1)/A]^2 \sigma$ (free) for Bragg scattering from a nucleus of mass A. The coherent scattering intensity, for various isotopes randomly distributed with abundances c_i, is $|c_1 f_1 + c_2 f_2 + \cdots|^2$. The effect of the random spins is obtained by weighting the appropriate amplitude for each spin state by its statistical weight. The weights can be found as in equation 10.22. The neutron has spin $\frac{1}{2}$; assume the nucleus which is scattering to have spin I. Then the total angular momentum of the colliding system, say J, must have either of the two values $J = I \pm \frac{1}{2}$. The higher J value has $2(I + \frac{1}{2}) + 1$ substates; the lower, $2(I - \frac{1}{2}) + 1$. Then the coherent scattered intensity from a nucleus of spin I must be given by the weighted amplitude squared:

$$f^2 \sim \left| \frac{I+1}{2I+1} f_{I+\frac{1}{2}} + \frac{I}{2I+1} f_{I-\frac{1}{2}} \right|^2 \tag{11.6}$$

The incoherent scattering due to temperature motion can be estimated on a model for the crystal. By use of the Debye model, the x-ray result of the Debye-Waller factor can be taken over to the neutron case [Weinstock, *Phys. Rev. 65*, 1 (1944)]. The corresponding decrease in the coherent scattering is not negligible, and it is the uncertainty of this correction which limits the accuracy of the method.

The spectrometer is first calibrated by diamond powder. The rather rare C^{13} contributes a negligible incoherent contribution from spin and isotopic randomness. Then temperature correction by means of the Debye-Waller factor gives the expected intensity of the Bragg peaks. Summing over all the Bragg peaks, using the known structure of the diamond lattice, we can express the intensity of a given peak in terms of the *total scattering cross section of the carbon nucleus*. σ (free) is measured by direct transmission experiments, and σ (bound) is obtained from equation 11.4. With this calibration, relative intensity measurements of other crystal powders of known structure can be given meaning as absolute scattered amplitudes. This was done carefully for sodium in several different compounds. Then the diffraction of sodium hydride (NaH) was studied, and in this way the coherent scattering amplitude of hydrogen was obtained, with f_{Na} known.   The result was

$$\sigma_{coh} = 4\pi|f_H|^2; \qquad f_H = +3.9 \times 10^{-13} \text{ cm} \qquad (11.7)$$

Now the neutron energy is small enough so that f_H can be written directly in terms of the Fermi scattering lengths, since, from equation 10.10, $1/a^2(k) + k^2 \simeq 1/a^2$.   We get*

$$f_H = -2(\tfrac{3}{4}a_t + \tfrac{1}{4}a_s) \qquad (11.8)$$

where the coefficients of a_t and a_s are the spin weighting factors, and the mass correction factor of equation 11.3 supplies the factor 2. Now the measurement of the total cross section at low energy, reported in Chapter X, yields

$$\sigma_0/4\pi = \tfrac{1}{4}a_s{}^2 + \tfrac{3}{4}a_t{}^2 = 20.4/4\pi \text{ barns}$$

$$= 162 \times 10^{-26} \text{ cm}^2 \qquad (11.9)$$

Obviously this is compatible with equations 11.7 and 11.8 only if a_s and a_t are substantially different.   This proves Wigner's hypothesis that the neutron-proton force is spin-dependent.

In fact, inspection of equations 11.7, 11.8, and 11.9 shows that a_s and a_t must have opposite signs.   We know from the discussion in Chapter X, especially equation 10.21, that a_t is positive, and therefore a_s is negative; i.e., the singlet state is virtual.   Equation 11.7 shows further that $|a_s| > 3a_t$.

It is important to obtain not only these qualitative results but also quantitative values for a_s and especially a_t, because a_t can then be used in equation 10.27 to determine the effective range r_{0t}.   Unfortunately, the accuracy of the crystal diffraction method is not very great.   It can be somewhat improved by examining empirically the variation of the peaks with temperature of the sample and fitting the data with what amounts to a more complicated and more adequate model of the lattice vibrations than the simple Debye description. This dependence on knowledge of the sodium hydride lattice oscillations still limits the accuracy of the method, however.

It is very interesting that the coherent scattering cross section of hydrogen (equation 11.7) is very small (less than 10 per cent) compared with the total cross section σ_0.   Thus most of the scattering is incoherent; it is connected to a "flip" of the spin of the proton.   In

* The sign convention here adopted, $f = -a$, follows from the direct definition of the scattered amplitude and from the discussion leading to equation 10.10. It is common in the literature to redefine f to have the same sign as a, and then one may refer to it as the "coherent scattering length."

other nuclei, the incoherent scattering is usually much less; for instance, for nuclei of zero spin there is no incoherent scattering of this type at all, and for the deuteron (spin 1) the coherent scattering is more than 70 per cent of the total. The coherent scattering of neutrons by hydrogen, however, is not small on an absolute scale and is amply sufficient to determine the position of H atoms in a crystal structure, a task which cannot be accomplished by x-rays whose scatter by an H atom is negligibly small. If it is desired to minimize the background from incoherent (spin flip) scattering for the purpose of crystal structure determination, deuterium can be substituted for hydrogen.

2. *Total internal reflection of neutrons.* The most accurate and certainly the most elegant method for measuring coherent scattering is the use of neutron mirrors. A measurement of the critical angle of internal reflection, and hence of the refractive index for slow neutrons, is made with a mirror of a liquid hydrocarbon. This determines the total coherent scattering of the liquid, and the hydrogen scattering amplitude is thus found in terms of the known value for carbon.

The method depends on an important and general theorem from physical optics which reads [see, e.g., M. Lax, *Revs. Mod. Phys.* *23*, 287 (1951)]:

$$n^2(k) = 1 + \left(\frac{4\pi}{k^2}\right) \sum N_i f_i(0) \tag{11.10}$$

where $n(k)$ is the index of refraction, k the incident wave number (in vacuum), N_i the number of nuclei of a given type i in the material per cubic centimeter, and $f_i(0)$ the coherent scattered amplitude in the forward direction for the nucleus i.

For most nuclei, the amplitude $f_i(0)$ turns out to be negative, corresponding to a *positive* Fermi scattering length a; for, unless the energy is near an absorption level, the nucleus acts more or less like an impenetrable sphere. The refractive index is therefore *less* than unity, and the passage of a neutron beam from vacuum into the material will show the phenomenon of total reflection beyond a certain (nearly grazing) angle of incidence. Using Snell's law at the mirror-vacuum interface, we write $\sin \theta_c / 1 = n/1$, where θ_c is the critical angle of incidence, measured from the normal. Since the index of refraction for neutrons is very near unity, we can write $\sin \theta_c \cong 1 - \delta_c^2 / 2$, where δ_c is the grazing angle measured from the mirror surface. Then

$$\delta_c^2 = -(4\pi/k^2) \sum N_i f_i(0) \tag{11.11}$$

Any neutron beam striking the surface at an angle $\delta < \delta_c$ will be totally reflected back into the vacuum. The limiting angle δ_c is clearly wavelength-dependent, and therefore for any given δ some neutron wavelengths will be totally reflected, but those so short that $\delta_c < \delta$ will not be.

Experimentally, a strong thermal beam of neutrons is directed from air (n_{air} is negligibly different from unity) down at a very small angle against the horizontal surface of a hydrogenous liquid acting as a mirror.* The collimation is made good enough to allow very precise determination of angles, with slits of a millimeter or so in width, and path lengths of 6 meters. The intensity of the reflected beam is measured as a function of angle of incidence. The reflected beam will contain all wavelengths of neutrons from the very longest present down to the critical wavelength, at which $\delta_c(\lambda_c) = \delta$, beyond which the intensity is known to decrease very rapidly. Even though the spectrum of the beam is not well known, it is seen that the reflected intensity is a sensitive function of critical wavelength. Now if several liquid hydrocarbon mixtures of different hydrogen/carbon ratio are used for mirrors, and the angle adjusted to give equal reflected intensity from each, the square of the angle δ_c for each must be proportional to ΣNf for each liquid. Extrapolating to zero δ_c, we get the condition $\Sigma N_i f_i = 0$. Knowing the extrapolated composition of this null-reflecting mixture, we have $N_C f_C + N_H f_H = 0$, where N_C and N_H are the atomic concentrations of C and H.

Thus the measurement gives a ratio for f_H/f_C as the result of a measurement of a liquid mixture. No neutron wavelengths need be known, no spectrum, no cross sections (except to obtain f_H absolutely from f_H/f_C). Moreover, because at the critical angles of reflection the wave penetrates deeply into the forbidden medium (in principle infinitely far at exactly $\delta_c = 0$), the medium is sampled over distances very large compared to atomic spacing. No surface film or the like can affect the result, and no sort of molecular aggregation. Since coherent scattering alone contributes to the refractive index, incoherent effects have no role, and in particular thermal motion cannot contribute, since only purely forward, zero-angle scattering is involved. This method is then intrinsically much more reliable than the others described.

The result [Burgy et al., *Phys. Rev. 84*, 1160 (1951)] is that $f_C/f_H = -1.753 \pm 0.005$. Using the best values of the free carbon cross section (with equation 11.4), and noting that a direct measurement of

---

* Pure H has a refractive index >1 ($f > 0$) and would not show total reflection. The presence of other nuclei with $f < 0$ makes the experiment feasible.

thermal incoherent scattering from carbon proves that the spin and isotopic incoherent contributions of C^{13} are less than 1 per cent, we get

$$f_C = \left(\frac{13}{12}\right)\left(\frac{\sigma_c}{4\pi}\right)^{\frac{1}{2}} = -6.63 \pm 0.03 \times 10^{-13} \text{ cm}$$

From this there follows

$$f_H = +3.78 \pm 0.02 \times 10^{-13} \text{ cm} \tag{11.12}$$

consistent with, but much more accurate than other experimental values.

3. *Scattering by ortho- and para-hydrogen.* The oldest method for the measurement of the coherent scattering is the comparison of the scattering of slow neutrons by ortho- and para-hydrogen. In an ortho-hydrogen molecule, the spins of the two protons are parallel (total proton spin 1); in para-hydrogen, they are antiparallel (total spin 0). Para-hydrogen has the lowest energy state and is therefore stable at low temperature. However, in the absence of a catalyst, the conversion of ortho- to para-hydrogen is very slow. It is therefore possible to "chill" hydrogen from room temperature to low temperatures and to preserve the ratio of ortho- to para-hydrogen that exists at room temperature, which is 3 to 1, the ratio of statistical weights. (See, e.g., Mayer and Mayer, *Statistical Mechanics,* John Wiley & Sons, New York, 1940.) It has thus been possible to measure separately the scattering of neutrons by para- and ortho hydrogen at low temperatures.

We shall now derive an expression for the scattered intensity from a molecule of ortho- or para-hydrogen when the incident neutron energy is so small that $1/k = \lambda_n$ is much greater than the distance between the atoms in the H_2 molecule (≈ 0.75 angstrom unit). This is true for neutrons at temperatures of 20° K or lower. The derivation follows that of Schwinger and Teller [*Phys. Rev. 52*, 286 (1937)].

Let the Pauli spin operators of neutron and proton be $\boldsymbol{\delta}_n$ and $\boldsymbol{\delta}_p$. (These are twice the spin operators $\mathbf{S}_n$ and $\mathbf{S}_p$ in units of $\hbar$.) We wish to investigate the eigenvalues of the operator $\boldsymbol{\delta}_n \cdot \boldsymbol{\delta}_p$. Let $\mathbf{S}$ be the total nuclear spin of the neutron and the proton:

$$\mathbf{S} = \mathbf{S}_n + \mathbf{S}_p \tag{11.13}$$

Therefore

$$\mathbf{S}^2 = \mathbf{S}_n{}^2 + \mathbf{S}_p{}^2 + 2\mathbf{S}_n \cdot \mathbf{S}_p \tag{11.14}$$

since $\mathbf{S}_n$ and $\mathbf{S}_p$ commute.

Now we already know that S^2, $S_n{}^2$, and $S_p{}^2$ are constants of motion, and we know their eigenvalues: $S(S + 1)$, $S_n(S_n + 1)$, and $S_p(S_p + 1)$, respectively, where S is 0 and 1 for the singlet and the triplet states of the deuteron, respectively, and S_n and S_p are each $\frac{1}{2}$. Equation 11.14 can therefore be used to determine

$$S_n \cdot S_p = \frac{1}{2}[S(S + 1) - S_n(S_n + 1) - S_p(S_p + 1)]$$

$$= S(S + 1)/2 - \tfrac{3}{4}$$

and therefore

$$\delta_n \cdot \delta_p = 2S(S + 1) - 3$$

$$= 1 \text{ for } S = 1 \text{ (triplet)} \qquad (11.15)$$

$$= -3 \text{ for } S = 0 \text{ (singlet)}$$

As in equation 11.8, the amplitudes of the scattered neutron wave in singlet and triplet state are just equal at these low energies to the Fermi scattering lengths, a_t and a_s (apart from a minus sign which does not affect their relative behavior).
Then the formula

$$\text{Scattered amplitude} = \frac{a_s + 3a_t}{4} + \frac{a_t - a_s}{4} \delta_n \cdot \delta_p \quad (11.16)$$

is easily seen to be correct for both triplet and singlet states, by direct substitution from equation 11.15.

Since the distance between protons in the molecule is assumed to be much smaller than λ_n, it is permissible to neglect the small phase difference in the scattering from the two protons and add amplitudes directly. Therefore the scattered amplitude from a molecule of H_2 is

$$-f_{H_2} = A = \frac{a_s + 3a_t}{2} + \frac{a_t - a_s}{4} \delta_n \cdot (\delta_{p_1} + \delta_{p_2})$$

$$= \frac{a_s + 3a_t}{2} + \frac{a_t - a_s}{2} \delta_n \cdot S_H \qquad (11.17)$$

where p_1 and p_2 denote the two protons and $\frac{1}{2}(\delta_{p_1} + \delta_{p_2}) = S_H$ is the total spin of the two protons in the H_2 molecule. Now in para-hydrogen the total spin S_H is zero. Therefore, the scattering amplitude for para-hydrogen is

$$f_{\text{para-}H_2} = -\tfrac{1}{2}(a_s + 3a_t) \qquad (11.18)$$

This is just twice the coherent scattering amplitude of a free H atom:

$$f_{\text{Hfree}} = -(\tfrac{3}{4}a_t + \tfrac{1}{4}a_s)$$

That f_{para} is twice f_{Hfree} is due to the fact that the two protons in the H_2 molecule scatter in phase.

The ortho-hydrogen cross section σ_{ortho} also follows from equation 11.17. The squared amplitude $|f_{\text{ortho}}|^2$ contains a cross term, linear in $\mathbf{d}_n$, which vanishes in averaging over the spin directions of the incoming neutron beam. The quadratic term remains and is proportional to the quantity

$$\langle(\mathbf{S_H} \cdot \mathbf{d}_n)(\mathbf{d}_n \cdot \mathbf{S_H})\rangle_{\text{av}} = \langle \mathbf{S_H}^2\rangle_{\text{av}} = S(S+1)$$

The result for the cross section is

$$\sigma_{\text{ortho}} = \sigma_{\text{para}} + 2\pi(a_t - a_s)^2 \tag{11.19}$$

Therefore, it suffices to show that the ortho-hydrogen cross section is greater than that of para-hydrogen in order to prove Wigner's hypothesis that the neutron-proton force is spin-dependent. This can be done by measuring the cross section of the "chilled" room-temperature mixture, brought to low temperatures without allowing time for the ortho-para conversion. In such a mixture the cross section is just

$$\sigma_{\text{mix.}} = \tfrac{3}{4}\sigma_{\text{ortho}} + \tfrac{1}{4}\sigma_{\text{para}} \tag{11.20}$$

This method in fact provided the first experimental proof of Wigner's hypothesis. The better experiments of the kind [R. Sutton et al., *Phys. Rev.* *72*, 1147 (1947)] gave $\sigma_{\text{ortho}} = 125$ barns, $\sigma_{\text{para}} = 4$ barns. Such an enormous ratio of ortho to para scattering means that the coherent scattering is only a small fraction of the total, as already mentioned in connection with crystal scattering (equations 11.7–11.9). It demonstrates that the singlet state is virtual; if it were real, one can show, using the observed total cross section σ_0 and the deuteron binding energy, that the ratio $\sigma_{\text{ortho}}/\sigma_{\text{para}}$ should have been only about 1.4.

If one wishes to derive a_s and a_t from these experiments, corrections must be made for the chemical bond effect, the molecular motion effect, and the slight phase shift, because the scattering protons are a finite though small fraction of a wavelength apart. There is another small correction for inelastic scattering in which the collision converts the molecule from the ortho to the para form. The amplitudes then become $a_t = 5.2 \times 10^{-13}$ cm, $a_s = -23.4 \times 10^{-13}$ cm. These are approximately right, but not nearly so reliable as those derived from the two other methods. There is in the ortho-para measurements an unevaluated systematic error which arises from a possible ortho contamination of the para-hydrogen. A small deviation from the thermal equilibrium concentrations expected after catalysis can have a big effect on the cross section, since $\sigma_{ortho}/\sigma_{para} \sim 30$.

C. RESULTS OF LOW-ENERGY SCATTERING EXPERIMENTS

The effective-range theory expresses the scattering cross section in terms of four parameters; Fermi scattering length and effective range, for both triplet and singlet states. The effective ranges are actually slightly energy-dependent, except in the limiting case of forces of zero range. This small dependence on energy makes possible some conclusions on the shape of the potential.

Three parameters are determined from the three measurements: coherent scattering; total scattering cross section with epithermal neutrons; and the deuteron binding, which corresponds to a virtual scattering at negative energy. From the first two data, one may obtain directly the Fermi scattering lengths a_s and a_t. The ground state of the deuteron, since it has a fixed spin of 1, can provide no information about the singlet interaction, but in combination with a_t it gives the effective triplet range r_{0t}. In the shape-independent approximation we may use equation 10.22 directly. If we include the last term in equation 10.20, then the value of the effective range r_{0t} deduced from γ and a_t will depend slightly on the value of P, i.e., on the shape of the well. Table XIA shows the variation in r_{0t}.

Table XIA.   Triplet Effective Range for Three Potential Shapes (in 10^{-13} Cm)

Well Shape	r_{0t}
Square	1.72 ($\pm$ 2% for all)
Exponential	1.69
Yukawa	1.64

To obtain also the singlet effective range r_{0s}, the fourth parameter, it is necessary to measure neutron-proton scattering at higher energies up to several Mev, but staying in the region where the partial wave of $l = 0$ still gives the only contribution. (Higher partial waves must be corrected for.)

Cross-section measurements of high accuracy (1 per cent or better) have been made for all energies at which monoenergetic neutron beams are available. Such neutron sources are obtained by using charged-particle beams of very homogeneous energies, produced usually by electrostatic generators. If a target is used in which some nuclear reaction yielding neutrons can occur, the neutron beam at a definite angle from the incident beam direction will be mono-energetic. The use of a lithium target with a proton beam produces neutrons from the endothermic reaction $Li^7(p, n)Be^7$ which vary in energy from a few tens of kilovolts for minimal yield up to the energy of the proton beam less the 1.647-Mev threshold. The reaction $H^3(d, n)He^4$ gives a strong neutron source of energy in the region of 13 to 15 Mev with the usual deuteron energies. These sources have made precise work possible for the energies they provide.

The statistical weight factors in equation 10.27 favor the triplet state contribution to scattering in the energy range studied. This is increased further because $1/a_t$ and $\frac{1}{2}k^2r_{0_t}$ in the denominator of the first term in the cross section of equation 10.27 tend to cancel, whereas the corresponding quantities in the second (singlet) term tend to add because of the negative sign of a_s. Moreover, at moderate energies the effective range enters the cross section mainly through the quantity $-k^2r_{0_s}/a_s$ in the denominator of the singlet term, which quantity is small just because a_s is so large. The cross section fit therefore determines r_{0_s} only rather inaccurately.

Since the triplet effective range must be known quite accurately before the singlet range can be determined from the measured cross section using equation 10.27, and since r_{0_t} depends somewhat on the potential shape (Table XIA), it is necessary to assume a definite shape to make the calculation of r_{0_s} possible. We tabulate a few values of the effective ranges as derived from the experiments at various neutron energies, with their errors.

Table XIB.   Values of the Effective Range for Singlet Neutron-Proton Scattering (in 10^{-13} Cm)

	Neutron Energy in Mev			
Well Shape	1.01	2.54	4.75	14.10
Square	2.56 ± .24	2.54 ± .21	2.48 ± .18	2.22 ± .24
Shape-independent	2.53 ± .24	2.48 ± .23	2.39 ± .20	
Exponential	2.51 ± .24	2.41 ± .22	2.33 ± .19	2.24 ± .33
Yukawa	2.46 ± .24	2.25 ± .23	2.02 ± .20	2.11 ± .40

Theoretically, r_{0_s} should be independent of energy. It is seen that this is roughly fulfilled both for the Yukawa and exponential wells, which are relatively long-tailed, and for the square well. It appears safe to take $r_{0_s} = 2.5 \pm 0.2 \times 10^{-13}$ cm.

Collecting the best values and their errors, we obtain a complete description of the S-wave neutron-proton scattering given by the four parameters (Table XIC).

Table XIC.   Shape-Independent Parameters for S-Wave Neutron-Proton Scattering (in 10^{-13} Cm)

$a_t(0)$	$a_s(0)$	r_{0_s}	r_{0_t}
$+5.38(1 \pm 0.004)$	$-23.7(1 \pm 0.003)$	$2.5(1 \pm 0.1)$	$1.70(1 \pm 0.017)$

$$\text{with } k^2 = ME/2\hbar^2 = 1.206 \ (E/\text{Mev}) \times 10^{24} \text{ cm}^{-2}$$

Scattering experiments at these energies cannot fix the shape of the potential. Only comparison of these results with those from other types of experiments will throw some light on the true shape of the potential. All that is shown by scattering results alone is the relative consistency of the description of the neutron-proton forces by non-relativistic quantum mechanics, using a simple potential function, and studying the region near 2 to 3×10^{-13}-cm separation and outside.

XII. INTERACTION OF THE DEUTERON
WITH RADIATION

A. PHOTODISINTEGRATION

Photodisintegration has been used to obtain the binding energy of the deuteron (Chapter IX). It will now be discussed from the point of view of its cross section. The discussion is restricted to low energies (several Mev) so that all the needed constants can be obtained from deuteron binding energy and neutron-proton scattering results. Furthermore, at these energies, the transition probability is attributable almost entirely to the dipole (electric and magnetic) moment. Quadrupole and higher multipole transitions would be important at high energies (100 Mev).

The cross section for γ-ray absorption is (compare Heitler, *Quantum Theory of Radiation*, 3rd ed., pp. 180 and 205, Oxford, 1954).

$$\frac{d\sigma}{d\Omega} = 2\,\frac{\omega m^2 v}{\hbar^3 c}\,|M|^2 \tag{12.1}$$

where $\omega = 2\pi\nu$ is the (circular) frequency of the incoming photon, m is the reduced mass of the system $= \frac{1}{2}M_{\mathrm{H}}$ and v is the velocity of the emitted particle. M is the matrix element, for the transition, of the electric or magnetic dipole moment.

We first discuss the effect due to *electric interaction*. Since the z component of the electric dipole moment of the proton in the center-of-mass system is $ez/2$, if z is the coordinate of the proton relative to the neutron, we have

$$M_{\mathrm{elec.}} = (e/2)\int\psi_i z\psi_f\,d\tau \tag{12.2}$$

where ψ_i is the wave function of the deuteron in the ground state.

The final state must be a P state to produce a non-vanishing matrix element. Since no stable P states exist (Chapter IX), it must be a P state of the continuous spectrum. For energies small compared to the well depth, the wave function of the P state will be practically zero inside the well. Thus the potential energy of the P state will be small, and the state will be only very slightly

75

distorted from that of a P state with no potential well. In the calculation of the matrix element, therefore, the wave function of a free particle of angular momentum 1 may be used for ψ_f. The free wave function is normalized per unit volume.

Since the contribution to the matrix element from the region inside the well is so small, it is nearly correct to replace ψ_i by its asymptotic expression: $\psi_i = c_i u_i/r$, $u_i \to e^{-\gamma r}$. Only the normalization constant c_i will involve the range of the forces. If we write $4\pi c_i^2 \int_0^\infty u_i^2\, dr = 1$ and recall the definition (equation 10.17) of $\rho(E_1, E_2)$,

$$\int_0^\infty u_i^2\, dr = \int_0^\infty (e^{-\gamma r})^2\, dr - \tfrac{1}{2}\rho(-W_1, -W_1)$$

$$\therefore c_i^2 = \frac{1}{4\pi}\left[\frac{2\gamma}{1 - \gamma\rho(-W_1, -W_1)}\right] \cong \frac{1}{4\pi}\left(\frac{2\gamma}{1 - \gamma r_{0_t}}\right) \quad (12.3)$$

If this is used with equation 12.1 and 12.2, the result is

$$d\sigma = 2\left(\frac{e^2}{\hbar c}\right)\cos^2\chi\left[\frac{\gamma k^3}{(\gamma^2 + k^2)^3}\right]\left(\frac{1}{1 - \gamma r_{0_t}}\right)d\Omega \quad (12.4)$$

where k is the wave number of the system after absorption of the quantum, so that

$$\left.\begin{array}{l} E \text{ of system} = h\nu - W_1 = \hbar^2 k^2/M \\ \text{Deuteron binding energy} = W_1 = \hbar^2\gamma^2/M \end{array}\right\} \quad (12.5)$$

χ is the angle between the direction of *polarization* of the γ-ray and the direction of motion of the proton. The factor $\cos^2\chi$ arises from the wave function of the final state. If the beam is unpolarized, and we average over all directions of polarization

$$\overline{\cos^2\chi} = \tfrac{1}{2}\sin^2\theta \quad (12.6)$$

where θ is the angle of the emitted proton with the direction of *propagation* of the incident photon. On the other hand, if we hold the direction of polarization fixed and average over all proton directions, we get

$$\int \cos^2\chi\, d\Omega = 4\pi/3 \quad (12.7)$$

From equations 12.3, 12.5, and 12.7, the total cross section becomes

$$\sigma_{\text{elec.}} = \frac{8\pi}{3}\frac{e^2}{\hbar c}\frac{\hbar^2}{M}\frac{W_1^{1/2}E_{\text{c.m.}}^{3/2}}{(E + W_1)^3}\left(\frac{1}{1 - \gamma r_{0_t}}\right) \quad (12.8)$$

where the last factor is the only correction to the zero-range cross section and is almost independent of potential shape.

The *photomagnetic disintegration* makes use of the magnetic dipole moment. If μ_p and μ_n are the moments of proton and neutron, respectively, in units of the nuclear magneton, then the magnetic dipole moment of the system is

$$(e\hbar/2Mc)(\mu_p \delta_p + \mu_n \delta_n) \qquad (12.9)$$

The initial state is, as before, the $^3S_1$ ground state of the deuteron the spatial dependence of which is given approximately by equation 12.3. The final state must also be an S state, or the integration over angles will vanish. However, all excited ^3S states are orthogonal to the ground state, since they are produced by the same potential well. The only possibility, therefore, is that the final state be the virtual $^1S_0$ state. Since this final state is an S state, the emitted protons will show isotropic distribution in angle, in contrast with the result (equation 12.4) for photoelectric disintegration in which the final state was a P state.

The matrix element for the transition is therefore given by

$$M_m = (e\hbar/2Mc) \sum_{\text{spin}} \chi_0 (\mu_p \delta_p + \mu_n \delta_n) \chi_1 \int \psi_i \psi_f \, d\tau \qquad (12.10)$$

where χ_1 and χ_0 are the spin functions of the triplet and the singlet states, and ψ_i is the wave function for the ground state which is approximated by equation 12.3. ψ_f is the wave function for the singlet S state in the continuous spectrum; for a plane wave exp (ikz), the S wave is just $(\sin kr/kr)$.

The matrix element can be computed in the same general way as that for the photoelectric effect; the integral is done using the asymptotic forms for both initial and final wave functions. The ground-state wave function and its normalizing factor are given by equation 12.3. For the singlet state, we can write the comparison function of equation 10.13, normalizing to approach asymptotically (apart from the phase shift) the S part of a plane wave normalized per unit volume:

$$\psi_f \cong c_s \frac{u_s}{r}; \quad u_s = \frac{\sin (kr + \delta_s)}{\sin \delta_s}; \quad c_s = \frac{\sin \delta_s}{(4\pi)^{1/2}k} \qquad (12.11)$$

and from the relation

$$k \cot \delta_s = -1/a_s(k) = -(1/a_s) + \tfrac{1}{2}k^2 r_{0_s}^2 + \cdots$$

we have

$$c_s^2 = \frac{1}{4\pi[k^2 + 1/a_s^2(k)]} \qquad (12.12)$$

The integral is elementary, and substituting the result into equation 12.10 and that in turn into the general formula (12.1), we get

$$\sigma_m = \frac{2\pi}{3} \frac{e^2}{\hbar c} \left(\frac{\hbar}{Mc}\right)^2 (\mu_n - \mu_p)^2 \frac{[\gamma - 1/a_s(k)]^2}{[k^2 + 1/a_s(k)]^2} \frac{k\gamma}{(k^2 + \gamma^2)} \frac{1}{(1 - \gamma r_{0_t})}$$

(12.13)

in a shape-independent approximation. Actually we have omitted correction terms to the integral $\int \psi_i \psi_f \, d\tau$ which are of the order of the k-dependent terms in $1/a(k)$. It is clear from equation 12.13, and also by correcting the integral, that r_{0_s} and r_{0_t} occur in the more accurate cross section. It turns out [Bethe and Longmire, *Phys. Rev.* 77, 647 (1950)] that only the difference of the effective ranges, $r_{0_s} - r_{0_t}$, determines the major correction to equation 12.13. On this argument alone, the quantity r_{0_s}, so hard to measure in scattering, might be determined from measurements of σ_m, but as we shall see in the next sections, other theoretical uncertainties have so far prevented the success of this method.

From equation 12.13 it can be seen that σ_m has a maximum where

$$k_m^2 = \frac{1}{a_s^2(0)}; \qquad W_0 = \frac{\hbar^2 k_m^2}{M} = \frac{\hbar^2}{M a_s^2(0)}$$

(12.14)

and W_0 is often called the energy of the virtual singlet state of the deuteron.

The cross section σ_m can be written in the notation of equation 12.8, giving

$$\sigma_m = \frac{2\pi}{3} \frac{e^2}{\hbar c} \left(\frac{\hbar}{Mc}\right)^2 (\mu_n - \mu_p)^2 \frac{W_1 E^{1/2}(W_1^{1/2} + W_0^{1/2})^2}{(E + W_1)(E + W_0)}$$

(12.15)

in which we have used the fact that a_s is negative, the virtual state energy of the singlet state defined in equation 12.14, and neglected the range correction factors.

The factor $(\mu_p - \mu_n)^2$ in equation 12.15 can be understood if we write the operator $\mu_p \delta_p + \mu_n \delta_n$ in the form

$$\tfrac{1}{2}(\mu_p + \mu_n)(\delta_p + \delta_n) + \tfrac{1}{2}(\mu_p - \mu_n)(\delta_p - \delta_n)$$

(12.16)

and note that the first term gives no contribution to the matrix element (equation 12.15). This follows from the fact that $(\delta_p + \delta_n)$, operating on the spin function χ_1, reproduces χ_1 multiplied by a constant factor, whereas we wish to produce χ_0.

Both the electric and magnetic cross sections decrease as $E^{-3/2}$ at high energies ($E \gg W_1 = 2.2$ Mev), but the magnetic cross section is smaller by a factor of about

$$\frac{\sigma_m}{\sigma_{\text{elec.}}} \simeq \frac{1}{4} \frac{W_1}{Mc^2} (\mu_p - \mu_n)^2 \tag{12.17}$$

$$\simeq \frac{1}{4} \frac{2.2}{931} (2.79 + 1.91)^2 = 0.013 = 1.3 \text{ per cent}$$

The smallness of this factor results from the smallness of the magnetic dipole moment $e\hbar/2Mc$ compared with the electric dipole moment $ez/2$, because the deuteron is large in size compared to a proton Compton wavelength.

At low energies ($E \ll W_1 = 2.2$ Mev) the electric cross section behaves as $E^{3/2}$, whereas the magnetic cross section behaves as $E^{1/2}/(E + W_0)$. Thus, for energies sufficiently near the threshold, the magnetic cross section will dominate by the factor

$$\frac{\sigma_m}{\sigma_{\text{elec.}}} \simeq \left[\frac{1}{4} \frac{W_1}{Mc^2} (\mu_p - \mu_n)^2 \right] \frac{W_1}{E} \frac{W_1}{W_0 + E} = 0.013 \frac{W_1}{E} \frac{W_1}{W_0 + E} \tag{12.18}$$

For the γ-ray energies studied in the region near threshold, the highest ratio of $\sigma_m/\sigma_{\text{elec.}}$ is ~ 0.7, given by the 2.507-Mev γ-ray from Ga^{72}. More precise evaluation [Salpeter, *Phys. Rev. 82*, 60 (1951)] gives values varying with potential shape from 0.65 to 0.68.

A plot of these photo cross sections as a function of energy is given in Fig. 11. The maximum photoelectric cross section, at $h\nu = 2W_1$, is about 2.3 millibarns, and the cross section at 25 Mev is 0.5 millibarn.

B. EXPERIMENTS ON PHOTODISINTEGRATION

The first observations of the photodisintegration of the deuteron were made in a cloud chamber, with the 2.62-Mev γ-rays from ThC″ [Chadwick and Goldhaber, *Nature 134*, 237 (1935)]. The determination of the cross section in this way is difficult: the sensitive time of a cloud chamber is hard to determine, and also a large error in the measured γ-ray intensity is possible.

The most complete measurements to date give the total cross section for half a dozen γ-ray energies from 2.5 to 17.6 Mev. The experimental values are compared with Fig. 11. The agreement with theory is excellent. The method used by Wilkinson and his co-workers [*Phys. Rev. 86*, 359, 383 (1952)] gave absolute cross sections to 5 or 10 per cent. They observed the disintegrations by counting ionization pulses from the photoprotons in a spherical chamber filled with

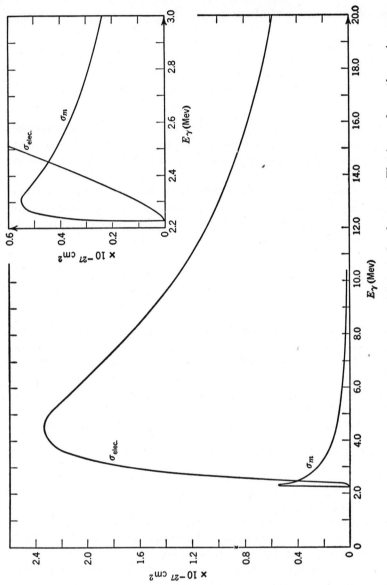

FIG. 11. Photoelectric and photomagnetic cross sections of the deutron. The inset shows the region near threshold energy much magnified.

deuterium gas, making careful corrections for the protons which struck the wall. The γ-ray flux was calibrated both by a measurement of the absolute ion current in a thick-walled graphite chamber and by a count of the α's accompanying the emission of γ's in the $F^{19}(p, \alpha)O^{16*}$ reaction, which was the source of γ's used at 6.14 Mev.

At energies where the magnetic photoeffect is still appreciable, the angular distribution of photoprotons will be given by interference between the outgoing S wave from the magnetic dipole interaction and the P wave from the electric dipole interaction, so that

$$\frac{d\sigma(\gamma, p)}{d\Omega} = a + b \sin \theta + c \sin^2 \theta \qquad (12.19)$$

Careful angular distribution measurements have been made.

The angular distribution measurements at energies not too far from threshold give good agreement with the theoretical values of $\sigma_m/\sigma_{\text{elec.}}$, as Table XIIA shows.

Table XIIA. Ratio of Photomagnetic to Photoelectric Cross Section

γ-Ray	Ga^{72}	ThC''	Na^{24}	$F(p, \alpha)O^{16*}$
Energy (Mev)	2.507	2.615	2.757	6.14
$\sigma_m/\sigma_{\text{elec.}}$ (observed)	0.61 ± 0.14	0.37 ± 0.12	0.26 ± 0.06	0.03 ± 0.06
$\sigma_m/\sigma_{\text{elec.}}$ (calculated)	0.67	0.40	0.25	0.026

Higher energies have not been fully investigated. The electric quadrupole transition to the ^3D state begins to contribute appreciably above 10 Mev or so and leads to a forward asymmetry of the photoparticles, an asymmetry which always implies interference between emerging waves of opposing parity. This effect has been clearly observed. The effect of tensor forces, modifying both the ground and the outgoing states, is complicated, but very small below 20 Mev.

C. CAPTURE OF NEUTRONS BY PROTONS

This is the process inverse to photodisintegration. The cross section for capture can be obtained from that for photodisintegration by statistical considerations such as those that follow.

Consider a box containing protons, neutrons, deuterons, and γ-rays in equilibrium. Let state 1 consist of deuteron and γ-ray and state 2 of neutron and proton. Then at equilibrium,

$v_1\sigma_{1\to2} \times$ [number of states 1]
$$= v_2\sigma_{2\to1} \times \text{[number of states 2]} \qquad (12.20)$$

This equation will still hold if the brackets are replaced by the density of states per unit energy. This quantity is in general

$$\frac{4\pi p^2}{(2\pi\hbar)^3}\frac{dp}{dE}\,g \tag{12.21}$$

per unit volume of the box, where p is the momentum and g is the statistical weight of the states. Using the relativistic relations

$$\frac{E^2}{c^2} = p^2 + m^2c^2; \quad \frac{dp}{dE} = \frac{E}{c^2p}; \quad \frac{Ev}{c^2} = p \tag{12.22}$$

equation 12.20 becomes

$$\frac{\sigma_{2\to1}}{\sigma_{1\to2}} = \frac{g_1\,p_1v_1E_1}{g_2\,p_2v_2E_2} = \frac{g_1\,p_1{}^2}{g_2\,p_2{}^2} \tag{12.23}$$

This is a general relation. To apply it to the definitions of states 1 and 2, set

$g_1 = g_dg_\gamma;\ p_1 = p_\gamma = \hbar\omega/c;\ \omega = 2\pi \times \gamma$-ray frequency
$g_2 = g_ng_p;\ p_2 = p_{n,p} = Mv/2;\ M =$ proton or neutron mass
$v =$ relative velocity of proton and neutron

g_d is 3 for the state $S = 1$, corresponding to the three possible directions of the spin. g_γ is 2, corresponding to the two possible directions of polarization of the photon. g_n and g_p are each 2, corresponding to the two directions of spin. Using expression 12.15 for σ_m, we get

$$\sigma_{\text{capture}} = \pi\,\frac{e^2}{Mc^2}\,\frac{\hbar}{Mc}\sqrt{\frac{2W_1}{E_0}}\,\frac{(W_1{}^{1/2} + W_0{}^{1/2})^2(W_1 + E_0/2)}{(W_0 + E_0/2)Mc^2}\,(\mu_p - \mu_n)^2 \tag{12.24}$$

where $E_0/2 = E = Mv^2/4 =$ energy of neutron and proton in the center-of-mass system. The σ_m has been used instead of the total photodisintegration cross section of the deuteron because σ_{capture} will be appreciable only at low energies and here σ_{elec} is small compared to σ_m. At very low energies σ_{capture} is proportional to $E_0{}^{-1/2}$, i.e., to $1/v$. But $\sigma_{\text{capture}}v$ is proportional to the number of capture processes per unit time; therefore, the probability (per second) of capture of slow neutrons by protons is *independent of the neutron velocity* (also of the proton velocity, if any).

At $v = 2200$ m/sec, $E_0 \simeq 0.025$ ev, $\sigma_{\text{capture}} = 0.330 \pm 0.005$ barn experimentally; theory roughly agrees. This is a rather large capture cross section as capture cross sections go. This accounts for the fact that hydrogen is not used as a moderator in "piles," operating with normal uranium. Carbon and deuterium have capture cross sections about 1/100 of that of hydrogen. One reason for the large value for hydrogen is the large size of $(\mu_p - \mu_n)$; another is the large scattering length of the virtual singlet state (near-resonance at zero energy).

D. INTERACTION AND MESONIC EFFECTS

The treatment given here was of course entirely phenomenological. The magnetic moments, for example, were regarded as fixed properties of the nucleons. The additivity of the free nucleon moments in the deuteron is at first sight strong evidence for this, but it has been shown that any forces of exchange nature could not change the expectation value of the deuteron magnetic moment but might well affect its fluctuations, i.e., the chances of magnetic dipole transitions in an external radiation field. Fitting the apparent exchange moment contribution in the pair of mirror nuclei H^3 and He^3, Austern and Sachs [*Phys. Rev. 81*, 710 (1951)] showed that this effect might mean an increase in the neutron capture cross section of some 2 to 4 per cent, and larger relative changes in the much less important magnetic part of the cross section at high energies. It has also been shown that the photomagnetic capture cross section of the *deuteron*, which is abnormally low, would in fact vanish strictly if H^3 had a simple spherically symmetric ground state and there were no exchange effects.

At high energies, of course, the simple dipole approximation is not good. Electric quadrupole terms especially become important for the deuteron photodisintegration. But experiment shows a very great increase over the cross section as calculated, even including all orders of multipole. The deviations first become serious at $h\nu \simeq 150$ Mev. It is likely that these processes involve the creation and reabsorption of π-mesons within the deuteron. The whole subject emphasizes the restriction of the rather static picture of nucleons interacting by a given potential to the region of classical nuclear physics, well below 100 Mev.

E. PHOTOEFFECT AND
THE POTENTIAL PARAMETERS

Evidently equation 12.8 gives a direct value for the triplet effective range r_{0t}, or more accurately $\rho_t(-W_1, -W_1)$, from the absolute photo cross sections. The good agreement in the energy dependence between experiment and theory confirms the effective-range procedure, and the absolute values determine $1/(1 - \gamma\rho_t)$ and thus

ρ_t. Some small shape-dependent corrections are made, but they represent effects not yet experimentally detectable. The value of r_{0_t} from the photoeffect is $1.7 \pm 0.1 \times 10^{-13}$ cm, in very good agreement with the more accurate but less direct value given in Chapter XI.

The occurrence of the term $1/a_s(k)$ in equation 12.13 means that careful measurements of the magnetic photo cross section can lead to a knowledge of the singlet effective range in terms of the triplet effective range r_{0_t}. This value can be obtained quite precisely from careful measurement of the neutron-proton capture cross section at thermal neutron energies. The value so obtained can be compared with that derived from the fit of $1/a_s(k)$ to the linear plot given by use of the scattering cross sections between ~ 1 and 15 Mev. Even more interesting is the fact that the small shape-dependent corrections to the approximate theory result in changes of opposite sign in the values of r_{0_s} coming from the two types of experiment. A long-tailed potential tends to yield a small effective range for a given scattering cross section, whereas it gives a large effective range for a fixed capture cross section. It may be easier experimentally to learn something about the shape of the potential function by this means than by the exceedingly accurate scattering cross-section measurements which would be necessary to obtain the deviations from the linear plot for $1/a_s(k)$ accurately enough to give information on the well shape. At present, however, the experimental data on the one hand, and the interaction corrections on the other, make any conclusion premature. The result from the capture experiments is roughly the same as that which follows from neutron-proton scattering but is less accurate.

XIII. SCATTERING OF PROTONS BY PROTONS

No stable state of He^2 is observed, and this is supported theoretically by the fact that the potential energy function for the proton-proton interaction which is derived from proton-proton scattering experiments leads to no bound state. Thus proton-proton scattering is the only way to get direct evidence on proton-proton forces. Proton-proton scattering experiments are easier to perform and interpret than proton-neutron experiments, for the following reasons:

1. Protons are readily available over a wide range of energies.

2. Protons can be made monochromatic in energy. The best reaction to produce monochromatic neutrons is $d + H^3 \rightarrow He^4 + n$; this is good for neutrons from 14 Mev to some 20 or 25 Mev; above these energies, only roughly monoenergetic neutrons can be produced.

3. Protons can be produced in well-collimated beams. Fast neutron beams are very hard to collimate.

4. Protons are easily detected by their ionization, which makes possible more accurate measurements of angular distribution than for neutrons.

5. Protons undergo Coulomb scattering simultaneously with nuclear scattering. This might seem to be a disadvantage, but actually it permits a determination of the interference between nuclear and Coulomb scattering, and this makes for greater sensitivity (in case one of the scattering probabilities is small) and also allows a determination of the sign of the phase shifts resulting from the nuclear scattering. Further, the Coulomb scattering is well known theoretically and experimentally and can be used to calibrate the nuclear scattering measurements.

6. The proton-proton combination obeys Fermi statistics, whereas in the neutron-proton combination states symmetric with respect to particle interchange as well as antisymmetric states occur. This simplifies the analysis of proton-proton scattering, but of course neutron-proton scattering still must be measured in order to get complete information.

A. THEORY OF PROTON-PROTON SCATTERING

The theory of proton-proton scattering is more complicated than that of neutron-proton scattering because of the presence of the Coulomb potential in addition to the nuclear potential. The Coulomb potential requires a rather special wave-mechanical treatment of the scattering problem because of the slow variation of the potential with distance.

Scattering by Coulomb field. Rutherford first investigated the scattering by a Coulomb field from the classical standpoint. His result is well known:

$$d\sigma = [e^4 Z_1{}^2 Z_2{}^2 / 4m^2 v^4 \sin^4 (\theta/2)] 2\pi \sin \theta \, d\theta \qquad (13.1)$$

where $Z_1 e$ and $Z_2 e$ are the charges of the particles, v is the velocity of the incident particle, m is the reduced mass, and θ is the scattering angle in the center-of-mass system. For two protons, $Z_1 = Z_2 = 1$, $m = M/2$, $\theta/2 = \theta_1$ (laboratory system). In the laboratory system equation 13.1 then becomes

$$d\sigma = (e^4/E_0{}^2)(1/\sin^4 \theta_1 + 1/\cos^4 \theta_1) \cos \theta_1 \, 2\pi \sin \theta_1 \, d\theta_1 \qquad (13.2)$$

The term containing $\cos^4 \theta_1$ is added because each proton at angle θ_1 in the laboratory system is accompanied by a recoil proton at angle $(\pi/2 - \theta_1)$, and these recoil protons are not counted in equation 13.1. A factor $4 \cos \theta_1$ arises from the transformation of the solid angle from the center-of-mass system to the laboratory system. $E_0 = \frac{1}{2} M v^2$ is the kinetic energy in the laboratory system.

As is well known, the Rutherford equation (13.1) agrees with the experimental results for the scattering of low-energy α-particles or protons by nuclei, the effect of the nuclear potential being negligible at these low energies. However, even at fairly low energies, the classical equation (13.2) does not give the correct scattering of protons *by protons*. One reason for this is the neglect of symmetry requirements by the classical theory. The wave-mechanical treatment of scattering in a Coulomb field by Mott showed that the correct result for identical scatterer and incident particle is

$$d\sigma = \frac{e^4}{E_0{}^2} \left(\frac{1}{\sin^4 \theta_1} + \frac{1}{\cos^4 \theta_1} \right.$$
$$\left. - \frac{\cos [(e^2/\hbar v) \ln \tan^2 \theta_1]}{\sin^2 \theta_1 \cos^2 \theta_1} \right) \cos \theta_1 \, 2\pi \sin \theta_1 \, d\theta_1 \qquad (13.3)$$

(see Mott and Massey, *Theory of Atomic Collisions*, 2nd ed., 303, Oxford, 1949). The extra term comes in because the identity of scattered particle and scatterer places symmetry requirements on the wave function. This term represents interference between the two parts of the wave function describing the two-proton system. The sign is negative because protons obey Fermi statistics. For unlike particles these terms drop out and the equation agrees exactly with the Rutherford equation (13.1).

For proton energies of 1 Mev and higher ($v > c/20$), $e^2/\hbar v < \frac{1}{4}$, so $\cos [(e^2/\hbar v) \ln \tan^2 \theta_1]$ is nearly unity except for θ_1 nearly zero or nearly $\pi/2$. Except in these regions, equation 13.3 is approximately

$$d\sigma = E_0{}^2 \left(\frac{1}{\sin^4 \theta_1} + \frac{1}{\cos^4 \theta_1} \right.$$
$$\left. - \frac{1}{\sin^2 \theta_1 \cos^2 \theta_1} \right) \cos \theta_1 \, 2\pi \sin \theta_1 \, d\theta_1 \quad (13.4)$$

However, experiments of White, and of Tuve, Heydenburg, and Hafstad in 1936, indicated considerably more protons at 45° than given by equation 13.4 at proton energies of about 1 Mev. This indicates that the nuclear potential already has an appreciable effect.

Effect of nuclear potential. It is reasonable to assume that the nuclear potential between two protons has the same characteristics as that between neutron and proton. The Wigner argument about short-range forces (Chapter VIII) involves both proton-proton and neutron-proton forces. The main difference between proton and neutron seems to be the electric charge, and the nuclear force apparently does not arise from charge. We assume therefore that the potential between two protons is confined within some short range a as before, although the value of a need not necessarily be the same.

Therefore, in proton-proton scattering *at low energies* it is expected that only the $l = 0$ scattering processes will be affected by the nuclear potential, just as in neutron-proton scattering.

We shall now merely outline the solution of the problem. (See Mott and Massey, *Theory of Atomic Collisions*, for a more complete development.)

In a purely Coulomb field, and in the center-of-mass system, an asymptotic solution of the Schrödinger equation for the scattering of two particles of equal mass M, one of which has laboratory energy $\frac{1}{2}Mv^2$, is

$$\psi(\mathbf{r}) = \exp [ikz + i\eta \ln k(r - z)]$$
$$+ (g(\theta)/r) \exp (ikr - i\eta \ln 2kr + i\pi + 2i\zeta_0) \quad (13.5)$$

where
$$g(\theta) = [e^2/Mv^2 \sin^2 (\theta/2)] \exp [-i\eta \ln \sin^2 (\theta/2)] \quad (13.5a)$$
and

$$\eta = e^2/\hbar v; \quad k = Mv/2\hbar; \quad e^{i\zeta_0} = \Gamma(1 + i\eta)/|\Gamma(1 + i\eta)| \quad (13.5b)$$

The first term in equation 13.5 is the incident wave, an almost plane wave with a small space-dependent phase shift caused by the long-range nature of the Coulomb potential. The second term is the spherical scattered wave. The square of the absolute value of $g(\theta)$ gives the cross section per unit solid angle, $d\sigma/d\Omega$, when there are no symmetry requirements on ψ. Note that $|g(\theta)|^2$ agrees exactly with equation 13.1, which is, therefore, correct for scattering of unlike particles with a pure Coulomb field.

Now let us consider the effect of the nuclear forces, but for the moment let the identity of the particles be disregarded. Then let $\psi(\mathbf{r})$ be expanded in Legendre polynomials of $\cos \theta$:

$$\psi(\mathbf{r}) = (1/r) \sum_l v_l(r)P_l(\cos \theta) \quad (13.6a)$$

and let the true wave function $\chi(\mathbf{r})$, which includes the effect of the nuclear forces, be also expanded:

$$\chi(\mathbf{r}) = (1/r) \sum_l u_l(r)P_l(\cos \theta) \quad (13.6b)$$

No ϕ dependence is required, because the incident wave is along the z axis (axis of the polar coordinate system). Such expansions are possible as long as both the Coulomb and the nuclear potentials are central. The lth term in the sums is the component of the wave with angular momentum l. $v_l(r)$ and $u_l(r)$ are solutions of the radial Schrödinger equation with pure Coulomb potential and with Coulomb-plus-nuclear potential, respectively. Thus $v_l(r)$ and $u_l(r)$ can be found; when they are calculated, it is found that asymptotically as $z \to \infty$, $u_l(kr) = v_l(kr + \delta_l)$, where δ_l is a constant phase shift depending on l.

Now for the present we shall treat only protons of low energy (<10 Mev, let us say); then only δ_0 is appreciable. We need therefore to correct only the wave with $l = 0$. In this case we may write

$$\chi(\mathbf{r}) = \psi(\mathbf{r}) + (1/r)[u_0(r) - v_0(r)] \quad (13.7)$$

When $u_0(r)$ and $v_0(r)$ are normalized correctly, it is found that
$$\chi(\mathbf{r}) = \exp [ikz + i\eta \ln k(r - z)]$$
$$+ (1/r) \exp [ikr - i\eta \ln 2kr + i\pi + 2i\zeta_0]f(\theta) \quad (13.8)$$

where

$$f(\theta) = \frac{e^2}{Mv^2} \frac{\exp\left[-i\eta \ln \sin^2\left(\theta/2\right)\right]}{\sin^2\left(\theta/2\right)} + \frac{i}{2k}\left(e^{2i\delta_0} - 1\right) \quad (13.9)$$

The difference between this $f(\theta)$ and the $f(\theta)$ of equation 13.5b is the added term containing δ_0 which describes the nuclear scattering.

Symmetry of wave function. Equations 13.8 and 13.9 give the correct results for the scattering of unlike particles with a Coulomb potential. We must now correct these equations to account for the identity of the two protons. The spatial wave function must be either symmetrical, with total spin = 0, or antisymmetrical, with total spin = 1. Now $\chi(\mathbf{r})$ of equation 13.5 is neither symmetrical nor antisymmetrical. But

$$\chi_s = (1/\sqrt{2})[\chi(\mathbf{r}) + \chi(-\mathbf{r})] \quad (13.10a)$$

is obviously symmetrical and

$$\chi_a = (1/\sqrt{2})[\chi(\mathbf{r}) - \chi(-\mathbf{r})] \quad (13.10b)$$

is obviously antisymmetrical. Replacing $(\mathbf{r})$ by $(-\mathbf{r})$ is equivalent to replacing r by r, z by $-z$, and θ by $(\pi - \theta)$. If the expansion is considered and it is remembered that

$$P_l[\cos\left(\pi - \theta\right)] = (-1)^l P_l\left(\cos\theta\right) \quad (13.11)$$

it is seen that in 13.10a components with odd l drop out, whereas in 13.10b components with even l drop out. The $f(\theta)$'s for χ_s and χ_a are

$$f_s(\theta) = \frac{e^2}{Mv^2}\left\{\frac{\exp\left[-i\eta \ln \sin^2\left(\theta/2\right)\right]}{\sin^2\left(\theta/2\right)}\right.$$
$$\left. + \frac{\exp\left[-i\eta \ln \cos^2\left(\theta/2\right)\right]}{\cos^2\left(\theta/2\right)}\right\} + \frac{i}{k}\left(e^{2i\delta_0} - 1\right) \quad (13.12a)$$

$$f_a(\theta) = \frac{e^2}{Mv^2}\left\{\frac{\exp\left[-i\eta \ln \sin^2\left(\theta/2\right)\right]}{\sin^2\left(\theta/2\right)}\right.$$
$$\left. - \frac{\exp\left[-i\eta \ln \cos^2\left(\theta/2\right)\right]}{\cos^2\left(\theta/2\right)}\right\} \quad (13.12b)$$

$f_s(\theta)$ comes from singlet $(S = 0)$ scattering, and $f_a(\theta)$ comes from triplet $(S = 1)$ scattering. The singlet and the triplet scattering add incoherently. Therefore, the total differential cross section is

$$d\sigma = \left[\tfrac{3}{4}\left|f_a(\theta)\right|^2 + \tfrac{1}{4}\left|f_s(\theta)\right|^2\right] \cdot 2\pi \sin\theta\, d\theta$$
$$= F(\theta) \cdot 2\pi \sin\theta\, d\theta \quad (13.13)$$

(definition of F).

To go to the laboratory system, replace θ by $2\theta_1$:

$$d\sigma = F(2\theta_1) \cdot 4 \cos \theta_1 \cdot 2\pi \sin \theta_1 \, d\theta_1 \qquad (13.14)$$

From equations 13.12 to 13.14, and with the small exponents in equation 13.12 again neglected [a complete formula, including these terms, was given by Breit, Thaxton, and Eisenbud, *Phys. Rev. 55*, 1018 (1939)], the cross section per unit solid angle is

$$\frac{d\sigma}{d\Omega} = \frac{e^4}{E_0{}^2} \left[\frac{1}{\sin^4 \theta_1} + \frac{1}{\cos^4 \theta_1} - \frac{1}{\sin^2 \theta_1 \cos^2 \theta_1} \right. $$
$$\left. - \frac{2\hbar v}{e^2} \frac{\sin \delta_0 \cos \delta_0}{\sin^2 \theta_1 \cos^2 \theta_1} + \left(\frac{2\hbar v}{e^2} \right)^2 \sin^2 \delta_0 \right] \cos \theta_1 \quad (13.15)$$

Note that equation 13.15 reduces to the Mott formula (13.4) for a pure Coulomb field when δ_0 is zero, i.e., when there is no nuclear scattering.

The fourth term in the bracket in equation 13.15 is an interference term between Coulomb and nuclear scattering. This is a very useful term, as it makes possible the experimental detection of quite small δ_0's because of the linear instead of quadratic dependence on δ_0.

The linearity in δ_0 of the interference term also permits determination of whether the nuclear potential is repulsive or attractive, as attractive potentials cause positive δ_0 and repulsive potentials cause negative δ_0. The experimental results indicate that the potential for $l = 0$ is attractive.

The last term in the bracket in equation 13.15 is exactly the scattering that would result if only the nuclear potential were present. For large energies this pure nuclear scattering becomes the most important because of the v^2 coefficient.

B. EFFECTIVE-RANGE THEORY; PROTON-PROTON SCATTERING

Just as for the neutron-proton case, an effective-range theory can be worked out for the proton-proton scattering, modified by the Coulomb forces. The entire nuclear effect at low energies can be described by the same two parameters: effective range and Fermi scattering length.

We develop this theory exactly as in the simpler case, where only the short-range nuclear forces enter. Taking S waves only ($l = 0$), and cross-multiplying the wave equations for two states of energies

E_1 and E_2 just as in equation 10.15, we obtain

$$\phi_1(r)\phi_2'(r) - \phi_2(r)\phi_1'(r) = (k_2{}^2 - k_1{}^2) \int_{r \ll r_0}^{\infty} (\phi_1\phi_2 - u_1 u_2)\, dr$$
$$(13.16)$$

where $u_{1,2}(r)$ are correct radial wave functions ($\psi = u/r$) of the system for two energies, E_1 and E_2, and the functions $\phi_1(r)$, $\phi_2(r)$ are the asymptotic forms approached by u_1, u_2 as r exceeds the range r_0 within which the nuclear potential is appreciable. The ϕ's are no longer portions of a plane wave but are now much modified by the long-range Coulomb forces. For the case of no long-range forces, two linearly independent solutions behave at great distances like $\sin kr$ and $\cos kr$. The boundary condition at the origin, that $u(0) = 0$, forces us to call $\cos kr$ the irregular solution, since it does not satisfy the condition required at the origin. Where Coulomb forces are present, the potential itself becomes infinite at the origin. This singularity in the differential equation brings about a related singularity in the solutions (hence the small but finite lower limit r in equation 13.16). For the Coulomb case, the regular and irregular solutions, which indeed reduce to $\sin kr$ and $\cos kr$ as $e^2 \to 0$, may be found by series expansion, or by using the properties of the confluent hypergeometric equation, of which this wave equation is a special case. [A review of the extensive theory is presented by Jackson and Blatt, *Revs. Mod. Phys.* **22**, 77 (1950). Valuable tables are found in Breit et al., *Revs. Mod. Phys.* **23**, 147 (1951).]

The regular solution can be so normalized that asymptotically it approaches exactly $\sin kr$ in the limit of no Coulomb field. In the actual case, it will not approach a plane wave at large r but one with a small space-dependent phase shift, as written in equation 13.5, behaving like $\sin (kr - \eta \ln 2kr + \text{const.})$, where the constant in the phase depends on η and vanishes for $\eta \to 0$. It is convenient to define a length R, the proton Bohr radius, by the formula

$$R = \hbar^2/Me^2 \cong 28.8 \times 10^{-13} \text{ cm} \qquad (13.17)$$

Now the relative kinetic energy and the quantity η may be written as before:

$$\eta = e^2/\hbar v = 1/(2kR); \qquad E = \hbar^2 k^2/M$$

With the normalization described above, the regular solution $F(r)$ becomes

$$F(r) = C(\eta)kr\,(1 + \tfrac{1}{2}r/R + \cdots) \qquad (13.18)$$

for $kr \ll 1$, and $r \ll R$, where

$$C^2(\eta) = e^{-\pi n}|\Gamma(1 + i\eta)|^2 = \frac{2\pi\eta}{e^{2\pi n} - 1} \qquad (13.19)$$

is the familiar Coulomb penetration factor, representing the probability of close approach of the protons for unit current far away. The irregular solution $G(r)$ is singular at $r = 0$. It can be written, with the symbols and normalization as above (asymptotically to $\cos kr$ for the field-free case),

$$G(r) = \left\{ 1 + \frac{r}{R}\left[\ln\frac{r}{R} + 2 \times 0.577 \cdots - 1 + h(\eta) \right] \cdots \right\} \qquad (13.20)$$

The function $h(\eta)$ is defined by

$$h(\eta) = \sum_{m=1}^{\infty} \frac{\eta^2}{m(m^2 + \eta^2)} - \ln\eta - 0.577 \cdots \qquad (13.21)$$

It varies rather slowly with proton energy, rising from 1.5 to only 2.5 as the laboratory kinetic energy rises from below 2 Mev to 10 Mev.

With these functions defined, we can write the asymptotic wave function $\phi(r)$ just as we wrote $\psi(r)$ for the neutron-proton case. There we had

$$\psi_1 = \sin(k_1 r + \delta_1)/\sin\delta_1 = \cos k_1 r + \cot\delta_1 \sin k_1 r$$

and here we write

$$\phi_1(r) = C[G(k_1 r) + \cot\delta_1 F(k_1 r)] \qquad (13.22)$$

Evaluating equation 13.16 with equation 13.22 and 13.20, setting $E_1 = 0$, and dropping the subscript 2, we obtain

$$\frac{C^2(\eta)\cot\delta}{\eta} + 2h(\eta) - \left[\frac{C^2(\eta)\cot\delta}{\eta} + 2h(\eta) \right]_{E=0}$$
$$= 2Rk^2 \int_0^{\infty} (\phi_0\phi - u_0 u)\, dr \qquad (13.23)$$

This equation can be rewritten to provide a close analog to the effective range theory of the neutron-proton system given in equation 10.16. For this purpose we introduce the function ρ:

$$\tfrac{1}{2}\rho(E_1, E_2) = \int_0^{\infty} (\phi_1\phi_2 - u_1 u_2)\, dr \qquad (13.24)$$

exactly as in the neutron-proton case, and a Fermi scattering length

a_p. The quantity in brackets in equation 13.23 is some number which we write

$$\left[\frac{C^2(\eta) \cot \delta}{\eta} + 2h(\eta) \right]_{E=0} = - \frac{2R}{a_p} \qquad (13.25)$$

Note that $\eta \to \infty$ as the energy decreases to zero. But the phase shift δ also goes to zero, since the nuclear forces can have no effect on the scattering for energies so low that the Coulomb barrier keeps the proton from seeing the nuclear well at all. The term in brackets is then indefinite as $\eta \to \infty$; it can be represented by expression 13.25. Here a_p is to be found from experiment. Finally, we can write for the proton-proton case:

$$K(k) = \frac{C^2(\eta) \cot \delta}{2\eta} + h(\eta) = R \left[- \frac{1}{a_p} + \frac{1}{2} k^2 \rho(0, E) \right]$$

$$\cong R \left(- \frac{1}{a_p} + \frac{1}{2} k^2 r_0 \right) \qquad (13.26)$$

where we have introduced the shape-independent approximation by setting

$$\rho(0, E) \cong r_0$$

where r_0 is the effective range for proton-proton scattering.

The phase shift δ, which is the additional phase shift over and above the shift due to the Coulomb forces, is not at all the same phase shift which a given nuclear potential would produce were the Coulomb forces switched off. Plainly the effect of the singular Coulomb potential cannot be neglected at short distances. It is interesting to ask what the scattering length for the proton-proton system would be if there were no Coulomb field, but the nuclear forces remained unchanged. The simplest method to answer this, given by Blatt and Jackson, is to treat the Coulomb potential as a perturbation, small compared to the nuclear forces within the nuclear well. This treatment yields an approximate result for the equivalent Coulomb-free scattering length $1/a_{eq.}$ which corresponds to an observed proton-proton length $1/a_p$:

$$\frac{1}{a_{eq.}} \cong \frac{1}{a_p} + \frac{1}{R} \ln \frac{R}{r_0} - \frac{1}{3R} \qquad (13.27)$$

Because the observed a_p is quite large compared to the nuclear force range, the value of a_p is rather sensitive to the depth of the nuclear well. Conversely, then, a knowledge of a_p to a few per cent implies an error of only tenths of a per cent in the well depth. Thus a rather inaccurate means to convert from a proton-proton scattering length to the equivalent Coulomb-free case is quite good enough. The comparison of a_{eq}. with the scattering length for the neutron-proton system in the corresponding state, ^1S, is one of the most direct means of examining the relation between the purely nuclear proton-proton and neutron-proton forces.

C. EXPERIMENTS ON PROTON-PROTON SCATTERING

Nuclear scattering appears as strong deviations from the Mott formula, especially at fairly large scattering angles. The observed cross section at a laboratory angle of 45° is forty-three times the Mott value for protons of 2.4 Mev, and the ratio increases with energy. Higher energies have been used not only to confirm the values found at more modest energies for the scattering parameters but also to look for the effects of the partial waves of $l > 0$ which will begin to contribute as the energy begins to surmount the centrifugal barrier.

Data have been obtained for proton beam energies all the way from 0.1 Mev to 32 Mev. The lower-energy protons are typically produced by electrostatic generators, with energy and beam direction very precisely controlled. The cross sections in this region have been measured with an absolute accuracy of a few parts per thousand; they are probably better known than any other nuclear cross sections. At higher energies the errors are not so small, especially if cyclotron beams are used. All these data can be treated as implied by equation 13.26, and the best straight-line fit found, to give values for the scattering length a_p and the effective range r_0. Figure 12 shows the plot, and the results are

$$a_p = -7.68 \pm 0.05 \times 10^{-13} \text{ cm}; \qquad r_0 = 2.65 \pm 0.07 \times 10^{-13} \text{ cm}$$
$$(13.28)$$

There is some indication from the higher-energy data that deviations from the linear fit are becoming appreciable. This implies that the shape-independent approximation is no longer adequate. The effective range $\rho(0, E)$ is no longer reliably energy-independent over such a wide variation in energy. The data do not allow any conclusion as to potential shape; they tend perhaps to suggest some tail like that of a Yukawa potential.

The fact that the intercept in Fig. 12 is positive, i.e., $a_p < 0$, demonstrates that the ^1S state for the proton-proton system cannot be bound. No nucleus He^2 can exist. The exclusion principle prevents any ^3S state, which would be the analog of the stable deuteron.

The absence of any bound state makes the proton-proton system more difficult to study than the neutron-proton system, where the properties of the deuteron help fix the scattering parameters.   But the possibility of destructive interference between scattering by the Coulomb field, known to be repulsive, and that of the nuclear forces enables an independent check of the attractive nature of the nuclear forces.   No such interference occurs for the neutron-proton system.

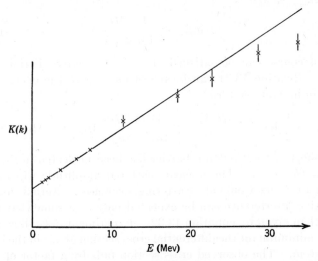

$K(k)$

0   10   20   30

E (Mev)

Fig. 12.   The effective-range theory applied to proton-proton scattering.   The straight line is the shape-independent approximation.   The experimental results begin to depart above 15 Mcv.

The interference depends on the angle of scattering.   Since the S wave is most affected by the nuclear forces, and since the P wave vanishes at 90° in the center of mass system, the cross section measured at this angle (45° in the laboratory system) shows the effect free of any confusion from possible triplet P-wave scattering.   From equation 13.9 we can estimate the energy of the cross-section minimum by setting $f(\theta_L = 45°)$ equal to zero.   With the small imaginary terms neglected, the scattering amplitude $f(\theta_L = 45°)$ becomes

$$f(\theta_L = 45°) = 0 = \frac{e^2}{Mv^2} \frac{e^{-i\eta \ln \frac{1}{2}}}{\frac{1}{2}} - \frac{e^{i\delta_0} \sin \delta_0}{k}$$

$$\cong \frac{2e^2}{Mv^2} - \frac{\delta_0}{k} \qquad\qquad (13.29)$$

so that the nuclear phase shift has to satisfy

$$\delta_0(k_m) \cong \frac{e^2}{\hbar v_m} = \frac{1}{137} \frac{c}{v_m} = \frac{1}{137} \cdot \frac{Mc}{2\hbar k_m} \qquad (13.30)$$

at the wave number k_m of the cross-section minimum. Using the general relation (from equation 13.26, with $\eta = 1/(2kR) \rightarrow 0$, $R \rightarrow \infty$) $k \cot \delta_0 = -1/a_p + \cdots$ as an adequate estimate of the phase shift, we get

$$-a_p k_m \cong \frac{1}{137} \frac{Mc}{2\hbar k_m} \qquad (13.31)$$

which of course can be satisfied only by a negative Fermi length, $a_p < 0$. Relation 13.31 can be rewritten to give the energy of the minimum in a simple form:

$$E_m = \frac{1}{2} M v_m^2 = \frac{2\hbar^2 k_m^2}{M} \cong \frac{1}{137} \frac{(\hbar/Mc)}{-a_p} Mc^2 \cong \frac{1}{4} \text{Mev} \qquad (13.32)$$

The effect of the Coulomb barrier has been neglected in this computation ($R \rightarrow \infty$). The nuclear scattered amplitude will increase with energy; the Coulomb scattering decreases. Actual complete destructive interference can be expected only at a somewhat higher energy than given by equation 13.32. Experiment does show a very striking minimum for the differential cross section at 45° in the laboratory system. The observed cross section falls by a factor of 4 and rises again within an energy range of only 50 kv. The minimum is actually found at 384 kv. This serves to determine a phase shift δ_0 accurately without any absolute measurement of a cross section. The result confirms the direct measurements of δ_0 from absolute cross-section data; it is not precise enough to allow any conclusion about the shape of the potential.

D. EQUIVALENCE OF NEUTRON-PROTON AND PROTON-PROTON FORCES

The equivalent Coulomb-free scattering length can be found from the experimental results quoted in equations 13.28 and 13.27. The computed value of the singlet scattering length and the effective range are then:

Proton-proton: ^1S

$$a_{\text{eq.}} = -17.2 \pm 3 \times 10^{-13} \text{ cm}; \qquad r_0 = 2.65 \pm 0.07 \times 10^{-13} \text{ cm}$$

Neutron-proton: ^1S

$$a_s = -24 \times 10^{-13} \text{ cm}; \qquad r_{0_s} = 2.5 \pm 0.25 \times 10^{-13} \text{ cm}$$

We have repeated the singlet parameters of the neutron-proton system from Table XIV for comparison. The effective ranges do not differ significantly, in view of their large experimental uncertainties. The scattering lengths are significantly different; but the definite 20 to 25 per cent difference implies, however, only a couple of per cent stronger interaction in the neutron-proton system. Such a difference might arise in part from the magnetic moment interaction. It is very tempting to conclude that to a good approximation, though perhaps not exactly, the specifically nuclear interaction between neutron and proton is the same as that between proton and proton. So far this can be said only of the singlet S states from direct scattering measurements; we shall discuss the generalization of this idea of the charge independence of the nuclear forces to all states and all nucleon pairs.

There is evidence that the neutron-neutron and proton-proton forces are equal (except for Coulomb effects) from the structure of complex nuclei. We have already pointed out (Chapter II) that the energy differences of the mirror nuclei could be ascribed to Coulomb energy entirely, and that doing so gave a reasonable value for the radius of the nuclear charge distribution. Moreover, once a small correction is made for Coulomb energy, the energy positions and the angular momentum properties of the first few excited states of light nuclei can be seen to be the same for the nucleus A^Z as for the mirror nucleus A^{4-Z}. Thus the forces

Neutron-proton = proton-proton, from scattering

Proton-proton = neutron-neutron, from mirror nuclei

Taken together these results imply that all the nucleon-nucleon forces are equal, at least in the ^1S state.

Direct evidence on the neutron-neutron forces, as distinct from the evidence inferred from the behavior of complex nuclei, comes from the observation of meson capture in deuterium, i.e., the reaction

$$\pi^- + d \rightarrow 2n + \gamma$$

Observation of the γ-ray spectrum permits conclusions on the interaction between the two outgoing neutrons and is consistent with an interaction in the singlet state of the di-neutron system the same as that in the singlet S state of the deuteron (H^2) or of the di-proton (He^2). All the somewhat rougher experiments support the conclusions of the detailed study of neutron-proton and proton-proton singlet scattering and tend to extend them to all nucleon pairs. A fuller discussion is given in Chapter XVI.

XIV. NON-CENTRAL FORCES

Central forces, i.e., forces which depend only on the distance between particles, have been adequate, so far, to explain binding energy and scattering experiments involving neutrons and protons. The existence of an electric quadrupole moment for the deuteron indicates a cigar-shaped distribution of charge which is not explainable by a central force. A force is needed which depends not only on the separation between neutron and proton but also on the angle which their spins make with the line joining the two particles. This interaction potential must have the form $S_{12} \, V(r)$, where

$$S_{12} = 3(\mathbf{\delta}_1 \cdot \mathbf{r})(\mathbf{\delta}_2 \cdot \mathbf{r})/r^2 - \mathbf{\delta}_1 \cdot \mathbf{\delta}_2 \qquad (14.1)$$

The first term gives the dependence of the interaction on spin angles. The second term has been subtracted so that the average of S_{12} over all directions $\mathbf{r}$ is zero. Formula 14.1 has the same dependence on direction as the interaction of two dipoles $\mathbf{\delta}_1$ and $\mathbf{\delta}_2$.

The non-central or tensor interaction (14.1) has been justified on very general grounds by Wigner [*Proc. Natl. Acad. Sci. U.S. 27*, 282 (1941)]. He has shown that, if the interactions are assumed to be invariant with respect to displacement, rotation, and inversion of the observer's coordinate system, as well as independent of the particle velocities, the most general interaction can be written in the form

$$V_1(r) + V_2(r) \, \mathbf{\delta}_1 \cdot \mathbf{\delta}_2 + V_3(r) \, S_{12} \qquad (14.2)$$

where the potentials V may depend on the orbital momentum of the two-particle system, as well as on the charge of the particles.

The reason for such a limited choice of interactions comes from the requirement of invariance against rotation and inversion (change of sign of all spatial coordinates). Thus the Cartesian components of $\mathbf{\delta}_1$ and $\mathbf{\delta}_2$ are not invariant against rotation, but $\mathbf{\delta}_1 \cdot \mathbf{\delta}_2$ is. On the other hand, $(\mathbf{\delta} \cdot \mathbf{r})$ is invariant against rotation, but not against inversion, since $\mathbf{r} \to -\mathbf{r}$ and $\mathbf{\delta} \to \mathbf{\delta}$ on inversion. ($\mathbf{\delta}$ behaves like an angular momentum $\mathbf{r} \times \mathbf{p} \to (-\mathbf{r}) \times (-\mathbf{p})$). Because of this, only even powers of $(\mathbf{\delta} \cdot \mathbf{r})$ may occur such as $(\mathbf{\delta}_1 \cdot \mathbf{r})(\mathbf{\delta}_2 \cdot \mathbf{r})$. However, higher powers than the second may be shown from the commutation relationships of the spin operators to be reducible to the second power or less, provided the spin of each particle is $\frac{1}{2}$. Thus equation 14.2 constitutes the most general two-body interaction consistent with the assumptions above.

Of the assumptions on which equation 14.2 rests, only the invariance arguments may be regarded as essential ones. There is no a priori reason why the forces should not be velocity-dependent. Velocity independence is assumed only for reasons of simplicity and in analogy to the classical forces derivable from a potential. Like the Lorentz force, other velocity-dependent forces might be expected to have a strength proportional to v/c and thus to be small in the non-relativistic limit. This is, of course, not known to be true. Indeed, there is strong evidence from the study of the heavier nuclei (see Chapter XIX) that one important non-central, velocity-dependent force does act on individual nucleons moving inside a heavy nucleus. This is the so-called spin-orbit force V_{LS}, here written for a nucleon in a central potential:

$$V_{LS}(r)\mathbf{l} \cdot \mathbf{\sigma} \qquad \mathbf{l} = \mathbf{r} \times \mathbf{p} \qquad (14.3)$$

where $\mathbf{l}$ is the orbital angular momentum and $\mathbf{\sigma}$ the spin operator belonging to the given nucleon. Such a force is not known to act between two nucleons, but its presence is by no means to be excluded, and it has been postulated to explain certain properties of nucleon scattering [Case and Pais, *Phys. Rev. 80*, 203 (1950)] It seems to produce effects not much different from those of the tensor force S_{12}, and, since there is some theoretical reason to expect S_{12} rather than V_{LS} from the meson theory of nuclear forces, S_{12} is the non-central force generally examined. Even in the heavy nuclei, it is entirely possible that sufficient S_{12} will produce an over-all effect which looks like the observed strong spin-orbit force and which is most simply described in this manner.

A. STATES OF THE DEUTERON

Central forces of the form

$$V_1(r) + V_2(r)\mathbf{\sigma}_1 \cdot \mathbf{\sigma}_2 \qquad (14.4)$$

are invariant with respect to rotations of space and spin coordinates *separately*. Since $\mathbf{L}$ and $\mathbf{S}$ correspond to infinitesimal rotation operators for space and spin coordinates (see Blatt and Weisskoff, *Theoretical Nuclear Physics*, pp. 781 ff., John Wiley & Sons, New York, 1952) these operators commute with the Hamiltonian formed by using expression 14.4 as the potential. Since L_z and S_z commute with H, both m_L and m_S represent good quantum numbers, or constants of the motion. Although L_x and L_y commute with H, they do not commute with L_z and thus cannot be quantized simultaneously with it. On the other hand $\mathbf{L}^2$ commutes with both H and L_z and has the quantized eigenvalues $\hbar^2 L(L + 1)$. Similar statements apply to $\mathbf{S}^2$. Thus the quantum numbers of a state, with a Hamiltonian containing only central forces, are L, S, m_L, and m_S.

If non-central forces of the type S_{12} are present, the Hamiltonian is invariant only under the *coupled* rotation of space and spin coordinates (rotation of the observer's point of view). Thus L and S are not in general expected to commute with the Hamiltonian, but $\mathbf{J} = \mathbf{L} + \mathbf{S}$ still must. Therefore J and m_J will be good quantum numbers.

Although S is not in general expected to be a good quantum number, it will be in this particular case involving *two particles, both of spin* $\frac{1}{2}$, for the Hamiltonian is symmetric in the spins of the two particles. From this, it follows, in a manner analogous to the discussion of parity given later, that the wave functions must be either *symmetric or antisymmetric in the spin coordinates* of the two particles. Thus the spin wave functions correspond to triplet or singlet states, and S is a good quantum number, even though m_S is not.

Parity. The Hamiltonian is also invariant with respect to inversion, i.e., replacement of $\mathbf{r} = \mathbf{r}_1 - \mathbf{r}_2$ by $-\mathbf{r}$. Thus the space wave functions must be either even or odd with respect to inversion. This fact is commonly denoted as even or odd *parity* of the wave function. The statement that parity is a good quantum number will now be proved, in general, for a system containing any number of particles, assuming invariance of the Hamiltonian for inversion

$$H(-\mathbf{r}_k) = H(\mathbf{r}_k) \qquad (14.5)$$

where the coordinates $\mathbf{r}_k$ of all the particles are inverted simultaneously. This assumption merely corresponds to the fact that all physical results should be independent of whether the observer uses a right- or left-handed coordinate system.

If we write Schrödinger's equation

$$H(\mathbf{r}_k)\psi(\mathbf{r}_k) = E\psi(\mathbf{r}_k) \qquad (14.6)$$

and replace all the coordinates $\mathbf{r}_k$ by $-\mathbf{r}_k$, we obtain

$$H(-\mathbf{r}_k)\psi(-\mathbf{r}_k) = E\psi(-\mathbf{r}_k) \qquad (14.7)$$

Using the symmetry of the Hamiltonian, we find

$$H(\mathbf{r}_k)\psi(-\mathbf{r}_k) = E\psi(-\mathbf{r}_k) \qquad (14.8)$$

or $\psi(-\mathbf{r}_k)$ satisfies the same differential equation as $\psi(\mathbf{r}_k)$. Disregarding degeneracies, for a given energy we see that the two solutions must be proportional to each other:

$$\psi(-\mathbf{r}_k) = K\psi(\mathbf{r}_k) \tag{14.9}$$

where K is a constant. Applying this operation twice,

$$\psi(\mathbf{r}_k) = K^2\psi(\mathbf{r}_k) \tag{14.10}$$

$$K = \pm 1 \tag{14.11}$$

Thus according to equations 14.9 and 14.11 parity is a good quantum number; i.e., all wave functions are either even or odd on inversion (they either remain unchanged or change sign). For the deuteron, therefore, there are four good quantum numbers: J, m_J, S, and parity.

In Chapter XVIII we discuss the concept of intrinsic parity, an extension of the idea of parity to cases like that of mesons in interaction with nucleons, in which the number of particles in the system can change.

Absence of electric dipole moments. An interesting consequence of the fact that parity is a good quantum number is that nuclei cannot have permanent electric dipole moments. The definition of the dipole moment is

$$\mathbf{D} = \int \sum_j e_j \mathbf{r}_j |\psi(\mathbf{r}_k)|^2 \, d\tau_k \tag{14.12}$$

If in this formula we introduce new variables ($\mathbf{r}_k \rightarrow -\mathbf{r}_k$), the first factor changes sign, whereas the second one, because of parity, remains identically the same. Thus $\mathbf{D} = -\mathbf{D}$, or $\mathbf{D} = 0$.

Such an argument does not exclude the possibility of an electric dipole moment arising from some other cause than the distribution of the nuclear protons; e.g., the nucleons themselves might have an intrinsic electric dipole moment. Experiment indicates that if any such dipole moment exists for a neutron, say, it is less than $\sim 10^{-4}(e\hbar/Mc)$ [cf. Purcell and Ramsey, *Phys. Rev.* **78**, 807 (1950)].

For a two-particle system *even parity* corresponds to a superposition of *even L's* and *odd parity* corresponds to a superposition of *odd L's*. Thus states of even and odd L do not mix. Now the only possible values of S are $S = 0$ and $S = 1$. But if $S = 0$, $L = J$, and thus L in this instance is a good quantum number. On the other hand, if $S = 1$, the laws of addition of angular momenta permit $L = J - 1, J, J + 1$. However, $L = J$ has opposite parity to that of $L = J - 1, J + 1$, so that $S = 1, L = J$ defines a state by itself, and the state of opposite parity will have $S = 1$ with a mixture of $L = J + 1$ and $L = J - 1$. Therefore, for a given J the possible states are in spectroscopic notation: ^1J_J, ^3J_J, and the mixture $^3(J - 1)_J + {}^3(J + 1)_J$. In particular, we have the following states of small J:

$$J = 0 \qquad {}^1S_0 \qquad {}^3P_0$$

$$J = 1 \qquad {}^1P_1 \qquad {}^3P_1 \qquad {}^3S_1 + {}^3D_1$$

$$J = 2 \qquad {}^1D_2 \qquad {}^3D_2 \qquad {}^3P_2 + {}^3F_2$$

The ground state of the deuteron has a measured total angular momentum of $J = 1$ and consists primarily of the triplet state $^3S_1$. When non-central forces are taken into account, therefore, it becomes the $^3S_1 + {}^3D_1$ state.

Range and magnitude of the tensor force. The deuteron ground-state wave function in the presence of the tensor force can be written

$$\psi = \psi_S + \psi_D = \frac{u(r)}{r}\, \chi_S + \frac{w(r)}{r}\, \chi_D \qquad (14.13)$$

where $\chi_{S,D}$ are functions of the angles describing the orientation of the neutron-proton separation vector $\mathbf{r} = \mathbf{r}_n - \mathbf{r}_p$ and of the spin variable of neutron and proton together. χ_S, corresponding to the S wave, is independent of angles and symmetric in the neutron and proton spin; χ_D, for the D-wave portion, has a rather complicated dependence on angles, involving the $Y_2{}^m$. They are chosen to be eigenfunctions of the total angular momentum operator, $J = S + L$. We shall deal in some detail with the radial factors only. The radial factors are normalized so that

$$\int_0^\infty u^2(r)\, dr + \int_0^\infty w^2(r)\, dr = 1; \quad p_S = \int_0^\infty u^2\, dr;$$

$$p_D = \int_0^\infty w^2\, dr \qquad (14.14)$$

where p_S and p_D are the probabilities of the system's being in the $^3S_1$ and $^3D_1$, states, respectively.

The Schrödinger equation contains the potential (equation 14.2). The tensor force operator S_{12} acts on the spin-angle functions according to the scheme

$$S_{12}\chi_S = C_S\chi_S$$

$$S_{12}\chi_D = C_{SD}\chi_S + C_D\chi_D \qquad (14.15)$$

where the C's are numbers. The Schrödinger equation for the ground state becomes a pair of coupled ordinary differential equations for the radial functions u and w. Even if the shape of $V_{1,2,3}(r)$ is assumed to be a square well, the equations must be solved numerically. The principal general result of a number of numerical investigations can be said to be that the range and depth of the tensor force are of the same order of magnitude as those of the ordinary forces usually employed. The deuteron quadrupole moment is the main property for which the tensor force must account, without disturbing the other known properties of the neutron-proton system at low energies.

Instead of reporting this elaborate and somewhat inconclusive numerical work, we present an approximate theory related to the effective-range theory of scattering already treated. The treatment will assume no particular shape for the tensor force $V_3(r)$.

Outside the range of nuclear forces, the deuteron ground-state S-wave function must be

$$u(r) = N_S e^{-\gamma r} \qquad (14.16)$$

and, in first approximation, $p_S \cong 1$, which fixes (with inside contribution neglected):

$$\int_0^\infty u^2 \, dr = 1 = N_S{}^2/2\gamma \qquad (14.17)$$

The D-wave part feels the centrifugal barrier, $\hbar^2 l(l+1)/Mr^2$, even at distances beyond the force range, which requires that the D wave behave like

$$w(r) = N_D e^{-\gamma r} \left(1 + \frac{3}{r\gamma} + \frac{3}{r^2\gamma^2} \right) \qquad (14.18)$$

at distances beyond the range of the specific potentials $V_{1,2,3}$. Inside the range of the forces, the high repulsive centrifugal barrier will cause the D wave to go rapidly toward zero as $r \to 0$, roughly like r^3 for small r. (The coupling of the two differential equations for ψ_S and ψ_D actually causes deviations from the ordinary power-law behavior of ψ_D for low r, but these are not strong effects.) Since beyond the range, which we can take as still fairly well within the "radius" of the deuteron $1/\gamma$, $w \sim e^{-\gamma r}/r^2$, the function must have a fairly sharp peak near R_T, the "range" of the tensor force. Now the integral of w^2 from the radius R_T on out is given by

$$\int_{R_T}^\infty w^2 \, dr \simeq \int_{R_T}^\infty \frac{9N_D{}^2}{(r\gamma)^4} \, dr = \frac{3N_D{}^2}{R_T{}^3\gamma^4} \qquad (14.19)$$

To take into account the contribution from $r < R_T$, we can very roughly double this and thus get the physically important quantity

$$p_D \simeq 2 \int_{R_T}^{\infty} w^2 \, dr \simeq \frac{6N_D^2}{R_T^3 \gamma^4} \tag{14.20}$$

in terms of the normalization of the outside part of $w(r)$.

The normalization of the outside portion of w can now be determined rather well by the quadrupole moment, Q. The quadrupole moment operator for the deuteron is defined as (cf. Chapter VIII):

$$Q = \tfrac{1}{4}(3z^2 - r^2) = \tfrac{1}{4}(3 \cos^2 \theta - 1)r^2$$

where the factor $\tfrac{1}{4}$ arises because the proton alone contributes to the charge density, and it always lies just $r/2$ from the center of mass. The expectation value of Q is

$$(\psi, Q\psi) = (\psi_S, Q\psi_S) + (\psi_D, Q\psi_D) + 2(\psi_S, Q\psi_D) \tag{14.21}$$

in which the S-wave part clearly vanishes because of its spherical symmetry. Since $p_S/p_D \gg 1$, the pure D term can be neglected, and only the cross term contributes. The cross term can give something only from overlap of the spin-angle functions χ_S, χ_D. The result of integrating with the correct χ's is

$$Q = \frac{1}{\sqrt{50}} \int_0^{\infty} r^2 u(r)w(r) \, dr \tag{14.22}$$

where the unusual constant comes from the spin sum and angular integration. Since the weighting factor r^2 favors the contribution of the outside wave function, and since $w(r) \to 0$ strongly at $r \to 0$, a good estimate of the integral can be obtained by using the asymptotic forms of $u(r)$ and $w(r)$, equation 14.18:

$$Q = \frac{N_S N_D}{\sqrt{8} \, \gamma^3} \tag{14.23}$$

The D-state probability can now be estimated directly in terms of the measured Q and the assumed value of R_T, the tensor force range. Combining equation 14.23 with equations 14.20 and 14.17,

$$p_D \cong \frac{24Q^2 \gamma}{R_T^3} \tag{14.24}$$

This relation makes it plain that very small ranges for the tensor force imply that the ground state becomes predominantly a D wave. But in that case the approximation of neglecting $(\psi_D, Q\psi_D)$ in equation 14.21 is wrong; the main quadrupole contribution comes no longer from the interference between S and D waves but from the direct D term. This term is negative, however; physically, it is clear that a high rotation will flatten the deuteron, not make it cigar-shaped, as required by a positive quadrupole moment. The value of R_T can therefore not be taken too small. Evidently neither too large nor too small a D-wave contribution is required by the data. Experimentally, the value of Q is

$$Q = +2.73(e \times 10^{-27} \text{ cm}^2) \qquad (14.25)$$

which means that $(Q\gamma^2) \sim 1\%$. A rough measurement of p_D is obtained from the deuteron magnetic moment, as described in the next paragraph. Even the uncertain value of p_D leads to a fair estimate of R_T, since it is the cube of R_T which occurs in equation 14.24. For wide limits in p_D, R_T must fall near 3×10^{-13} cm., rather longer than the range of the central forces.

Percentage of D state from magnetic moment of deuteron. As indicated in Chapter VIII, the small discrepancy between the sum of the magnetic moment of proton and neutron and the measured value for the deuteron can be interpreted as a contribution of the rotational current of a D wave proton in the deuteron ground state. This leads to a simple estimate of the D state probability, p_D.

The magnetic moment operator for the deuteron is

$$\mathbf{\mu} = \mu_p \mathbf{\delta}_p + \mu_n \mathbf{\delta}_n + \mathbf{L}_p \qquad (14.26)$$

where μ_p and μ_n are the magnetic moments of the two nucleons, $\mathbf{\delta}_n$, $\mathbf{\delta}_p$ their unitary spin operators, and $\mathbf{L}_p = \mathbf{r}_p \times m\mathbf{v}$ the orbital angular momentum of the proton, all measured in nuclear Bohr magnetons, $e\hbar/2Mc$. The uncharged neutron can contribute no magnetic moment by orbital motion alone. Now $\mathbf{L}_p = \mathbf{L}/2$, and we can eliminate the $\mathbf{\delta}$'s by using $\mathbf{J} = \mathbf{L} + \frac{1}{2}(\mathbf{\delta}_n + \mathbf{\delta}_p)$. Writing $\mathbf{\mu}$ in terms of $\mathbf{\delta}_n + \mathbf{\delta}_p$, $\mathbf{\delta}_n - \mathbf{\delta}_p$, and recalling that $\mathbf{\delta}_n - \mathbf{\delta}_p$ vanishes for a triplet state,

$$\mathbf{\mu} = (\mu_n + \mu_p)\mathbf{J} - (\mu_n + \mu_p - \tfrac{1}{2})\mathbf{L} \qquad (14.27)$$

The expectation value of $\mathbf{\mu}$ is given by $\langle \mathbf{\mu} \rangle = (\mathbf{\mu} \cdot \mathbf{J}/J^2)\mathbf{J}$, as usual. There results, with $J(J+1) = S(S+1) = 2$,

$$\langle \mu \rangle_z = \mu_n + \mu_p - 0 \times p_s - \tfrac{3}{2}(\mu_n + \mu_p - \tfrac{1}{2})p_D \qquad (14.28)$$

The numerical result was already given. Taking the theory at face value, $p_D = 4\%$. But there are many reasons to doubt that the simple additivity of the free nucleon magnetic moments can hold to this accuracy in the deuteron; one may expect that p_D is really between, say, 2 per cent and 8 per cent. Even from this it follows that the tensor force range is about 2 to 3×10^{-13} cm, very like that of the ordinary forces, or somewhat longer.

The approximations of this discussion are not very accurate, but the results are semi-quantitative at least. Full discussion of this complicated topic will in the end demand both a better theory of the nucleons and a great deal of high-speed calculation.

B. NEUTRON-PROTON SCATTERING

The partial-wave treatment of scattering is in principle very much altered by non-central forces. The separation of the various partial waves is no longer complete, since the orbital angular momentum l is not a constant of the motion. Even at the lowest energies the tensor force mixes some ^3D wave in with the S part of the incoming wave. But the effect is small, since at low energies the D wave is small close to the center of scattering. It turns out that the coefficient of $P_2(\theta)$ in the angular distribution is only about 1 per cent even at 10 Mev, for neutron-proton scattering. This is hard to separate from the small effects of the P wave at this energy and has not been observed. The triplet parameters a_t and r_{0t} are not much affected by tensor forces, especially if the potentials $V_{1,2,3}$ all have similar shape.

C. PHOTODISINTEGRATION
AND NEUTRON CAPTURE BY PROTONS

The electric dipole photodisintegration will be modified by the presence of an initial ^3D wave in the deuteron, giving possible transitions $^3D_1 \rightarrow {}^3P_{0,1,2}$ which adds an unobservably small isotropic term to the cross section. The total cross section tends to be 1 or 2 per cent smaller.

The photomagnetic cross section at low energies is rather more strongly modified but is itself very small except at the lowest energies. A non-isotropic term arises from the $^3D_1 \rightarrow {}^1D_2$ transitions, behaving like $\cos^2 \theta$. It is too small to be seen.

The radiative capture, which is a magnetic dipole transition at the lowest energies, just above threshold, is decreased slightly by the presence of the interference term between ^1D and ^1S final states caused by the tensor force. Uncertainties about meson exchange currents mask this effect as well.   [See Austern, *Phys. Rev. 85*, 283 (1952).]

In general, the tensor force affects low-energy processes very little, except for the deuteron quadrupole moment, for which it is essential. Only at energies where other than S waves are important will the tensor force become determining.

XV. SATURATION OF NUCLEAR FORCES

The binding energy and volume of nuclei are proportional to A, the mass number. This is not in accord with a law of force which gives equal interactions between all pairs of particles in the nucleus, for there are then $A(A-1)/2$ distinct interacting pairs, and a binding energy at least proportional to $A(A-1)/2$ might be expected, if not to a higher power of A due to increased packing with more interaction. Instead, the nuclear binding energies seem similar to the internal energies of bulk matter, in which 2 pounds has twice as much energy and volume as 1 pound.

To account for this phenomenon of "saturation of nuclear forces," in which one particle apparently interacts with only a limited number of others, various hypotheses have been made, and various other assumptions about the nature of the forces can be shown to be impossible.

Among the impossible assumptions is that which has been used in this book so far, namely, an ordinary potential, attractive at all distances and independent of the angular momentum, because it is easily shown that such a potential does not give saturation. This is so even if the Coulomb repulsion of the protons is taken into account. The proof can be carried out with various degrees of exactness, using the variational method. This method is based on the Schrödinger variational theorem which states that the quantity

$$\Omega = \int \psi H \psi \, d\tau / \int \psi^2 \, d\tau \qquad (15.1)$$

is a minimum when ψ is the correct eigenfunction of the lowest eigenvalue E_0 of H, and the minimum value of Ω is E_0. Thus, if the assumed Hamiltonian operator representing the interaction of the particles in a given nucleus is sandwiched between any *arbitrary* ψ in the expression for Ω, the value of Ω must be greater (i.e., less negative) than the correct energy of that nucleus. The simplest ψ's are plane waves inside a box representing the nucleus. If the size of the box is adjusted to give as low an Ω as possible, this size comes out about equal to the range of nuclear forces, which is clearly much too small. Further, it gives a potential energy proportional to A^2, and a kinetic energy proportional to $A^{5/3}$. The size of the coefficients of these powers is such that the potential energy dominates for $A > 50$; for $A = 238$ the binding energy is greater than 238 mass units. This is convincing evidence that the ordinary potential will not work, and this is true independently of the shape of the potential (square well, exponential, Gaussian, etc.).

A tensor force also is not sufficient to give saturation, regardless of its sign. This has been shown by Volkoff [*Phys. Rev. 62*, 134 (1941)].

What is needed is a potential which prevents the particles from getting too close together. The observed part of the forces, which has been described so far, *binds* the particles. Three suggestions have been made to explain saturation, none completely satisfactory as yet:

1. A potential which is repulsive at short distances. There is some evidence that the meson theory of forces implies such a potential, and high-energy scattering at least may suggest its presence. Whether if present it would be adequate to provide saturation without extending out so far as to conflict with the low-energy information is still not known.

2. A non-linear theory has been proposed. This is to say that the forces between two nucleons would depend on the number of nucleons present surrounding the interacting pair. Such forces are many-body forces and could not be obtained by any phenomenological theory of the two-nucleon interaction. The question is open.

3. Exchange forces. These are known to be present (see Chapter XV).

A. EXCHANGE FORCES

In the first paper on nuclear forces, Heisenberg proposed, in order to explain the saturation of nuclear forces, that these forces are "exchange" forces, similar to the force that binds ordinary chemical molecules. Without inquiring into the origin of these exchange forces, let us write down the various types of exchange forces that can exist between two particles, and then examine the effects of these forces on the properties of the deuteron, and on the saturation of the binding energy.

For an ordinary (non-exchange) central force the Schrödinger equation for two particles is (in the center-of-mass system)

$$[(\hbar^2/M)\nabla^2 + E]\psi(\mathbf{r}_1, \mathbf{r}_2, \sigma_1, \sigma_2) = V(r)\psi(\mathbf{r}_1, \mathbf{r}_2, \sigma_1, \sigma_2) \quad (15.2)$$
$$\text{(Wigner)}$$

In nuclear physics, such forces are called Wigner forces. The interaction does not cause any exchange between coordinates of the two particles. Another type of interaction is one that interchanges the space coordinates of the two particles in addition to multiplication of ψ by some $V(r)$; for such an interaction, the Schrödinger equation is:

$$[(\hbar^2/M)\nabla^2 + E]\psi(\mathbf{r}_1, \mathbf{r}_2, \sigma_1, \sigma_2) = V(r)\psi(\mathbf{r}_2, \mathbf{r}_1, \sigma_1, \sigma_2) \quad (15.3)$$
$$\text{(Majorana)}$$

Such a force is called a Majorana force. Two other possibilities are: (1) the Bartlett force, with interchange of spin coordinates, and (2) the Heisenberg force, with interchange of both space and spin coordinates. The Schrödinger equations are, respectively,

$$[(\hbar^2/M)\nabla^2 + E]\psi(\mathbf{r}_1, \mathbf{r}_2, \sigma_1, \sigma_2) = V(r)\psi(\mathbf{r}_1, \mathbf{r}_2, \sigma_2, \sigma_1) \quad (15.4)$$
$$\text{(Bartlett)}$$

$$[(\hbar^2/M)\nabla^2 + E]\psi(\mathbf{r}_1, \mathbf{r}_2, \sigma_1, \sigma_2) = V(r)\psi(\mathbf{r}_2, \mathbf{r}_1, \sigma_2, \sigma_1) \quad (15.5)$$
$$\text{(Heisenberg)}$$

Effects of exchange forces. Exchange forces, with a $V(r)$, are central forces and do not cause mixing of l's. However, it is of course possible to substitute for $V(r)$ in equations 15.2 to 15.5 a potential of the type (equation 14.2) which includes a tensor force: This will then mix different l's, just as it does for ordinary forces, and permits the explanation of the quadrupole moment of the deuteron.

Majorana force. The Majorana interaction replaces $(\mathbf{r})$ by $(-\mathbf{r})$ in ψ. Using the well-known behavior of the wave function on such an inversion, the Schrödinger equation (15.3) may be rewritten

$$[(\hbar^2/M)\nabla^2 + E]\psi(\mathbf{r}) = (-1)^l V(r)\psi(\mathbf{r}) \quad (15.6)$$

This is equivalent to having an ordinary potential that changes sign according to whether l is even or odd and is independent of spin.

Bartlett force. Considering still a system of two particles, we find that the spin function is symmetric if the total spin S is 1, and antisymmetric if the total spin is 0. Thus, the Schrödinger equation (15.4) for the Bartlett force may be rewritten

$$[(\hbar^2/M)\nabla^2 + E]\psi(\mathbf{r}) = (-1)^{S+1}V(r)\psi(\mathbf{r}) \quad (15.7)$$

This is equivalent to an ordinary potential which changes sign between $S = 0$ and $S = 1$. Since we know from neutron-proton scattering data that both the ^3S and ^1S potentials are attractive, the nuclear force cannot be totally of the Bartlett type.

Heisenberg force. Combining the arguments of the two last paragraphs, we may rewrite the Schrödinger equation (15.5) for the Heisenberg force:

$$[(\hbar^2/M)\nabla^2 + E]\psi(\mathbf{r}) = (-1)^{l+S+1}V(r)\psi(\mathbf{r}) \qquad (15.8)$$

This is equivalent to an ordinary potential which changes sign according to whether $l + S$ is even or odd. For example, the effective potential is:

$$
\begin{array}{ccccc}
\text{For} & ^3S & ^1S & ^3P & ^1P \\
\text{potential} + V(r) & -V(r) & -V(r) & +V(r)
\end{array}
\qquad (15.9)
$$

The reversal of sign between ^3S and ^1S states indicates, as for the Bartlett force, that the nuclear force cannot be wholly of the Heisenberg type. However, the difference between the neutron-proton interactions in the ^3S and ^1S states can be explained by assuming that the interaction is roughly 25 per cent Heisenberg or Bartlett and 75 per cent Wigner or Majorana.

Exchange forces and saturation. The Bartlett spin-exchange force does not lead to saturation of the binding energy per particle. If the nuclear force were of the Bartlett type, heavy nuclei should exist with all spins aligned where the number of interacting pairs is $A(A - 1)/2$, which leads to binding energy proportional to at least the square of A.

However, the space exchange in the Majorana and the Heisenberg forces does lead to saturation because of the alternation in sign of the potential between odd and even l. For example, assume that the nuclear force is the Majorana type (we already know it cannot be more than about 25 per cent Heisenberg). Then saturation should not be apparent in nuclei up to He^4, for in He^4 the spatial wave function can still be symmetrical in all four particles, without violating the Pauli principle. We need only give antiparallel spins (antisymmetric spin wave functions) to the two neutrons, and likewise to the two protons. Thus the Majorana force does not alter the Wigner argument about the short range of the forces based on the binding energies of He^4 and lighter nuclei.

In the next heavier nucleus—He^5 or Li^5—the Pauli principle can no longer be satisfied by spin wave functions alone; therefore, the spatial wave function must have at least one node. In other words, only four particles can be in an s state, whereas the last has to be put in a p state, and will therefore be repelled by the other particles. He^5 and Li^5 should thus be unstable, in agreement with experiment. This is a first sign of saturation.

To investigate saturation in heavy nuclei, one may employ the same variational method presented at the beginning of the present chapter to prove that ordinary forces do *not* give saturation. It is satisfactory that this calculation, in the case of the Majorana force, does *not* lead to non-saturation. On the other hand, since the variational method gives only a maximum to the true energy, it cannot be used to prove that the Majorana force *does* give saturation. But Wigner has given a conclusive argument that saturation is achieved with the space-exchange Majorana force [*Proc. Natl. Acad. Sci. U.S. 22*, 662 (1936)]. The space-exchange part of the Heisenberg force would also cause saturation.

B. SPIN AND ISOTOPIC SPIN

It is often convenient to write exchange forces in a slightly different way. Since for two particles

$$\mathbf{\delta}_1 \cdot \mathbf{\delta}_2 = +1 \qquad \text{for } S = 1$$
$$= -3 \qquad \text{for } S = 0 \tag{15.10}$$

the Bartlett force between two particles can obviously be written

$$\tfrac{1}{2}V(r)(1 + \mathbf{\delta}_1 \cdot \mathbf{\delta}_2) = \begin{cases} +V(r) & \text{for } S = 1 \\ -V(r) & \text{for } S = 0 \end{cases} \tag{15.11}$$

The spin-exchange part of the Heisenberg force could be written in the same way.

In order to be able to use a similar notation for the space-exchange part of forces, we introduce the concept of the charge of a particle as a coordinate; i.e., neutron and proton are regarded as different eigenstates of the same particle, called a *nucleon*. We choose the symbol τ for this charge coordinate and we define

$$M_\tau \equiv \quad \tfrac{1}{2} \text{ for the proton}$$
$$M_\tau \equiv -\tfrac{1}{2} \text{ for the neutron} \tag{15.12}$$
$$T \equiv \quad \tfrac{1}{2} \text{ for both}$$

using $\pm \tfrac{1}{2}$ in analogy with the spin coordinate. We also define the charge functions:

$$\text{Charge function} = \gamma \text{ for the proton}$$
$$= \delta \text{ for the neutron} \tag{15.13}$$

in analogy with the spin functions α and β.

The nucleons must obey Fermi statistics in order to be consistent with the ordinary theory (this will become apparent shortly, if it is not immediately obvious). Thus the total wave function (including the charge function) for two or more particles

$$\psi = \psi_{space}(\mathbf{r}) \, \psi_{spin}(\sigma) \, \psi_{charge}(\tau) \qquad (15.14)$$

must be antisymmetric with respect to interchange of *all* coordinates of two nucleons. We therefore look for symmetric and antisymmetric charge functions for two particles. There are four of these, as given in Table XVA.

Table XVA.   Two-Particle Charge Functions

State	Function	Representing	Symmetry	Net Charge
I	$\gamma(1)\gamma(2)$	He^2	Symmetric	$2e$
II	$\delta(1)\delta(2)$	n^2	Symmetric	0
III	$(1/\sqrt{2})[\gamma(1)\delta(2) + \gamma(2)\delta(1)]$	H^2	Symmetric	e
IV	$(1/\sqrt{2})[\gamma(1)\delta(2) - \gamma(2)\delta(1)]$	H^2	Antisymmetric	e

Again, in analogy to spin, two quantum numbers are defined to describe these functions: T to describe symmetry, and M_τ to describe the net charge. These quantities have the values given in Table XVB.

Table XVB.   Quantum Numbers for Charge States

State	T	M_τ
I	1	1
II	1	−1
III	1	0
IV	0	0

T is 1 for symmetric functions, 0 for the antisymmetric function, in analogy to spin. M_τ is the sum of the M_τ's for the two nucleons.

In the literature τ is called the "isotopic spin," T is called "the total isotopic spin," and M_τ may be called the "component of τ in the direction of positive charge." T is analogous to total sin S, and M_τ to S_z. For a given T, M_τ can have the values T, $T - 1$, $\cdots$, $-T$.

From Table XVA it is seen that a sytem containing two neutrons or two protons has a symmetric charge function. Since we are assuming nucleons to obey Fermi statistics, the remainder of the wave function (15.14) must be antisymmetric. This implies (correctly) Fermi statistics for neutrons and protons, disregarding charge as a coordinate. But in a system containing a neutron and a proton the charge function can be either symmetric or antisymmetric, and so also can the remainder of the wave function. Therefore, the treatment of proton and neutron as two eigenstates of the same particle does not in this case introduce any restrictions, consistent with the ordinary theory of statistics.

It is also convenient to introduce an operator τ in analogy to the δ operator, defined by its effect on the "charge coordinate" M_τ.* The eigenvalue of its absolute square is, again in analogy with spin,

$$|\tau|^2 = 4T(T + 1) \tag{15.15}$$

Then, just as for spin, in a system of two nucleons

$$\begin{aligned} \tau_1 \cdot \tau_2 = +1 \quad &\text{for } T = 1 \\ -3 \quad &\text{for } T = 0 \end{aligned} \tag{15.16}$$

Now the Heisenberg interaction can be written (letting $V(r)$ absorb the factor -1) as

$$\tfrac{1}{2}V(r)(1 + \tau_1 \cdot \tau_2) \tag{15.17}$$

To prove this, we note that equation 15.17 changes sign according to whether the charge part of the wave function (equation 15.14) is symmetric or antisymmetric, i.e., according to whether the product of space and spin functions is antisymmetric or symmetric, which is just what is required according to equations 15.8 and 15.9.

The types of interaction between the two particles discussed so far may now be summarized by listing the various types of operators, which when multiplied by some $V(r)$ give the interactions listed in Table XVC.

Eisenbud and Wigner [*Proc. Natl. Acad. Sci. U.S. 27*, 281 (1941)] have shown that these interactions and their linear combinations are the only ones possible under certain reasonable invariance

Table XVC.   Types of Interactions

Ordinary	1	(Wigner)
Spin exchange	$\delta_1 \cdot \delta_2$	(Bartlett)
Space-spin exchange	$\tau_1 \cdot \tau_2$	(Heisenberg)
Space exchange	$(\delta_1 \cdot \delta_2)(\tau_1 \cdot \tau_2)$	(Majorana)
Tensor	$(\delta_1 \cdot r)(\delta_2 \cdot r)$	
Tensor exchange	$(\delta_1 \cdot r)(\delta_2 \cdot r)(\tau_1 \cdot \tau_2)$	

* The operator whose eigenvalues are $M_{\tau_1} = \pm \tfrac{1}{2}$ is written as $\tfrac{1}{2}\tau_{z_1}$.

requirements, namely, excluding interactions depending on total charge or on the momentum. (The interaction $(\mathbf{\sigma}_1 + \mathbf{\sigma}_2) \cdot \mathbf{L}$ depends on the momentum.)

C. CHARGE INDEPENDENCE

The isotopic spin formalism serves as a useful way of classifying nucleon systems. But it is more than a handy way of keeping track of symmetries allowed by the exclusion principle, for we know that neutron and proton can change into one another by meson capture. The states $M_r = \pm\frac{1}{2}$ are not merely formally related but are physically similar. This strongly suggests, but does not prove, that to some degree of approximation the total isotopic spin T is a constant of the motion and is conserved in all processes, at least with a high probability. The differences between neutron and proton mass, Coulomb forces, and magnetic moment surely mean that two states of different M_r cannot be exactly equal in energy, but for the purposes of nuclear force study, such small effects ought to be negligible. We know that the z component of T, M_r, which is just the electric charge, is strictly conserved. But the total isotopic spin, which for a set of N nucleons is just

$$T = \sum_1^N \tau_i \qquad (15.18)$$

is something entirely different.

If T^2 is to be a constant of the motion, it must commute with the Hamiltonian, H. For a two-particle system, there are just two isotopic spin vectors, τ_1 and τ_2, which may occur in H. If the Hamiltonian is to be independent of the orientation of T (in the isotopic spin space), it must be a scalar, and it can consist only of the linear combination

$$a + b\tau_1 \cdot \tau_2 \qquad (15.19)$$

The very definition of $\mathbf{T}$ implies that it will commute with $\tau_1 \cdot \tau_2$:

$$T^2 = \tfrac{1}{4}(\tau_1{}^2 + \tau_2{}^2 + 2\tau_1 \cdot \tau_2) \qquad (15.20)$$

and since T^2 commutes with M_r, evidently $\tau_1 \cdot \tau_2$ does also. If the Hamiltonian of a nucleon system commutes with T^2, the forces present are said to be charge-independent.

The most direct evidence that the nuclear forces possess at least approximate charge independence is the low-energy scattering discussed at the end of Chapter VIII. The agreement between the scattering lengths and effective range parameters of the two singlet S

states is evidence for the similarity of neutron-proton and proton-proton forces in a given space and spin state. Table XVD lists

Table XVD. Properties of a Two-Nucleon System

State	Parity	Spin (S)	$M_S \equiv S_z$	Isotopic Spin, (T)	$M_\tau \equiv T_z$	$\mathbf{\delta}_1 \cdot \mathbf{\delta}_2$	$\tau_1 \cdot \tau_2$	Possible Nuclei
$^1S_0$	Even	0	0	1	$\pm 1, 0$	-3	$+1$	$He^2, H^2, 2n$
$^3S_1$	Even	1	$\pm 1, 0$	0	0	$+1$	-3	H^2
$^1P_1$	Odd	0	0	0	0	-3	-3	H^2
$^3P_{0,1,2}$	Odd	1	$\pm 1, 0$	1	$\pm 1, 0$	$+1$	$+1$	$H^2, He^2, 2n$

various properties of the two-nucleon system. It can be seen from the table that the ^1S state has $T = 1$ and can thus occur with $M_\tau = \pm 1, 0$: Thus the experiments show indeed that the scattering behavior at low energy is independent of M_τ (i.e., of the charge) as long as T (and S, L) are the same. Then the potential must take the form of equation 15.19 for its behavior with respect to isotopic spin.

As we said in Chapter VIII, the energy-level structure of mirror nuclei shows also that T is a good quantum number and provides further evidence for charge independence. But it must be observed that as far as mirror nuclei go (here the low-energy proton-proton scattering gives more information) a somewhat weaker symmetry would be adequate. Symmetry with respect to the transformation

$$M_\tau \rightarrow -M_\tau; \quad \tau_x \rightarrow \tau_x; \quad \tau_y \rightarrow \tau_y$$

is enough to give the same results as full charge independence *for any system in which the number of neutrons equals the number of protons*. Such a property, called charge symmetry, merely means that the neutron-neutron and proton-proton interactions are equal but says nothing about the relations of neutron-proton interaction to the others. The evidence from nuclear levels and scattering supports the more restrictive charge independence.

Information on charge independence comes from the properties of nuclei which have $N \neq Z$ so that charge symmetry can be ignored, but in which A is even. For them the possible values of T are integer, not half-integer as for the nuclei with odd A, true mirror nuclei. The simplest cases will have $T = 1$ or 0. Such nuclei exist in triads of three isobars, all with mass A, but with differing Z, and therefore with differing M_τ. A good example is the set of mass 10: C^{10}, B^{10}, Be^{10}. It is plausible to assume that the ground state of each of these nuclei has the lowest value of T which it can possibly assume.

The quantum numbers can then be listed, with the relative binding energies.

	C^{10}	B^{10}	Be^{10}
M_τ	-1	0	$+1$
T	1	0	1
Relative binding energy	-4.72 Mev	0	$+0.23$ Mev

With the neutron-proton mass difference, only the Coulomb interaction can act to split apart the otherwise degenerate substates $M = \pm 1, 0$ of the isotopic spin triplet $T = 1$. Thus there ought to be an excited state in B^{10} with the quantum numbers $T = 1$, $M_\tau = 0$. This will lie at the same energy after Coulomb correction as do its partner substates with $M_\tau = \pm 1$, the ground states of C^{10} and Be^{10}. The Coulomb correction can be made very simply by writing the Coulomb energy for a nucleus with Z protons.

$$E_c = aZ(Z - 1)$$

The energy of the $T = 1$ states is then just

$$E_1 = \Delta + E_c$$

and we can find a and Δ from the two experimental binding energies. The predicted state of B^{10} lies about $\Delta = 1.9$ Mev above the ground state. Indeed, a state is found at 1.74 Mev, and it is a state which appears to have the zero angular momentum and even parity consistent with the various known properties of the ground states of C^{10} and Be^{10}, although it is very different from the ground state of B^{10}, which is known to have an angular momentum of three units. More careful semiempirical estimates of the Coulomb energy give even closer agreement. Studies of inelastic scattering of deuterons by B^{10} show that the 1.74-Mev state takes no observable part in absorbing deuterons, just as one would expect, since the deuteron has $T = 0$, and cannot combine with the B^{10} ground state to form a state with $T = 1$.

Similar results have been found for the mass number 14.

These ideas have been carried much further in studying the structure of complex nuclei. The notion of isotopic spin is due to Wigner, who introduced the name "super-multiplet" to refer to the several substates corresponding to a given value of T. The whole topic is well reviewed in a paper by Feenberg and Wigner, *Repts. Progr. in Phys. 8*, 274 (1941)].

The fact that Coulomb interaction (or indeed any other electromagnetic effect, such as the interaction of magnetic moments or currents with magnetic fields) tends to split the degenerate isotopic spin states is made clear by writing down the operator for the electric charge of a nucleon:

$$Q_i = \frac{+|e|}{2} (1 + \tau_{iz})$$

Now the Coulomb energy operator of a pair of nucleons is just

$$V_{ij} = \frac{e^2}{4r_{ij}} (1 + \tau_{iz})(1 + \tau_{jz})$$

and evidently this is not a scalar in the $\mathbf{T}$ space, because of the occurrence of $\tau_{iz}\tau_{jz}$ instead of the desired $\boldsymbol{\tau}_i \cdot \boldsymbol{\tau}_j$. And so the Coulomb energy itself does not commute with a charge-independent Hamiltonian, and the same holds for the operators of the magnetic and electric multipole interactions with the electromagnetic field. Another appreciable source of splitting is the small mass difference between proton and neutron. Thus heavy nuclei, with $N \gg Z$, and large Coulomb energies, will not markedly show the properties of charge independence.

How far charge independence is to be expected to hold is still uncertain; it is certainly desirable on grounds of simplicity, and it is fully compatible as well with all that is now known of mesons. The conservation of isotopic spin is probably, but not yet certainly, a very general property of nuclear forces and of nucleon-meson interactions as a whole, disturbed only slightly by electromagnetic and mass effects.

XVI. NUCLEON SCATTERING
AT HIGH ENERGIES

The low-energy nucleon scattering data give information on a few states of the two-nucleon system, namely, the states described by $T = 1$, ^1S; $T = 0$, ^3S. The deuteron ground state tells us mainly about the ^3S wave. The accuracy of this information is high, and the strong suggestion of charge independence means that only four parameters, a_s, a_t, r_{0_s} and r_{0_t}, are needed, instead of the six possible ones. We know that there is a tensor force, mainly from the observed distortion of the deuteron charge density. About the detailed shape of the potential little can be said.

To go beyond this information higher energies are needed, so that the short-wavelength nucleons may probe the details of the potential, or so that the centrifugal barrier for the high-l states can be surmounted, and information collected for the partial waves of $l \geq 1$, without demanding infinite experimental accuracy. The high-energy data are not yet all reliably in (early 1955), but, from the bombarding energy of about 14 Mev up to nearly 600 Mev, we have fairly good results for theoretical interpretation. The experimental techniques differ widely over this large energy range; we shall not attempt to describe them even briefly. The chief experimental results are total cross sections for neutron-proton and proton-proton elastic scattering (capture and meson production are both small, and we omit discussion of these effects) and angular distribution of the collision products. Angular distributions must be expressed in the center-of-mass system for direct theoretical interpretation; this transformation is important at such high energies. Relativity will be neglected, except that the relativistic mass increase will be considered in computation of k. Polarization experiments are of increasing importance (see Chapter XVII).

In the center-of-mass system, conservation of momentum requires that the two nucleons after the collision travel in opposite directions—i.e., at angles θ and $180° - \theta$ to the incident nucleon, respectively. In the laboratory system the two nucleons leave at right angles to each other and the angles between them and the incident nucleon are $\theta/2$ and $90° - \theta/2$, respectively. At higher energies, relativity effects modify the kinematics, and the angle included between the two outgoing nucleons in the laboratory system is reduced from $\pi/2$ to

$$\text{Included angle} \cong \pi/2 - (E/4Mc^2) \sin \theta \qquad (16.1)$$

where E is the kinetic energy of the incoming nucleon in the laboratory. The neutron-proton mass difference is neglected.

A. NEUTRON-PROTON SCATTERING

The onset of anisotropy. Equation 10.7 estimated the energy above which the P wave, with $l = 1$, might be expected to appear. Interference between the P wave and the S wave, proportional to the P-wave amplitude, ought to show up at energies above 10 or 12 Mev, with an observed cross section (as always, in the reference frame in which the center of mass is at rest) like

$$a_0 + b \cos \theta + c \cos^2 \theta \qquad (16.2)$$

The relative strength of the $\cos \theta$ term ought to measure the P-wave probability amplitude. Experiments [Barschall and Taschek, *Phys. Rev.* **75**, 1819 (1949)] indicate no such terms and are consistent with isotropic scattering, within the experimental accuracy of about 5%. (Note that this differs very much from the earlier results cited in the first edition of this book; the later results have been fully confirmed.)

Why is there so little P wave apparent? The answer comes from the values of the phase shifts δ_0, δ_1. For the early appearance of the P wave, expected, say, in the neighborhood of 12-Mev energy incident, we can be sure that $\delta_1 \ll 1$, and

$$\frac{e^{2i\delta_1} - 1}{2i} \cong \delta_1$$

But the ^3S-wave phase shift δ_{0t} is given by equation 10.16 with Table XIC, and from this $\delta_{0t} = \pi/2$ at $k = 0.48 \times 10^{13}$ cm^{-1}, or 18 Mev. So as the P wave begins to show up, the interfering S-wave amplitude becomes pure imaginary, the interference term tends to vanish, and all that is left of the P wave in the cross section is the $\cos^2 \theta$ term, which depends on the square of the P-wave amplitude and is much smaller. This argument is at least qualitatively correct, as more detailed calculations show. Very precise work has lately shown P-wave effects ($< \frac{1}{2}\%$) even at 2 to 3 Mev.

The next careful measurements, at 27 Mev, show considerable anisotropy, with a cross section about like

$$\sigma(\theta) \cong \text{Const. } (1 + \tfrac{1}{3} \cos^2 \theta) \tag{16.3}$$

and the P wave itself appears reasonably strong.

Exchange forces. At still higher energies, the neutron-proton scattering provides quite direct evidence for strong exchange forces. To discuss this evidence, there is need of a formula for scattering cross section which is easier to handle at high energies than equation 10.1 with the required sum over many partial waves. Such a method is the Born approximation, valid for weak interactions. Although the nucleon interactions are not weak, the Born approximation can be expected to give some indication of the true behavior at least of the less strongly interacting partial waves of higher l. The approximate formula derived for the scattering amplitude in the Born approximation (see, e.g., Bohm, *Quantum Theory*, Prentice-Hall, New York, 1951) supplants the exact but hard-to-apply equation 10.1. The Born approximation formula reads:

$$f(\theta) = -(M/4\pi\hbar^2)\int d\mathbf{r} \, V(\mathbf{r}) \exp(i\mathbf{q} \cdot \mathbf{r}) \tag{16.4}$$

where M is the nucleon mass, $V(\mathbf{r})$ the interaction potential, and $\mathbf{q}$ the momentum transferred in scattering; $\mathbf{q} = \mathbf{k}_{\text{final}} - \mathbf{k}_{\text{initial}}$, so that for elastic collisions with $E_f = E_i, |\mathbf{q}| = 2k \sin \theta/2$; θ is the angle of deflection in the center-of-mass frame; $2\hbar^2 k^2/M = E_{\text{incid.}}$. The approximation (equation 16.4) is not satisfactory for quantitative work at any energy in nucleon scattering, but it is not qualitatively wrong for energies well above the depth of the nuclear well, say 30 Mev or so.

If the potential $V(\mathbf{r})$ vanishes outside of some range R, the Born approximation predicts isotropic scattering, more or less independent of energy if $qR \ll 1$. For $qR \gg 1$, the oscillations of $\exp(i\mathbf{q} \cdot \mathbf{r})$ cause the scattering to fall off rapidly. Near $q = 0$, forward scattering, the cross section should stay rather large even as the energy increases; the cross section for backscattering, $q = 2k$, will fall rapidly with increasing energy. Figure 13 shows the expected general behavior of equation 16.4.

The recoil energy is large for large q, of course. On the basis of formula 16.4, neutrons scattered at energies in the 100-Mev range would go mostly forward, and the recoil protons would mostly have low energies, in the neighborhood of 10 Mev. All the energetic particles emerging from the collision would be slightly scattered neutrons, so that $qR \ll 1$. But the early observations, reported in the first edition as a note added in proof (middle of 1947), immediately contradicted this expectation. The majority of the emergent particles were fast protons, moving with nearly the energy and the direction of the incident neutrons. This can be explained if the neutron and proton change roles; the neutron retains the energy of the order of 10 Mev, and the proton is the particle continuing forward only slightly scattered. This is exactly the consequence of exchange

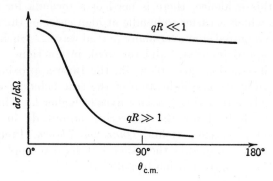

FIG. 13.   Born approximation results for neutron-proton differential cross section, with ordinary forces.

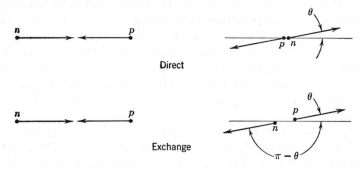

FIG. 14.   Schematic momentum vectors in the center-of-mass system for direct and for exchange neutron-proton scattering. Small-angle direct scattering is equivalent to nearly backward exchange scattering.

forces, of the type of equation 15.6. The momentum transfer q is given by

$$\mathbf{q} = \mathbf{k}_{\text{final proton}} - \mathbf{k}_{\text{initial neutron}} \qquad (16.5)$$

and the predictions of the Born approximation are then just reversed along the axis of scattering angle, as sketched in Fig. 14. Strong exchange forces are demonstrated by many fast proton tracks in the cloud chamber where the scattering of the neutrons in hydrogen was observed; no more direct evidence for space exchange could be hoped for.

Serber force. Analysis of the angular dependence of the neutron-proton scattering in the region of 100 Mev suggested a particular mixture, equal parts of ordinary and Majorana forces. This may be represented by the expression

$$V(\mathbf{r})[1 - \tfrac{1}{4}(1 + \mathbf{\delta}_1 \cdot \mathbf{\delta}_2)(1 + \mathbf{\tau}_1 \cdot \mathbf{\tau}_2)] \tag{16.6}$$

and is called the Serber force. According to equation 15.6 and Table XVD, the Serber force will be attractive (with $V(\mathbf{r})$ attractive) for states of even l, independent of spin, and will vanish in all states of odd l. Such an assumption, viz., that there is no force in any state of odd l, of course greatly simplifies all calculations. The angular distribution of scattering produced by a Serber force must be given by the linear combination

$$\left| \sum_{l \text{ even}} (2l + 1)(e^{2i\delta} - 1)P_l (\cos \theta) \right|^2 \tag{16.7}$$

and since every $P_{l \text{ even}}$ is an even function of $\cos \theta$, the cross section will be symmetric fore and aft in the center of mass system, i.e.,

$$d\sigma(\theta)/d\Omega = d\sigma(\pi - \theta)/d\Omega \tag{16.8}$$

This symmetry is apparently observed, at least approximately, up to about 200 Mev, although the experiments are somewhat conflicting.

Experiments at energies just above 250 Mev do not show the symmetry forward and backward which supports the idea of a nearly pure Serber force. Instead, the cross section per unit solid angle for neutrons scattered nearly backward—180° in the center-of-mass system—is about double the forward cross section. The forward-scattered protons are the result of the exchange forces, at these energies about twice as effective as the ordinary forces (see Fig. 15).

The analysis of the proton-proton scattering (see below) shows strong contributions from states of odd angular momenta. If we believe in charge independence, these same states must also contribute to neutron-proton scattering and thus give direct evidence against the Serber type of exchange force.

The presence of exchange forces, so clearly evident in the scattering experiments, is qualitatively what the requirements of saturation had led theorists to expect. But quantitative calculations of nuclear binding energy, subject to some limitations with respect to the accuracy of the wave functions employed, suggest that saturation would require a ratio of ordinary to exchange forces of about ¼, smaller than any scattering data indicate. It is probable that the exchange forces do not constitute the only reason for saturation.

Total cross section. The total cross section falls faster than $1/E$ in the region above 30 Mev. Some effect in this direction can be expected if we have a Serber force because this force removes more or less completely any effects of the odd l states and thus reduces the cross section at high energy, while leaving that at low energy unchanged. But this effect is not sufficient to allow a good fit with the experimental data. The tensor force, according to calculations, does not appreciably change this situation. Perhaps the repulsive core which has been introduced to explain the proton-proton scatter-

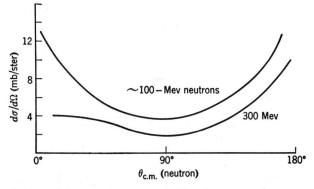

Fig. 15. Differential scattering cross section in center-of-mass system for neutron-proton collisions at two laboratory energies. There is a marked shift away from forward-backward symmetry with increasing energy. The curves are idealized versions of the still rather uncertain data.

ing at high energies (see below) should be invoked: If the interaction is repulsive at small distances and attractive at large ones, then at least for moderate momentum change q the scattering amplitude (equation 16.4) is decreased. Since moderate q give the largest contribution to the cross section, this would explain the observed effect.

On the other hand, a strong repulsion increases the value of equation 16.4 for large q. Indeed, the differential cross section at 90°, which corresponds to the largest momentum transfer, is observed to stay remarkably high even at 280-Mev neutron energy, higher than can easily be explained in terms of potential which is everywhere attractive and not very singular at the origin. This observation can be well correlated to the proton-proton scattering experiments by the assumption of charge independence (see below).

The two surest conclusions from the neutron-proton data are these: (1) Strong exchange forces exist; (2) a simple potential description works very well at low energies, though it may be deficient at higher energies.

B. PROTON-PROTON SCATTERING

This system can be formed only in the triplet isotopic spin state, so that scattering experiments study only a part of the states reached in neutron-proton scattering.   Table XVD indicates the first few

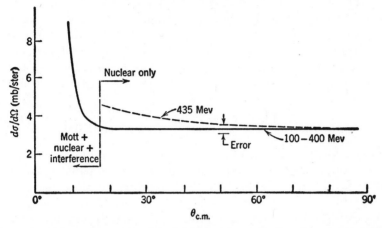

FIG. 16.   Differential cross section in center-of-mass system for proton-proton scattering.   The solid curve is approximately valid for all laboratory energies between about 100 Mev and 400 Mev.   The arrows mark off the range of variation from isotropy and energy independence which might be consistent with experiment in that energy range.   Above 400 Mev the scattering begins to be anisotropic, as shown by the dashed curve.

states, and the rules for forming the higher ones are implied by the table.   For spin 0, only states with even l can exist; for $S = 1$, only states with odd l.   This apparently simpler system has given the hardest problems for theoretical interpretation.

Summary of the data.   Between the 30-Mev region, where the $l \neq 0$ states might first be expected to appear, and energies around 400 Mev, the properties of the proton-proton cross section are simple and puzzling.   The curve of Fig. 16 shows the main features of the results: at low angles, a strong increase in the cross section per unit solid angle, ascribed to the long-range Coulomb interaction, and of interest mainly to check the phase of the specifically nuclear part. For angles above some small θ_C, the value of $d\sigma/d\Omega$ is independent of angle for all the measured energies. Apart from the Coulomb effect, the scattering is isotropic. The accuracy is not high at all energies, but around 150 Mev it is good enough to put the departures from isotropy at less than 3 per cent.

The total cross section is also constant with energy, within experimental error. From about 150 to 400 Mev, the elastic cross section in the center-of-mass system can be fitted by the value:

$$d\sigma/d\Omega = 3.4 \pm 0.4 \text{ millibarns/steradian*} \tag{16.9}$$

By 600 Mev there is a marked forward scattering.

The obvious hypothesis that the isotropic scattering below 400 Mev arises because even at such high energies only the S wave contributes is immediately excluded by the absolute cross-section data. For in equation 13.29 we can evaluate the last term with $\sin \delta_0 = 1$, corresponding to the maximum pure nuclear S-wave scattering, which is:

$$\frac{d\sigma_0}{d\Omega} = 4\left(\frac{\hbar}{Mv}\right)^2 = \frac{1}{k_{rel.}^2} = \frac{830}{E(Mev)} \frac{\text{millibarns}}{\text{steradian}} \tag{16.10}$$

too low for the experimental values. (The general formula of equation 10.1 gives a result small by a factor of 4 compared to equation 16.10 because of the identity of the two protons in the present case.) The conclusion seems final, though the alternative is not very satisfactory: The total cross section can be explained only by invoking contributions from the waves of higher l, but the isotropy of $d\sigma/d\Omega$ is then explained only as an accidental result of the combination of many states involved. However, the need for invoking states with $l \neq 0$ is proved by the polarization observed in proton-proton scattering at high energy (Chapter XVII): S scattering alone can never lead to polarization. Moreover, polarization is possible only if the total spin of the system $S = 1$, not if $S = 0$. But $S = 1$ is related to odd values of the orbital momentum l, as shown above; hence, the large polarization shows that states of odd l, particularly P states, must have a large interaction.

Closer study of polarization, and of the interference between Coulomb and nuclear scattering, is expected to give further information.

C. INELASTIC PROTON-PROTON SCATTERING

Only elastic scattering is possible in proton-proton collisions, unless enough energy is available to create a π-meson in the collision. Some electromagnetic radiation is in fact emitted at all energies,

* 1 barn $\equiv 10^{-24}$ cm^2; 1 millibarn $\equiv 10^{-3}$ barn.

but the probability of radiation is very small.   If a particle with
mass M_i is incident upon a stationary target particle of mass M_t,
the kinetic energy T required at threshold to produce new particles
with a total mass μ is

$$T = \mu c^2 \left[1 + \left(M_i + \frac{\mu}{2} \right) \Big/ M_t \right]$$

so that a single π-proton can just be made in proton-proton collisions
with 290 Mev proton kinetic energy in the laboratory system.
Discussion of the meson production process is excluded from the

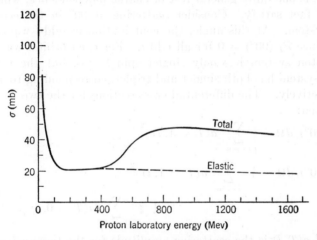

Fig. 17.   Observed total proton-proton cross section (solid curve), and observed
elastic proton-proton cross section (dashed curve) vs. laboratory energy.

scope of this book, but it is interesting to observe that the proton-
proton total cross section, which remains so constant with energy
from 150 to above 400 mev, begins to rise just beyond 400 Mev, at
which energy the production of single mesons begins to become
important.   The observed total proton-proton cross section is
plotted in Fig. 17, with the elastic cross section dotted, and the
presence of a real change above 400 Mev is clear.   The deviation
from isotropy first noticed in elastic scattering at about this same
energy surely is to be understood only when the meson production
processes are considered.   With such an energy, one leaves the realm
of nuclear physics and enters the realm of physics of the fundamental
particles themselves.

Neutron cross sections have not been studied as yet at such high
energies.

D. CHARGE INDEPENDENCE

Since the simple notion of pure S-wave proton interaction cannot be maintained, it is at least satisfactory that the neutron-proton data also make very clear the presence of waves of $l > 0$. If charge independence holds, the proton-proton scattering forces are present for those states of the neutron-proton system which have $T = 1$, and the much more complex-appearing neutron-proton cross sections reflect the presence of the states with $T = 0$ which are excluded in the system of two like particles.

There is one quite general test of charge independence, which the data in fact satisfy. Consider scattering at 90° in the center-of-mass system. At this angle, the contribution of odd-l waves vanishes, since $P_l (90°) = 0$ for all odd l. For even orbital waves the two-proton system has only singlet spin states, but the neutron-proton system has both singlet and triplet, corresponding to $T = 1$, 0, respectively. The differential cross sections for the two cases can be written:

$$d\sigma_{p-p}(90°)/d\Omega = \left| \sum_{l \text{ even}} {}^1a(T = 1, l) \right|^2$$

$$d\sigma_{n-p}(90°)/d\Omega = \tfrac{1}{4} \left| \sum_{l \text{ even}} {}^1a(T = 1, l) \right|^2$$

$$+ \tfrac{3}{4} \left| \sum_{l \text{ even}} {}^3a(T = 0, l) \right|^2 \quad (16.11)$$

where[3,1] $a(T, l)$ is the scattering amplitude for the two-nucleon system in the triplet or singlet spin state, and with the indicated values of isotopic spin T and of l. If the amplitude depends only on the variables indicated, for a given momentum, as required by the assumption of charge independence, then at any energy it follows that

$$d\sigma_{n-p}(90°)/d\Omega \geq \tfrac{1}{4}d\sigma_{p-p}(90°)/d\Omega \quad (16.12)$$

Since σ_{n-p} falls rapidly with energy, and σ_{p-p} remains about constant, the test is most severe at the highest energies. Recent values [Hartzler and Siegel, *Phys. Rev.* **95**, 185 (1954), and references in that paper] are:

$$90°, 400 \text{ Mev: } d\sigma_{n-p}/d\Omega = 1.5 \text{ millibarns/steradian}$$

$$d\sigma_{p-p}/d\Omega = 3.5 \text{ millibarns/steradian} \quad (16.13)$$

easily satisfying the test. Charge independence is not excluded by any measurements yet made, in spite of the wide apparent difference in the cross sections.   It seems to be a more trustworthy guide than the idea that nearly isotropic scattering is almost all S-wave.

The comparison of equation 16.11 with equation 16.13 shows that at 90° the $T = 0$ scattering is much less than the $T = 1$.   On the other hand, at 180° the neutron-proton differential cross section is much larger than the proton-proton (about four times), and this must be attributed to the contribution of $T = 0$.   Hence the $T = 0$ scattering is strongly dependent on angle, as would be expected for a "reasonable" potential at such a high energy, from the approximation formula (16.4) or from more general qualitative arguments such as those given below in connection with equation 16.15.   In any case, $T = 0$ scattering is markedly different from $T = 1$ scattering. Unfortunately, it is not possible to deduce the $T = 0$ scattering uniquely from the difference between the neutron-proton and proton-proton scattering because (1) the relative statistical weights of $T = 0$ and 1 differ from those of equation 16.11 for angles other than 90° and depend on the (unknown) contributions of $S = 0$ and 1 to both proton-proton and neutron-proton scattering, and (2) the contributions from $T = 0$ and $T = 1$ interfere.

Neutron-neutron scattering, which cannot be studied directly, should be similar to proton-proton scattering except for the absence of Coulomb effects.

E. THE NUCLEON CORE

A very attractive qualitative picture of the unusual features of the proton-proton scattering was suggested by Jastrow [*Phys. Rev. 81*, 185 (1951)].   He pointed out that the near-isotropy of the cross section ruled out potentials for which the phase shift in states of successively higher l had the same sign and suggested that the effect might be obtained at least in part by alternating negative and positive phase shifts with increasing l.

Consider a simple example, assuming pure Serber force, and energies near 300 Mev or so, so that only the first two even-l values, $l = 0$ and $l = 2$, contribute.   Then singlet states only are involved, and the differential cross section can be written down from formula 10.1:

$$d\sigma/d\Omega = \lambda^2 \left| e^{i\delta_0} \sin \delta_0 + 3e^{i\delta_2} \sin \delta_2 P_2(\cos \theta) \right|^2 \quad (16.14)$$

where δ_0, δ_2 are the S and D phase shifts.   Expression 16.14 can be rewritten as:

$$d\sigma/d\Omega = \lambda^2 [\sin^2 \delta_0 + 9 \sin^2 \delta_2 P_2{}^2(\cos \theta)$$
$$+ 6 \sin \delta_0 \sin \delta_2 P_2(\cos \theta) \cos (\delta_0 - \delta_2)] \quad (16.15)$$

Now the interference term, in equation 16.15, has the sign of $\sin \delta_2$ $\sin \delta_0 P_2(\cos \theta)$. If δ_2 and δ_0 are both greater than zero, the interference will be negative wherever $P_2 = (3 \cos^2 \theta - 1)/2$ is negative and will reduce the cross section materially at 90°. The angular dependence may show some wrinkles from the $P_2{}^2$ term, but this term also is greater at 0° than at 90°, so that the distribution will be generally V-shaped about 90°. To eliminate the dip near 90°, it is only necessary to give δ_0 and δ_2 opposite signs. Then the interference term will tend to reduce the forward peak and build up the 90° value, exactly as needed to make approximate isotropy. Some triplet contributions, and even tensor force contributions, will add further cross section as needed near the zeroes of $P_2(\cos \theta)$, $\sim$60°.

A change of sign between S and D waves may be obtained by introducing a strongly repulsive core in addition to the attractive singlet potential observed for low energies. The S wave will have a phase shift which will depend on this central core and become repulsive over-all at high-enough energies. The higher l waves are kept away from the core by centrifugal forces and will therefore display the normal positive phase shift of an attractive well. The S-wave phase shift for the core alone, with core radius R_c, would be given by

$$\delta_0 \cong -kR_c \qquad (16.16)$$

To this is added a positive term, arising from the relatively long but shallow attractive tail, the ordinary nuclear potential of low energies. This positive term will rapidly decrease as the kinetic energy grows beyond the depth of the well, and the net S-wave phase shift will change over in sign from the low-energy positive value to negative values at an energy which depends on the choice of constants. To make the change occur at about 150 Mev, one has to take $R_c \cong 0.5$ $- 0.6 \times 10^{-13}$ cm, depending somewhat on the shape of the attractive well. (The attractive well must itself be modified in order to retain agreement with the low-energy data in the presence of the repulsive core, but the effective range method can be preserved.)

The net change in sign might be expected to show up also in the low-angle dependence of the cross section, below, say, 10 or 15°, where interference between nuclear scattering and the Mott scattering of formula 13.4 should be appreciable. The experiments do not agree on this point as yet; but the strongly destructive interference of the low-energy experiments, which demonstrates the over-all attractive nature of the S-wave proton-proton nuclear interaction at low energies, has certainly been much reduced by 300 Mev.

The possibilities for saturation which a core might provide are evident.   The simple hard-sphere radius of 0.6×10^{-13} cm is much too small to explain the observed radius of $\sim 1.2 \times 10^{-13}$ cm for the volume per nucleon, but zero-point energy effects have also to be taken into account, a task not yet successfully undertaken.   The origin of saturation probably has no single explanation but is a combination of hard core effects, including zero-point energy, exchange forces, and perhaps many-body interactions.

Other indications of a core are provided by the optical model (see Chapter XXII) for high-energy scattering, which indicates a refractive index corresponding to a decrease in nuclear potential with increasing energy, exactly what would be expected from a core. The meson theory of nuclear forces also indicates the plausibility of such an effect (Chapter XVIII).

It must be kept in mind that the repulsive core alone is not the full answer to the problem of the proton-proton interaction.   The observation of strong polarization shows that strong non-central forces must be present as well.

F. PHASE-SHIFT ANALYSIS

The Schrödinger treatment with given potentials is not to be counted on at such high energies that relativistic effects may be important.   For protons of 400 Mev, $(E_{c.m.}/Mc^2) \sim 0.2$.   A more direct method of discussing scattering, not limited to the dynamics implied by a particular wave equation, is that of simply computing phase shifts for a small number of states which might plausibly be involved.   Requirements like charge independence, and certainly smooth variation of phase shifts with energy, may help in determining the correct set.   Then it is the task of some better dynamical theory to explain the actual phase shifts and their energy course. This approach is much more general, of course, than that of constructing potential wells, but it lacks the pictorial character of the older scheme.

It has proved possible to fit the proton-proton scattering, with its unusual isotropy, by employing only S and P waves, using all the three possible P waves, those which with the spin have total angular momentum $J = 0$, 1, and 2.   The phase shifts needed for the P states of various J differ strongly.   The fit therefore makes an implied use of strong non-central forces, a feature emphasized by the direct polarization measurements for high-energy proton scattering.   It has been possible [Thaler, Bengston, and Breit, *Phys. Rev.* *94*, 683 (1954)] to fit the neutron-proton data with phase shifts derived from the proton-proton results and the requirement of charge independence. The ^3S and ^1P waves must be considered in the neutron-proton case. The fit is far from unique, even apart from the intrinsic ambiguities of sign which occur. However, when the complete scattering matrix has been determined from polarization measurements (see Chapter XVII), the phase-shift analysis will become much more definite. In the end it is likely that the precise study of nucleon interactions will rest upon such phase-shift analyses rather than upon the wholly non-relativistic idea of a two-body potential.

The importance of non-central forces was exploited by some authors who earlier used spin-orbit forces, or tensor forces, to replace the qualitative features of the hard core model. Such forces, if chosen with strong singularities at the origin, can give rough fits to the data, perhaps not quite so easily as can the hard core. The phase-shift analyses confirm those earlier approaches, without making any statements about the r-dependence of the forces, of course.

G. CONCLUSIONS

In the absence of any real theory of the high-energy interactions, we must summarize the qualitative conclusions somewhat tentatively. The high-energy nucleon interaction seems to show over-all:

1. The definite presence of (a) exchange interactions, (b) strong non-central forces (either tensor or spin orbit), (c) very strong repulsion at close range (perhaps a hard core). None of these effects is adequate alone to explain all the data.

2. The simple and attractive assumption of charge independence is consistent with all observations, up to around 600 Mev at least.

3. A simple, velocity-independent, two-body potential well, of whatever shape and whatever angular behavior, cannot account for all the data, though a set of phase shifts can always be chosen to do so.

XVII. POLARIZATION OF NUCLEONS

A. QUANTUM MECHANICS OF POLARIZED BEAMS

The beams and the targets usually employed in nuclear physics consist of unpolarized particles, i.e., particles whose spins are randomly oriented. The probability for any process involving inter-action of particles with spin is in general a function of spin orienta-tion. The probability of the process for an unpolarized set of par-ticles is found by averaging the probability for a definite orientation of the spin, $w(S_z)$, over the spin directions possible, with equal weight for all directions:

$$\text{Probability} = \frac{1}{2S + 1} \sum_{S_z = -S}^{+S} w(S_z) \tag{17.1}$$

No single quantum wave function can, however, represent unpolar-ized particles, since writing down a wave function presupposes some assumption about the relative phases of the parts of the wave function which refer to the various alternative orientations of spin, and these cannot be defined for an unpolarized beam. This is familiar in the classical electromagnetic theory of light, where a plane wave written as $\mathbf{E} = \text{Re}\,[(a_x\mathbf{e}_1 + a_y\mathbf{e}_2)e^{i(kz-\omega t)}]$ with $\mathbf{e}_1$ and $\mathbf{e}_2$ unit vectors in the x and y directions, would correspond to a light beam with two orthogonal components of the electric vector, $a_x\mathbf{e}_1$ and $a_y\mathbf{e}_2$, having amplitudes and phases given by a_x and a_y. A plane-polarized beam, electric vector in the y direction, is represented by setting $a_x = 0$; a beam with electric vector along x, by $a_y = 0$. If $a_x = a_y$, the beam is still plane-polarized, but at 45° to the x axis. For a beam of right (or left) circular polarization, $a_y = a_x e^{\pm i\pi/2}$; for any general (complex) values of the constants a_x and a_y, the beam is elliptically polarized. There is *no* definite choice of a_x and a_y which will yield an unpolarized beam; for that, some random variation of relative phase is needed.

For nucleons or electrons, as for light, only two alternatives need be assumed for the direction of polarization. (Photons have, in fact, a spin $S = 1$, and thus ought to have $2S + 1 = 3$ possible directions of polarization, but the requirement that electromagnetic waves must be transverse serves to reduce the number of alternative to two, exactly the same as for a particle of spin $\frac{1}{2}$.) We can write out the spin part of a wave function for a beam of spin $\frac{1}{2}$ particles as a column vector with just two components, each giving the amplitude and phase of a possible polarization type (or spin orientation):

$$\psi = \begin{pmatrix} a_1 \\ a_2 \end{pmatrix} = a_1\varphi_1 + a_2\varphi_2 \qquad \varphi_1 \equiv \begin{pmatrix} 1 \\ 0 \end{pmatrix}, \; \varphi_2 = \begin{pmatrix} 0 \\ 1 \end{pmatrix} \qquad (17.2)$$

where we have expanded the column vector in terms of two normal and orthogonal functions φ_1, φ_2, which are spin eigenfunctions, for example indicating that the spin is directed in either positive or negative sense along any line in space. The functions $\varphi_{1,2}$ are just like the functions α, β of equation 10.25; they are eigenfunctions of the Pauli operator σ_z where the z axis is taken in an arbitrary direction. The intensity of the beam is evidently the sum of the probabilities for the two alternative polarizations:

$$I = |a_1|^2 + |a_2|^2 \qquad (17.3)$$

and we can write this in the form

$$I = (a_1{}^* + a_2{}^*) \begin{pmatrix} a_1 \\ a_2 \end{pmatrix} \equiv \sum_{i=1,2} \psi_i{}^+\psi_i \qquad (17.4)$$

where we have introduced the symbol $\cdots +$ (read $\cdots$ adjoint) to stand for the quantity obtained by taking the complex conjugate of each element of a vector (or matrix), and interchanging rows and columns. Thus the column vector ψ becomes ψ^+, a row vector with complex conjugate components. The intensity I is plainly just the scalar product of the two vectors ψ^+, ψ in the spin space of two components.

The identical information given by the column vector wave function ψ can be expressed in another way, which is, however, capable of generalization to include beams of any degree of polarization. We use, instead of I, a 2×2 matrix ρ_{ij} to describe the system:

$$\rho_{ij} \equiv \psi_i\psi_j{}^+; \qquad \rho = \begin{pmatrix} a_1{}^*a_1 & a_1a_2{}^* \\ a_2a_1{}^* & a_2{}^*a_2 \end{pmatrix} \qquad (17.5)$$

The matrix ρ is called the density matrix for the system and is here given for a system with definite wave function ψ. (This is a special case of a very general method encountered in quantum statistical mechanics.) Now the intensity I can be written

$$I = \Sigma\rho_{ii} = \text{Trace } (\rho) \qquad (17.6)$$

Plainly ρ is Hermitian; i.e.,

$$\rho = \rho^+$$

Three independent numbers serve to fix ρ; these are discussed with equation 17.27.

The degree of polarization along the axis of quantization is defined as the net fraction of the beam which is aligned in the positive z direction:

$$P_z = (|a_1|^2 - |a_2|^2)/I \qquad (17.7)$$

and can be written in the compact form

$$P_z = \mathrm{Tr}\,(\rho\sigma_z)/\mathrm{Tr}\,(\rho) \qquad (17.8)$$

The beam is characterized completely by the intensity, the degree of polarization in the direction given, and the relative phase between a_1 and a_2, which is supplied by the off-diagonal elements of ρ. Now, it is always possible to diagonalize such a matrix. But the off-diagonal elements cannot be zero unless either a_1 or a_2 vanishes, so that the matrix ρ_{ij} is always of the form

$$\rho = \begin{pmatrix} I & 0 \\ 0 & 0 \end{pmatrix} \quad \text{or} \quad \rho = \begin{pmatrix} 0 & 0 \\ 0 & I \end{pmatrix} \qquad (17.9)$$

in some system. In this sense a beam represented by such a ρ, arising from a single wave function, is always polarized completely.

To represent a more general beam, we have only to *average* the density matrix over, say, N states, *each* with a density matrix $\rho^{(\alpha)}$ and weight $w(\alpha)$

$$\overline{\rho_{ij}} = \sum_{\alpha=1}^{N} \rho_{ij}^{(\alpha)} w(\alpha) \equiv \overline{\psi_i\psi_j^+} \qquad (17.10)$$

The density matrix $\bar{\rho}$ of this so-called mixed case (no single wave function) now is less restricted. For example, $\bar{\rho}_{12}$ may vanish while $\bar{\rho}_{11}$ and $\bar{\rho}_{22}$ both remain finite, because of canceling off-diagonal terms in the various $\bar{\rho}_{12}^{(\alpha)}$. The resulting matrix $\bar{\rho}$ gives the most general description of the spin properties of a beam of spin $\frac{1}{2}$ particles. Since every 2×2 matrix can be written as a linear combination of the Pauli matrices (and the unit matrix), we can write

$$\rho = a\mathbf{1} + \mathbf{b} \cdot \mathbf{\sigma} \qquad (17.11)$$

The constants a and $\mathbf{b}$ can be chosen to have a direct physical meaning by observing that the total beam intensity is given by

$$I = \mathrm{Tr}\,(\bar{\rho}) = 2a$$

since Tr $[(\mathbf{\sigma}_m)] = 0$.   The degree of polarization, with its direction, is specified by a vector **P**.   From equation 17.11 and the cyclical relations among the Pauli matrices,

$$\sigma_x\sigma_y = -\sigma_y\sigma_x = i\sigma_z \quad \text{with } \sigma_x^2 = \sigma_y^2 = \sigma_z^2 = 1$$

gives the components of P as

$$(\mathbf{P}_m) \equiv \text{Tr } [\bar{\rho}(\mathbf{\sigma})_m]/\text{Tr } (\bar{\rho}) = 2(\mathbf{b})_m/2a$$

where the subscript m signifies the component of the vector in a direction m.   Then the density matrix for an arbitrary beam becomes, dropping the bar on $\bar{\rho}$,

$$\rho = \tfrac{1}{2}I(1 + \mathbf{P} \cdot \mathbf{\sigma}) \tag{17.12}$$

A completely polarized beam, polarized for example in the $+z$ direction, is represented by

$$\rho = \tfrac{1}{2}I(1 + \sigma_z) = \begin{pmatrix} I & 0 \\ 0 & 0 \end{pmatrix}$$

and an unpolarized beam, whose polarization vector **P** vanishes in any direction, must be

$$\rho = \tfrac{1}{2}I \begin{pmatrix} 1 & 0 \\ 0 & 1 \end{pmatrix} = \tfrac{1}{2}I\mathbf{1}$$

In this way an arbitrary beam of spin $\frac{1}{2}$ particles can be specified by the four real and measurable numbers, I and **P**.   [See Tolhoek and DeGroot, *Physica 17*, 1 (1951); or McMaster, *Am. J. Phys. 22*, 351 (1954).]

B. THE SCATTERING MATRIX

The scattering cross section, for processes involving polarized beams, polarized targets, or both, must also be generalized.   In general it may be represented by a matrix in the spin space appropriate to all the alternative orientations of the whole system.   We will for the most part consider only spin $\frac{1}{2}$ particle beams and spin zero (or unpolarized) targets, so that the scattering cross section will, like the density matrix, be a 2×2 matrix.   (Again this is but the special case of a much more general method of quantum mechanics, valid for collisions of every kind, whenever several alternative results of a collision are possible.)

The effect of a scattering may be represented by the result of a matrix operation on the column vector of the incoming wave function

ψ_0, to produce an outgoing scattered wave ψ_f, in this way:

$$\psi_f = S\psi_0 \quad \text{and} \quad \psi_f{}^+ = (\psi_0{}^+S^+) \tag{17.13}$$

where S is the scattering matrix. If the incoming beam is represented by a density matrix ρ_0, we have the scattered beam

$$\rho_f = \overline{\psi_f\psi_f{}^+} = \overline{(S\psi_0)(\psi_0{}^+S^+)} = S\rho_0 S^+ \tag{17.14}$$

since

$$\rho_0 = \sum_\alpha \psi_{(\alpha)}\psi_{(\alpha)}{}^+w(\alpha) = \overline{\psi_0\psi_0{}^+} \tag{17.15}$$

The wave functions can be so normalized that the expectation value of the scattered amplitude gives the differential cross section per unit solid angle, $d\sigma/d\Omega$, for a unit incident beam. Then

$$d\sigma/d\Omega = \mathrm{Tr}\,(\rho_f)/\mathrm{Tr}\,(\rho_0) \tag{17.16}$$

The matrix S will of course depend on the scattering angle, the energies of incoming and outgoing beam, and the type of particles; the rows and columns simply index the spin dependence. Just as for the density matrix ρ, the scattering matrix S can be written as the linear combination

$$S = g\mathbf{1} + \mathbf{h} \cdot \mathbf{\sigma} \tag{17.17}$$

where the scalar g and the vector $\mathbf{h}$ are complex functions of angle, energy, and particle type.

The use of the spin vectors $\mathbf{\sigma}$ in equation 17.17 turns out to be a practically indispensable way of carrying out calculations for polarization processes, but it somewhat conceals the simpler physical relations. Before working out more practical cases by means of equation 17.17, it is worth while to look at a few very simple cases in a more direct way.

Take the scattering matrix S for a case in which all polarization effects are along a certain fixed direction of quantization. Then we can write the S matrix in the diagonal form:

$$S = \begin{pmatrix} a_+ & 0 \\ 0 & a_- \end{pmatrix} \tag{17.18}$$

where a_+ is the scattering amplitude for scattering the particles incident with spin up, and a_- that for the spin-down part of the beam. Now an incident unpolarized beam with

$$\rho_0 = \tfrac{1}{2}I\begin{pmatrix} 1 & 0 \\ 0 & 1 \end{pmatrix}$$

becomes polarized after one scattering:

$$\rho_1 = S\rho_0 S^+ = \tfrac{1}{2}I \begin{pmatrix} |a_+|^2 & 0 \\ 0 & |a_-|^2 \end{pmatrix}$$

and the amount of polarization is given by

$$P = (|a_+|^2 - |a_-|^2)/(|a_+|^2 + |a_-|^2) \tag{17.19}$$

Only the absolute squares $|a_+|^2$ and $|a_-|^2$ are relevant for this process; the relative phases do not affect the result. If the incoming beam is totally polarized,

$$\rho_0 = I \begin{pmatrix} 1 & 0 \\ 0 & 0 \end{pmatrix}$$

the scattered beam will retain complete polarization.

If we use relation 17.17 for the first case above, taking the direction of quantization to be the z axis, we get

$$\begin{pmatrix} a_+ & 0 \\ 0 & a_- \end{pmatrix} = g + h_z\sigma_z = \begin{pmatrix} g + h_z & 0 \\ 0 & g - h_z \end{pmatrix}$$

and the polarization after scattering becomes:

$$P = \tfrac{1}{2} (|g + h_z|^2 - |g - h_z|^2)/(|g|^2 + |h_z|^2)$$
$$= 2 \text{ Re } (gh_z{}^*)/(|g|^2 + |h_z|^2) \tag{17.20}$$

where now the real part of the product $gh_z{}^*$ determines the polarization. This apparent interference between the two parts of equation 17.17 is characteristic of this way of writing a scattering matrix; the effect of scattering is divided into two parts—one which cannot affect the spin and one which can flip it—instead of into parts giving an amplitude for each spin direction, as in the simple expression of equation 17.18. It is the vector nature of the spin operators which gives the present formalism its great usefulness.

If the scatterer is oriented in some way by external conditions, as in a piece of polaroid, the matrix S will depend on the direction of that orientation. A target which absorbed all particles with spin up, say, along a fixed direction $\mathbf{A}$, would have the matrix

$$S = \text{Const. } (\mathbf{1}|\mathbf{A}| + \mathbf{A} \cdot \boldsymbol{\sigma}) \tag{17.21}$$

But for scattering by an unoriented target, we can insist that the matrix S be independent of any external direction and depend only on the geometry of the collision, i.e., on the initial and final momentum vectors $\mathbf{k}_0$ and $\mathbf{k}_f$ (in the system in which the target is at rest). Now the quantity g must be a scalar and the vector $\mathbf{h}$ an axial vector (since $\mathbf{\sigma}$, analogous to $\mathbf{L} = \mathbf{r} \times \mathbf{p}$, is a pseudo or axial vector in ordinary three-dimensional space). From $\mathbf{k}_0$ and $\mathbf{k}_f$ can be built the familiar scalar $\mathbf{k}_0 \cdot \mathbf{k}_f$, which depends only on the cosine of the scattering angle $\cos\theta = \mathbf{k}_0 \cdot \mathbf{k}_f / |\mathbf{k}_0| \cdot |\mathbf{k}_f|$ and the axial vector $\mathbf{k}_0 \times \mathbf{k}_f$. The most general form of S matrix possible for collisions between a spin $\tfrac{1}{2}$ beam and an unoriented or spin-free target is then

$$S = g(\theta, E_0, E_f)\,\mathbf{1} + h(\theta, E_0, E_f)\mathbf{n} \cdot \mathbf{\sigma} \qquad (17.22a)$$

where we have used as arguments the energies E_0, E_f instead of the magnitudes of the momenta, and the unit vector $\mathbf{n}$, normal to the plane containing the incident and outgoing momenta, is defined by

$$\mathbf{n} = (\mathbf{k}_0 \times \mathbf{k}_f)/|\mathbf{k}_0 \times \mathbf{k}_f| \qquad (17.22b)$$

Expression 17.22 is the basis of all polarization calculations for nucleon beams. (We will ordinarily suppress the unit matrix $\mathbf{1}$ in writing 17.22.)

C. MEASUREMENT OF POLARIZED BEAMS

For visible photons and for thermal neutrons, oriented scatterers exist, either single or oriented crystals in the case of light, or magnetically oriented nuclei, in the slow neutron case. Here the usual unpolarized beam may be polarized by passage through one scattering layer and analyzed by its scattering in another. Some external direction determines the geometry of polarization. No such devices are known for nucleon beams at any but the lowest energies, at which atomic orientation may affect the long-wavelength nucleons. These experiments are discussed in Section D of this chapter. Normally, nucleon beams are produced unpolarized and must be studied by interaction with unpolarized, and not with oriented, layers of scatterer. This is possible because an unpolarized beam becomes partially polarized with one scattering, and the nature of this polarization may be studied by its effect on the scattered intensity, at various angles, of successive scatterings of the once-scattered beams.

Consider an unpolarized beam of well-defined energy and direction. It is caused to scatter from the original direction $\mathbf{k}_0$, to a direction and energy fixed by $\mathbf{k}_1$ (see Fig. 18). The resultant beam will have the density matrix:

$$\rho_1 = S_1\rho_0 S_1{}^+ = \tfrac{1}{2}I(g_1 + h_1\,\mathbf{n}_1 \cdot \mathbf{\sigma})(g_1{}^* + h_1{}^*\mathbf{n}_1 \cdot \mathbf{\sigma})$$

$$g_1 = g_1(\theta_1, E_1, E_0)$$

$$h_1 = h_1(\theta_1, E_1, E_0) \qquad (17.23)$$

The polarization of this singly scattered beam is given by the vector

$$\mathbf{P}_1 = P_1\mathbf{n}_1 \tag{17.24}$$

$$P_1(\theta_1, E_1, E_0) = 2 \operatorname{Re} (g_1 h_1{}^*)/(|g_1|^2 + |h_1|^2)$$

where $\mathbf{n}_1$ is given by equation 17.22. Now the once-scattered beam is brought against a second target and allowed again to scatter, the

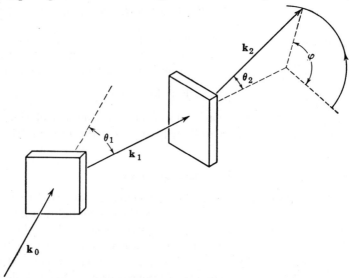

Fig. 18. Geometry of the double-scattering experiment for the detection of polarization. The initially unpolarized nucleon beam is incident on the first target with wave vector $\mathbf{k}_0$. It is scattered through the angle θ_1, taking the new direction $\mathbf{k}_1$. It is scattered a second time in the second target, through the angle θ_2, into the direction $\mathbf{k}_2$, specified by θ_2 and by the azimuthal angle φ. Any polarization resulting from the first scattering is now analyzed by observing the dependence of the intensity of the twice-scattered beam upon the angle φ.

resultant doubly scattered beam having the momentum $\mathbf{k}_2$. Then the beam is given by:

$$\rho_2 = S_2 \rho_1 S_2{}^+ \qquad S_2 = (g_2 + h_2 \mathbf{n}_2 \cdot \mathbf{d})$$

$$\mathbf{n}_2 = (\mathbf{k}_1 \times \mathbf{k}_2)/|\mathbf{k}_1 \times \mathbf{k}_2|$$

If the beam entering the second scatterer, with momentum $\mathbf{k}_1$, were polarized, the effect of the second scatterer acting alone would be to produce a polarization we call $\mathbf{P}_2$:

$$\mathbf{P}_2 = P_2\mathbf{n}_2$$

$$P_2 = 2 \operatorname{Re} (g_2 h_2{}^*)/(|g_2|^2 + |h_2|^2) \tag{17.25}$$

P_1 and P_2 may be made equal, or nearly so, if the angles θ_1 and θ_2 are correctly chosen; the equality is in general only approximate, both for instrumental reasons and because the beam loses energy (measured in the laboratory system) after the first scattering, even if it is elastic. Going on to consider the beam emerging from the second scatterer, we can measure the differential cross section (equation 17.16):

$$d\sigma_2/d\Omega = \mathrm{Tr}\ (\rho_2)/\mathrm{Tr}\ (\rho_1)$$

and, carrying out the indicated products, we obtain

$$d\sigma_2/d\Omega = (|g_2|^2 + |h_2|^2)(1 + P_1(\theta_1)P_2(\theta_2)\mathbf{n}_1 \cdot \mathbf{n}_2) \quad (17.26)$$

where use has been made of the relation (Dirac)

$$(\mathbf{a} \cdot \mathbf{\sigma})(\mathbf{b} \cdot \mathbf{\sigma}) = \mathbf{a} \cdot \mathbf{b} + i\mathbf{a} \times \mathbf{b} \cdot \mathbf{\sigma}$$

The result of equation 17.26 is directly measurable, because it implies a variation of the measured intensity of the twice-scattered beam with azimuthal angle.

Suppose first, for simplicity, that the first and second scatterings lie in the same plane. Then the differential cross section is just

$$d\sigma_2/d\Omega = (|g_2|^2 + |h_2|^2)(1 \pm P_1P_2) \quad (17.27)$$

the plus-or-minus sign being taken depending on whether the vectors $\mathbf{n}_1 \cdot \mathbf{n}_2$ are parallel or antiparallel, that is, whether the angle of deflection θ_2 lies to the right or to the left of the beam direction k_1. From this left-right asymmetry e the polarization can be measured.

$$e_{l-r} = (d\sigma_2{}^l - d\sigma_2{}^r)/(d\sigma_2{}^l + d\sigma_2{}^r) = P_1P_2 \quad (17.28)$$

If conditions are arranged to make $P_1 \cong P_2$, equation 17.28 gives $P_1 = \sqrt{e}$. If the two scatterings do not lie in the same plane, the azimuthal angle φ (Fig. 18) is introduced to measure the angle between the first and second scattering planes. The cross section is in general then

$$d\sigma_2(\theta_2, \varphi)/d\Omega = (|g(\theta_2)|^2 + |h(\theta_2)|^2[1 + P_1(\theta_1)P_2(\theta_2) \cos \varphi] \quad (17.29)$$

Such a variation with the angle φ is in fact observed. In double scattering of both neutrons and protons against spinless or unoriented nuclear targets, the observed asymmetries approach $e \sim 50$ per cent, or $P \sim 70$ to 90 per cent, for energies above ~ 100 Mev. This implies that g and h are closely similar in magnitude, at least at some angles.

If the incident beam is totally polarized, formula 17.29 gives the left-right asymmetry in the single scattering of a fully polarized beam; this may be regarded as the simplest physical significance of P.

At a given energy and angle, for the collision of spin $\frac{1}{2}$ particles of a definite type with a specific target, the matrix S in equation 17.22 is specified completely by the two complex functions g, h, which we can write

$$g(\theta, E) = |g| e^{i\alpha_0}; \qquad h(\theta, E) = |h| e^{i\alpha}$$

so that

$$S = e^{i\alpha_0}(|g| + |h| e^{i(\alpha-\alpha_0)} \mathbf{n} \cdot \mathbf{\sigma})$$

The absolute phase α_0 of the scattered amplitude has a physical meaning only in terms of possible interference with scattered amplitudes arising from different interactions, so that for purely nuclear scattering the matrix S is fixed by three real parameters, g, h, and $(\alpha - \alpha_0)$. Ordinary single scattering, with unpolarized beams and polarization-insensitive detectors, allows measurement of $|g|^2 + |h|^2$, the cross section. Double scattering allows measurement of the polarization, which from equation 17.29 determines $|g||h|\cos(\alpha - \alpha_0)$. But the third parameter is still undetermined by these experiments. A triple-scattering experiment, which may be thought of as an experiment to analyze the effect of the scatterer on a partially polarized beam, serves to fix a third relation among $|g|$, $|h|$, and $(\alpha - \alpha_0)$, and thus to determine the scattering matrix completely, up to a phase factor $e^{i\alpha_0}$. The triple-scattered beam may be calculated along the same lines. [See Wolfenstein, *Phys. Rev. 96*, 1654 (1954).]

This theory may be generalized to more complicated cases than that of the spin $\frac{1}{2}$ beam against a spinless target. Deuteron scattering against a spinless target has been studied, for example. The density matrix here is a 3×3 matrix, because there are three orientations possible for the spin 1 deuteron. The azimuthal dependence on double scattering turns out to be like

$$d\sigma_0/d\Omega = a(\theta_2) + b(\theta_2) \cos \varphi + c(\theta_2) \cos 2\varphi$$

instead of the simpler form (equation 17.29). This is exactly as predicted by the theory. Perhaps the most interesting extension is to the 4×4 spin space required for nucleon-nucleon scattering to describe the resultant spin quartet (triplet plus singlet) well known for a system of two spin $\frac{1}{2}$ particles. The scattering matrix at a given energy and angle, for proton-proton collisions, for example, is specified in general by not less than nine real parameters. These can in principle be fixed only by the use of polarized targets together with repeated scattering, spin correlation experiments using both collision partners, and magnetic fields.

D. EXPERIMENTS WITH POLARIZED NEUTRONS

Magnetic polarization of thermal neutrons.   Polarized nucleons were first obtained by passing thermal neutrons through magnetized iron targets, which can serve both as polarizers and as analyzers.   Here the polarization is produced by the orientation of the scattering centers with respect to the direction of the applied magnetic field. The *nuclei* of the target are not aligned (at ordinary temperatures and field strengths); the only aligned elements of the scatterer are the electrons of the iron atoms.   These can affect the neutron spin because the magnetic dipole moment of the neutron and that of the aligned electron have a magnetic interaction energy which depends on their relative orientation.   Though this interaction energy is small, it persists over the whole atomic volume.   If the atom can scatter more or less as a whole, the net atomic scattered amplitude turns out to be of the same order of magnitude as that scattered from the much more strongly interacting, but compactly localized, nuclear interaction.   For this large effect, the neutron wavelength must be comparable with atomic dimensions, and therefore thermal neutrons are necessary.   Higher-energy neutrons, with much shorter wavelength, are not appreciably scattered from atoms, since now the scattered contributions from various parts of the atomic magnetic field interfere destructively, except in the forward direction.

We can describe this process also by a minor modification of the general methods of this chapter.   The scattered neutron amplitude will contain a nuclear part, independent of the atomic magnetic moment, and a magnetic part, which must depend on the direction of the magnetic moment of the atom, **m**.   So the general scattering matrix S becomes

$$S = a + b\boldsymbol{\sigma} \cdot \mathbf{m} \qquad (17.30)$$

where external magnetic fields now determine **m**, and we can no longer impose the requirement of equation 17.22 that S be independent of direction in space.   Since thick targets are ordinarily used, we will not directly take S to calculate their effect but will rather take the result of repeated scatterings through a thickness of scatterer dx, which can be written in the form

$$d\rho(x)/dx = (1/\lambda)(1 + \mathbf{M} \cdot \boldsymbol{\sigma})\rho(x) \qquad (17.31)$$

Here $\rho(x)$ represents the density matrix at thickness x, λ is an effective scattering mean free path for the medium, and **M** is a vector representing the magnetic scattering effect of the medium.

M is determined by the external magnetization and by the magnetic properties of the medium. The form $(\mathbf{M} \cdot \mathbf{\sigma})$ is general, and can be thought of as obtained by a repeated application of $S \cdots S^+$.

The usual thick-target integration gives

$$\rho(x) = e^{-(x/\lambda)(1+\mathbf{M}\cdot\mathbf{\sigma})}$$

$$= e^{x/\lambda}(\cosh Mx/\lambda + \mathbf{M} \cdot \mathbf{\sigma} \sinh Mx/\lambda)\rho(0) \qquad (17.32)$$

and we can see the polarization properties directly. Magnetizing the medium, with an unpolarized beam incident, produces a relative change in transmitted intensity

$$\mathrm{Tr}(\rho_{\mathbf{M}} - \rho_0)/\mathrm{Tr}(\rho_0) = \cosh Mx/\lambda - 1$$
$$\cong \tfrac{1}{2}(Mx/\lambda)^2 \qquad \text{if } Mx/\lambda \ll 1 \quad (17.33)$$

and a polarized beam emerges with polarization:

$$\mathbf{P} = \mathrm{Tr}\ (\rho\mathbf{\sigma})/\mathrm{Tr}\ (\rho) = \mathbf{M} \tanh Mx/\lambda \qquad (17.34)$$

This polarized beam can be sent through another magnetized sample acting as analyzer, and the whole arrangement becomes a complete analog to a beam of optical light passing through two Nicol prisms. The direction of polarization is fixed now by the external conditions, and not by the plane of scattering, as in the earlier discussion of unoriented targets. Polarization by unoriented targets is plainly the analog of polarization by Rayleigh scattering of light.

The actual value of λ and the direction and magnitude of M are hard to give. They depend not only on the neutron energy and the nuclear properties of the material but on its lattice, atomic, microcrystalline, and magnetic domain characteristics as well. Their study is a specialized topic of solid-state physics.

The principal nuclear use of this phenomenon has been in the determination of the magnetic moment of the free neutron. To do this a partially polarized neutron beam is set up by a polarizer magnet and then passed through an analyzer. A uniform magnetic field is produced in the intervening space through which the beam passes. The neutron spin will be unaffected by such a uniform field. But if a weak radio-frequency field is impressed on the beam in that space, transitions will be induced between the spin-parallel and spin antiparallel states of the neutron, which have different energies in the uniform field B. The resonant frequency for such transitions is given by the relation:

$$\hbar\omega_0 = 2\mathbf{B} \cdot \mathbf{\mu} \qquad (17.35)$$

and the measurement of the magnetic moment can be made by observing at what impressed frequency ω_0 the polarization state of the neutrons in the intermediate space is caused to change, as indicated by observed changes in transmission of the analyzer. As was seen in Chapter VIII, the method can be made enormously accurate, especially if not an absolute μ but a ratio μ_1/μ_2 is wanted.

If the plane-polarized radio-frequency field is replaced by a circularly polarized one (rotating instead of simple sinusoidal radio-frequency field), the *sign* of the magnetic moment also can be measured. Resonance absorption will then occur only if the direction of field rotation is the same as that of the Larmor precession of the nucleon moment in the uniform field. This method confirms the indirect evidence for the negative sign of the neutron moment.

Some work has been done on neutron polarization with targets in which the *nuclei* have been aligned by strong magnetic fields at very low temperatures in paramagnetic salts. The results so far are mainly of interest in the study of low temperatures.

Polarization in nucleon-nucleon scattering. Low-energy nucleon scattering cannot show any polarization, because only the S wave contributes. Up to about 100 Mev, the polarization is unobservably low in neutron-neutron or proton-proton scattering. But beginning at about that energy, experiments show strong and complex polarization in nucleon-nucleon scattering. The observed polarization varies in such a complicated way with energy that in the proton-proton case, for example, it seems necessary to invoke partial waves of at least $l = 3$ to explain the results at 200 Mev. The polarization found in proton-proton scattering reaches a peak value around 40 per cent in the energy region below some 400 Mev, for special angles and energies. Neutron-proton scattering is similar.

It has been observed in Section C of this chapter that a full description of the nucleon-nucleon scattering can be given only by the measurement of no less than nine real numbers for each energy and angle of scattering. This prodigious task will not soon be completed, even with the remarkable contemporary techniques of triple scattering and coincidence recoil polarization.

Polarization in nucleon-nucleus scattering. In the energy range above 100 Mev, the scattering of protons and neutrons from heavier nuclei, Be on up, has been observed to polarize the nucleon beam. Two features of the rather voluminous and complicated data stand out:

1. The polarization, for favorable energies and angles, can reach values as high as 90 per cent, even though nucleon-nucleon scattering

does not exceed 40 per cent polarization. This is observed for a variety of target nuclei.

2. High polarization is associated experimentally with elastic scattering. The more strictly the energy of the scattered beam is held to be that of the incident beam, the higher is the polarization. Indeed, the angular distribution of polarization seems to reflect the angular distribution of the shadow scattering, which certainly confirms the inference from direct energy selection.

Tamor [*Phys. Rev. 97*, 1077 (1955)] has given a qualitative explanation for these two unexpected phenomena. He observes that in nucleon-nucleon scattering the scattering matrix may be written:

$$S = a + b(\mathbf{d}_1 \cdot \mathbf{n})(\mathbf{d}_2 \cdot \mathbf{n}) + c(\mathbf{d}_1 + \mathbf{d}_2) \cdot \mathbf{n} + e(\mathbf{d}_1 \cdot \mathbf{\kappa})(\mathbf{d}_2 \cdot \mathbf{\kappa}) + f(\mathbf{d}_1 \cdot \mathbf{p})(\mathbf{d}_2 \cdot \mathbf{p}) \quad (17.36)$$

for the two nucleons 1 and 2, where $\mathbf{n}_1$, $\mathbf{\kappa}$, and $\mathbf{p}$ are the three orthogonal unit vectors:

$$\mathbf{n} = \mathbf{k}_i \times \mathbf{k}_f / |\mathbf{k}_i \times \mathbf{k}_f|; \qquad \mathbf{\kappa} = \mathbf{k}_f - \mathbf{k}_i / |\mathbf{k}_f - \mathbf{k}_i|; \qquad \mathbf{p} = \mathbf{n} \times \mathbf{\kappa} \quad (17.37)$$

If we consider the incoming polarization to be along $\mathbf{n}$, say, then only the terms e and f in equation 17.36 can contribute to collisions in which the value of S_z changes sign. These can be called spin-flip collisions. Now, whenever spin flip occurs for incoming particle 1, the struck nucleon 2 must also flip its spin. If we allow only elastic events, however, and nucleon 2 is bound into a nucleus, a spin flip for 2 is forbidden, for any flip must produce a new nuclear state. This is true in so far as the effect of the nucleus can be regarded as the sum of the effects of scattering by free nucleons, and it should hold to a good approximation at these energies. Thus the terms e and f cannot contribute to the elastic scattering. But the terms e and f never contribute to the polarized intensity, because of their symmetry. Thus if they are suppressed in elastic nuclear scattering, the polarized intensity remains unchanged, but the total cross section is reduced, so that the relative number of polarized nucleons should increase in elastic nuclear scattering over that expected from nucleon-nucleon collisions, just what is observed. Actually term b is also affected by the suppression of spin flip, so that it cannot be shown that such an increase is always present, but only that the maximum possible polarization is increased by this process.

XVIII. SKETCH OF THE MESON THEORY
OF NUCLEAR FORCES

It may now be regarded as well established that the forces between nucleons are transmitted by mesons. The quantitative explanation of nuclear forces in terms of the meson theory is still extremely tentative and incomplete, but the theory supplies a valuable point of view and will presumably develop rapidly in the future.

When we describe the Coulomb force between two charges, we introduce the electric field surrounding a charge, and consider the field surrounding one charge as acting on any other. Similarly, we may introduce a new "nuclear field" surrounding each nucleon, and consider the nuclear force as the action of the nuclear field surrounding the first nucleon on the second, or vice versa.

In quantum theory, every field must be "quantized." In the electromagnetic field, this procedure leads to the concept of light quanta (photons). The "quanta" of the nuclear force field are called mesons. Yukawa, in initiating the meson theory [*Proc. Physico-Math. Soc. Japan 17*, 48 (1935)], suggested that if the mesons are given a finite rest mass m, the range of the forces arising from the meson field will be $\hbar/mc$, the Compton wavelength for the meson. The electromagnetic field in contrast falls off smoothly as the square of the separation, having therefore essentially infinite range; photons have zero rest mass. But the effective range of nuclear forces, as we have seen, is of the order of 2×10^{-13} cm, and we should therefore expect the meson mas to be around 200 electron masses. Indeed, about two years after Yukawa's theory, particles of mass about $200 m_e$ were discovered in cosmic radiation.

By 1947, when the first edition of this book appeared, the properties of the meson abundant in cosmic rays near sea level were fairly well known. This is the μ-meson (see Chapter VII). It was natural to think this meson the Yukawa particle, but two results obtained that very year led to our present understanding: The Yukawa particle is not the μ-meson but is its parent, the shorter-lived π-meson.

The first of these results was the observation by Conversi et al. that negatively charged μ-mesons, when stopped in matter, showed β-decay in preference to nuclear capture for elements as heavy as $Z \sim 6$. Since the velocity of a μ-meson in the K shell of carbon is about 10^9 cm/sec, it travels about 10^3 cm in its lifetime of roughly 1 microsecond. A large fraction of this path is spent traversing nuclear matter. Indeed, the fractional volume of the meson K shell which is occupied by nuclear matter in carbon is about

$$\left(\frac{\text{Radius of nucleus}}{\text{Radius of meson } K \text{ orbit}}\right)^3 = \left(\frac{r_0 A^{\frac{1}{3}}}{\hbar^2/m_\mu Z e^2}\right)^3 \cong 3 \times 10^{-4} \quad (18.1)$$

in an obvious notation. It follows that the mean path of such a meson within a nucleus is a few millimeters. Evidently, if it interacted with nucleons strongly enough to be responsible for the nuclear forces, its mean free path within the nucleus should be about the same as is that of a nucleon, or only $\sim 10^{-13}$ cm. The discrepancy is too great to blame on the roughness of this estimate. It was explained only when C. F. Powell, also in 1947, found the decay of the π-meson into the μ-meson in his pioneer work with photographic emulsions. Powell also observed directly strong interactions between π-mesons and nuclei: The Yukawa theory applies to the π-meson, not to the μ. By now the π-meson is a laboratory, and not merely a cosmic-ray, particle, and its properties have been well investigated (see Chapter VIII).

To determine the shape of the nuclear forces in meson theory, at least in first approximation, we shall derive an equation for the meson field, analogous to the equation $\nabla^2 \psi = -4\pi\rho$ which describes the static part of the electromagnetic field. The wave equation describing the field must also be the Schrödinger equation for an individual field quantum, in our case a meson. It is known from experiment that mesons have no spin. The relativistic wave equation for such particles, with a finite rest mass m, is the Klein-Gordon equation:

$$\nabla^2 \psi + (1/\hbar^2 c^2)[(E - V)^2 - (mc^2)^2]\psi = 4\pi\rho \quad (18.2)$$

with

$$E = i\hbar(\partial/\partial t) \quad (18.3)$$

where ρ in this case is proportional to the density of nucleons. In free space, $V = 0$. For a *static* meson field, according to equation 18.3, we must put $E = 0$. Furthermore, if there is one point-nucleon at the origin, the Klein-Gordon equation becomes

$$\nabla^2 \psi - (mc/\hbar)^2 \psi = 4\pi g_1 \delta(\mathbf{r}) \quad (18.4)$$

where δ represents the Dirac δ-function, and g_1 is a constant replacing the electronic charge in electrodynamics.

The solution of this equation is

$$\psi = -(g_1/r) \exp\left[-(mc/\hbar)r\right] \tag{18.5}$$

and the potential acting on a second nucleon is given by:

$$V = g_2\psi \tag{18.6}$$

where g_1 and g_2 are the effective nucleonic "charges" or coupling constants.

The Yukawa scalar meson theory just described produces the required range for nuclear forces for the measured mass of the π-meson is 273 times the mass of the electron. This gives $\hbar/mc = 1.4 \times 10^{-13}$ cm. The effective range of nuclear forces in the singlet state is about $2.2\hbar/mc$ if the interaction has the "Yukawa shape" given by equation 18.5. This gives a slightly larger result than the observed singlet effective range, about 2.6×10^{-13} cm; the difference is usually attributed to the effect of higher-order interactions in which two or more mesons are simultaneously transmitted between the nucleons. Since in this theory the nuclear particle does not change its nature (i.e., charge), we find that according to the theory the neutron-neutron, neutron-proton, and proton-proton forces are all equal. However, the theory does not explain the exchange nature of nuclear forces, which is well established from high-energy scattering experiments (Chapter XVI) and also valuable to help account for the saturation of nuclear forces (Chapter XV). Neither does the theory in this simple form explain the spin dependence or the presence of non-central forces. The theory must therefore be modified in several ways.

A. CHARGED AND NEUTRAL MESONS; SYMMETRIC THEORY

Since the mesons first found in cosmic rays (μ-mesons) were all charged positively or negatively, a theory involving charged mesons was developed. According to this theory, the following reactions can take place:

$$p \rightleftharpoons n + \pi^+ \qquad \text{or} \qquad n \rightleftharpoons p + \pi^- \tag{18.7}$$

Thus protons and neutrons can transform into each other by the emission or absorption of positive or negative mesons. The interaction of two particles, 1 and 2, can take place, for instance, by the following scheme:

$$p_1 \to n_1 + \pi^+ \qquad n_2 + \pi^+ \to p_2 \qquad (18.8)$$

This interaction has the advantage over the one previously discussed, involving mesons without electric charge, that it gives exchange forces between proton and neutron. But it is plain that the interaction (18.8) can occur only between a proton and a neutron, not between two like nucleons. This is in contradiction with experimental evidence and rules out the charged-meson theory. The symmetric-meson theory was developed on this account, long before neutral mesons were discovered.

The discovery of the neutral meson, π^0, and the fact that charge independence is now consistent with all nuclear data, confirm fully the use of the symmetric-meson theory (Kemmer, 1939), containing positive, negative, and neutral mesons, described by three wave functions ψ_1, ψ_2, and ψ_3. Here neutron-neutron and proton-proton forces will exist and will be equal.

The theory is best formulated using the isotopic spin. The single equation (18.2) becomes a set of three equations, one for each of the three charge types of mesons with wave function ψ_α:

$$\nabla^2 \psi_\alpha - (mc/\hbar)^2 \psi_\alpha = 4\pi g_1 \tau_\alpha \delta(\mathbf{r}) \qquad (18.9)$$

and the operators τ_α work on the charge wave function of the nucleon. The τ_α are to be chosen so that the emission (or absorption) of charged mesons takes place according to equation 18.7, and in addition the emission of neutral mesons can occur in the reactions

$$n \rightleftharpoons n + \pi^0$$
$$p \rightleftharpoons p + \pi^0 \qquad (18.10)$$

We shall also require charge independence; i.e., both $|\tau|^2$ and τ_z shall be constants of the motion.

Consider reaction 18.10 involving a neutral meson. Let us designate the τ_α for this case as τ_3. Then τ_3 must leave a proton a proton and a neutron still a neutron:

$$\tau_3 \psi_p \sim \psi_p \qquad \psi_p \equiv \gamma = \begin{pmatrix} 1 \\ 0 \end{pmatrix}$$

$$\tau_3 \psi_n \sim \psi_n \qquad \psi_n \equiv \delta = \begin{pmatrix} 0 \\ 1 \end{pmatrix} \qquad (18.11)$$

where we have used the charge wave functions as in equation 15.13.

The constants of proportionality in equations 18.11 are not determined by charge conservation alone; but since we want to guarantee charge independence, we can choose them by writing

$$\tau_3 = \tau_z = \begin{pmatrix} 1 & 0 \\ 0 & -1 \end{pmatrix} \tag{18.12}$$

and τ_z will be conserved. With the other two components, τ_1 and τ_2, we have to represent reactions 18.8, so that we must have

$$\tau_1 \psi_p = 0; \qquad \tau_1 \psi_n = c_1 \psi_p$$

$$\tau_2 \psi_n = 0; \qquad \tau_2 \psi_p = c_2 \psi_n \tag{18.13a}$$

where the constants c_1 and c_2 are still at our disposal. We can now express these operators as linear combinations of the old τ_x, τ_y (which are the same as the Pauli spin matrices σ_x, σ_y; see chapter XV):

$$\tau_1 = c_1 \frac{(\tau_x + i\tau_y)}{2} = c_1 \begin{pmatrix} 0 & 1 \\ 0 & 0 \end{pmatrix}$$
$$\tau_2 = c_2 \frac{(\tau_x - i\tau_y)}{2} = c_2 \begin{pmatrix} 0 & 0 \\ 1 & 0 \end{pmatrix} \tag{18.13b}$$

and we have still to choose the constants. We do this so as to maintain the value of $|\tau|^2$, for the total isotopic spin must have unchanged eigenvalues. Then we write

$$|\tau|^2 = \tau_z^2 + \tau_x^2 + \tau_y^2 = \tau_z^2 + \frac{c_1 c_2}{2} (\tau_1 \tau_2 + \tau_1 \tau_2) \tag{18.14}$$

and if we take

$$c_1 = c_2 = \sqrt{2} \tag{18.15}$$

all the conditions are satisfied. Note that this corresponds to choosing complex axis directions in the x-y plane of the space of the three isotopic spin operators, $\tau = (\tau_x, \tau_y, \tau_z)$. Since only the z axis in that space has a physical meaning, this choice is entirely allowable; it implies that the scalar product of two τ vectors must be taken as

$$\tau_a \cdot \tau_b = \tau_{3a}\tau_{3b} + \tau_{1a}\tau_{2b} + \tau_{2a}\tau_{1b}$$

instead of the form usual with real orthogonal axes.

The appearance of the constants $\sqrt{2}$ in equation 18.15, from what is essentially a normalization requirement on $|\tau|$, ensures that charged mesons (which can be emitted only by one type of nucleon for each charge) are as strongly coupled to nucleons as are neutral ones (which can be emitted by either neutron or proton). The most interesting feature of the symmetric theory is that the neutral meson field of a neutron is equal in strength but opposite in sign to that of a proton, as can be seen from equation 18.12.

The interaction potential between two nucleons now becomes

$$V(\mathbf{r}_{ij}) = -(g^2/r_{ij}) \exp\left[-r_{ij}/(\hbar/mc)\right]\boldsymbol{\tau}_i \cdot \boldsymbol{\tau}_j \qquad (18.16)$$

where i and j designate the two interacting nucleons. This interaction is a scalar in the isotopic spin space and therefore maintains charge independence. The symmetric theory was constructed for this end.

With the form of equation 18.16 for scalar mesons, it is easy to see that the π-meson cannot be scalar, for the value of $\boldsymbol{\tau}_1 \cdot \boldsymbol{\tau}_2$, given by Table XVD, changes sign as T goes from 0 to 1. The singlet proton-proton state is known to be attractive, and thus the deuteron ground state would on this theory have a repulsive force, which is absurd.

B. SCALAR AND PSEUDOSCALAR MESONS

The π-meson is known to have zero spin by direct experiment. It must then have only a single component wave function. But the scalar theory above led to an absurd result. There is only one open possibility, and in order to discuss it we shall have to introduce a new physical concept, the idea of intrinsic parity.

Intrinsic parity. This is an extension of the notion of parity (Chapter VIII) made use of in the theory of the fundamental particles. In the derivation of equation 14.11 it was implicitly assumed that on an inversion of coordinates the space wave function changed only by the replacement, $\mathbf{r}_k \rightarrow -\mathbf{r}_k$ and $\psi(-\mathbf{r}_k) = K\psi(\mathbf{r}_k)$ (equation 14.9). But the phase of a wave function is not directly measurable, and it would be entirely consistent to change the sign of the wave function itself on inversion, as well as the sign of coordinates. The absolute square of the wave function, or the relative phase of several wave functions, which alone are observable, are not affected by such change of sign. It would be a purely conventional possibility, as long as the wave functions of all particles followed the same convention. But if there are present in the system more than one type of particle, with different wave function behaviors on inversion, then the intrinsic change of sign of the wave function on inversion becomes meaningful. For a particle whose wave function has but one component, there are two possibilities:

$$\psi(-\mathbf{r}_k) = \pm K\psi(\mathbf{r}_k) \qquad (18.17)$$

where K is the constant of the previous section which determines the space behavior of the wave function on inversion. If the plus sign holds in equation 14.9, the particle is said to be *scalar;* if the minus sign holds, it is *pseudoscalar.* The distinction has meaning only if the number or type of particles present in a system can change, for the absolute sign of an entire wave function cannot be meaningful. Especially if the system changes by the creation or destruction of a particle of given intrinsic parity can the effect of this constant of motion be observed. For in such a change the spatial parity of the residual system adjusts to compensate the change in intrinsic parity caused by the gain or loss of the particle.

The intrinsic parity of the π-meson is odd (compared to the nucleon, taken as having even parity.) Since its spin is zero, it is thus not a scalar particle but a pseudoscalar one (analogous to an axial rather than to a polar vector). (A pseudoscalar changes sign when the sign of the time is reversed, or on inversion of all spatial coordinates; under proper Lorentz transformations, it is invariant.)

A typical piece of evidence for the pseudoscalar character of the π-meson is the capture of slow negative π-mesons in deuterium. The stopped π-meson falls eventually into the innermost atomic orbit available to it, the K shell. Here it stays until the proton captures the π-meson, to give the reaction

$$\pi^- + H^2 \rightarrow n + n + 140 \text{ Mev} \qquad (18.18a)$$

One alternative reaction is the emission of most of the energy as γ-radiation:

$$\pi^- + H^2 \rightarrow n + n + \gamma \qquad (18.18b)$$

Now the total angular momentum of the deuteron plus the π-meson in the K shell is plainly $J = 1$, since the meson has zero spin. The two recoil neutrons in reaction 18.18a must therefore also have $J = 1$ and can be only in the quantum state ${}^3P_1{}^-$. The Pauli exclusion principle forbids the over-all symmetric states ${}^3S_1$, ${}^3D_1$, ${}^1P_1$.

If the intrinsic parity of the system were unchanged by the disappearance of the captured meson, the final state would have the even parity of the initial deuteron, since the initial space wave function of the π-meson has even parity. But the only possible final state permitting reaction 18.18a, the ${}^3P_1$ state, has *odd* parity. Therefore conservation of parity requires that the intrinsic parity of the π-meson also be *odd*, since the two reactions (18.18a and 18.18b) are observed to go roughly equally often. The final state of reaction

18.18b has three particles and therefore no such restricted parity value.

C. COUPLING OF PSEUDOSCALAR MESON AND NUCLEON

The intrinsic parity is a notion essentially relativistic in nature, for it depends on the appearance or disappearance of particles, described only in relativistic quantum theories. The coupling of a pseudoscalar meson with a nucleon can be represented correctly only by means of the Dirac theory, with an operator designated usually as γ_5, which has matrix elements connecting nucleon states with positive energy strongly to antinucleon states (negative energy) (cf. Chapter XX). This means that the virtual creation of nucleon-antinucleon pairs becomes an essential part of the meson exchange process. Only the quantum field theory can include this possibility consistently.

A non-relativistic approximation to the pseudoscalar theory turns out to amount to introducing into the Hamiltonian of nucleon plus meson field an interaction energy containing the factor $\mathbf{\sigma} \cdot \nabla \psi_\alpha$, where $\mathbf{\sigma}$ is the nucleon spin. Since ψ_α is a pseudoscalar, $\mathbf{\sigma}$ an axial, and ∇ a polar vector, the product $\mathbf{\sigma} \cdot \nabla \psi_\alpha$ is invariant with respect to inversion of the spatial coordinates, and hence a scalar, as the Hamiltonian should be.

If we assume the nucleons to be point particles, moving with non-relativistic velocities, then it is possible to solve the field equations in the first approximation, i.e., assuming that only one meson is exchanged between two nucleons. This leads to an interaction potential between two nucleons of the form:

$$V(\mathbf{r}_{ij}) = \frac{g^2}{(2M)^2} \, \mathbf{\tau}_i \cdot \mathbf{\tau}_j \left[S_{ij} \left(\frac{1}{r^3} + \frac{\mu}{r^2} + \frac{\mu^2}{3r} \right) e^{-\mu r} \right.$$
$$\left. + \mathbf{\sigma}_i \cdot \mathbf{\sigma}_j \left(\frac{\mu^2 e^{-\mu r}}{r} - 4\pi \delta(\mathbf{r}) \right) \right] \quad (18.19)$$

where $\mu = \hbar/mc$, $r = |\mathbf{r}_{ij}|$, and S_{ij} is the tensor force (equation 14.1). The term $(\mathbf{\tau}_i \cdot \mathbf{\tau}_j)(\mathbf{\sigma}_i \cdot \mathbf{\sigma}_j)$ in equation 18.19 gives a central force. In both the ^3S and the ^1S states, $(\mathbf{\tau}_i \cdot \mathbf{\tau}_j)(\mathbf{\sigma}_i \cdot \mathbf{\sigma}_j) = -3$, so that the predicted central force for both these states is the same and is attractive. The tensor force S_{ij} has the correct sign to explain the deuteron quadrupole moment. Since the tensor force acts in the ^3S state and not in the ^1S, it lowers the energy of the former. It is therefore entirely acceptable to have the same central force for ^1S and ^3S, as equation 18.19 predicts; the difference between the scattering lengths for these states is then attributed to the effect of the tensor force. A number of calculations have been done which show that, with appropriate magnitude and shape of central and tensor force— not those given by the first approximation (equation 18.19)—the experimental facts on the ^1S and ^3S state can indeed be explained assuming the same central force for both states.

The last term in equation 18.19 is a δ-function which is repulsive for the S states. An exact δ-function would have no effect on the energy levels. However, Levy pointed out in 1952 that the positions of the two nucleons can never be regarded as exactly fixed but that they must be smeared out by the quantum uncertainty of at least $\hbar/Mc$. The term $\delta(\mathbf{r})$ smeared out yields then a very strong and small repulsive core, just what was suggested on quite different grounds by Jastrow (see Chapter XVI). This core turns out to be two or three times $\hbar/Mc$; i.e., perhaps one-third of the range $\hbar/mc$ of the Yukawa force. Unfortunately, this core is obtained from meson field theory for both $T = 0$ and $T = 1$, whereas the high-energy scattering experiments seem to require it only for $T = 1$.

One can try to determine the value of g such that the potential (equation 18.19) yields the correct scattering length for the ^1S state of the deuteron. (The singlet state is chosen because it is simpler, owing to the absence of the tensor force.) This gives approximately $g^2/\hbar c = 17$, which may be compared with the corresponding quantity for the electromagnetic field; i.e., the fine structure constant $e^2/\hbar c = \frac{1}{137}$. The very large value of the dimensionless coupling constant $g^2/\hbar c$ is the reason why it is so difficult to obtain reliable theoretical results from meson theory. The usual perturbation methods of quantum field theory are well adapted to the treatment of the electromagnetic field with its small coupling constant $e^2/\hbar c$, but they fail completely for the strongly coupled meson field. Only very tentative approximation methods have so far been developed.

One consequence of the large coupling constant is clear: It must happen very frequently that more than one meson is transferred simultaneously between two nucleons. Fortunately, the transfer of *very many* mesons probably does not need to be considered: If n mesons are transferred, this leads to an interaction behaving approximately as

$$\exp\,(-n\mu r) \tag{18.20}$$

from arguments similar to those leading to equation 18.16 or 18.19; hence the range of these forces is effectively $1/n\mu$. But for small distances, we have the strong repulsive core arising from the δ function in equation 18.19.   This core prevents the nucleons from coming close together with any appreciable probability; therefore it does not matter much whether the transfer of n mesons adds an attractive or a repulsive interaction at these small distances, or what the magnitude of this interaction is.   For the same reason, the interaction of the nucleon with heavier mesons (e.g., the K mesons which have a mass of about 1000 electron masses) will not have much influence on the nuclear forces at low energy.   (The repulsive core is not caused by the interaction of the nucleon with these heavier mesons, as was at one time suggested, but comes out naturally from its interaction with the ordinary π-mesons.)   This conclusion is very important, because it makes it likely that the nuclear force problem can be solved, at least in principle, without first understanding the very complicated behavior of the elusive heavy mesons.

Of course, when two nucleons collide at very high energy (billions of electron volts), all these arguments break down.   Then the nucleons *can* penetrate or disturb each other's "core"; this manifests itself experimentally by the multiple production of π-mesons and the frequent production of heavy mesons.

Encouraged by the general argument that only the exchange of a relatively small number of mesons can have an appreciable effect on the nuclear force at low and medium energies, many authors have tackled the nuclear force problem.   In this more complete treatment, it is no longer possible to derive a potential between two nucleons which can be used in a differential Schrödinger equation in configuration space, but one obtains instead an integral equation in momentum space.   No such calculation has yet been carried to a point which agrees quantitatively with experiment; yet every point in the summary on page 132 is *qualitatively* predicted by pseudoscalar symmetric meson theory.*   How long this situation will continue we do not know.

* A similar qualitative, or in this case semiquantitative, understanding has been gained of the interaction of the mesons themselves with nucleons, as manifested by their scattering from nucleons and their production from nucleons by γ rays, at moderate energies (up to about 400 or 500 Mev).

C.

COMPLEX NUCLEI
β-DECAY

XIX. THE STRUCTURE OF NUCLEI

From a detailed knowledge of the forces between nucleons it would be possible to calculate the properties of all nuclei. The solution of the many-body problem involved would doubtless be impossible except approximately. Not much progress has been made toward this ambitious future program [although a possible route has been pointed out by Brueckner, *Phys. Rev. 95*, 217 (1954)], but a good deal of insight has been gained into the structure and properties of all nuclei by the use of various more or less physical models whose consequences are capable of calculation.

A. THE LIQUID DROP;
SEMI-EMPIRICAL ENERGIES

The simplest of these models is the analogy between a nucleus and a drop of an ordinary liquid. A liquid drop has a uniform central density, independent of its size, and outside this a surface layer; so has the nucleus. In this quite crude model nuclei are treated as though individual nucleons had no special role, and the special properties of nuclei like the α-particle are forgotten. The principal use of this model is the prediction of nuclear binding energies. We can write the mass defect of a nucleus of mass number A in this way:

$$M(A, Z) - A = -a_v A + a_s A^{2/3} + a_c Z^2/A^{1/3} \qquad (19.1)$$

Here the first term represents a uniform binding energy per unit volume of nuclear matter; the second term, a surface energy, repulsive in effect, and standing for the unsaturated "bonds" of those nucleons which are present on the surface of the nuclear drop; the last term is

157

the classical energy of electrostatic repulsion, the Coulomb energy of the Z protons of the nucleus. The latter term is of course just

$$\frac{1}{2} \iint \frac{\rho(\mathbf{r})\rho(\mathbf{r}')}{|\mathbf{r} - \mathbf{r}|} \, d\mathbf{r} \, d\mathbf{r}' = \frac{3}{5} \frac{Z^2 e^2}{R} = \frac{3}{5} \frac{Z^2 e^2}{r_0 A^{1/3}} \tag{19.2}$$

for a uniform charged sphere.

The mass defect of such a classical liquid drop of constant density and uniform charge bears little similarity to the real state of affairs. On that basis the most stable nuclei would have no protons but would have $Z = 0$ and $A = N$, the number of neutrons. For light nuclei, where the Coulomb energy is not large, neutrons and protons in fact tend to occur in the same number. We therefore add a term called the symmetry energy, which gives its biggest binding for equal N and Z, and varies in the simplest symmetrical way with $N - Z$, namely quadratically. Such a contribution will be associated with strong space-exchange forces, of the kind discussed in Chapter XV. These forces attract if the nucleons interacting have a relative motion which is space-symmetric, e.g., if the two are in a relative s wave of orbital angular momentum. (Higher angular momenta contribute only a little, because they correspond to a greater separation of the nucleon pair.) For particles with opposed spin directions, such relative motion is always possible. But two particles with parallel spin orientation cannot interact in a symmetric state, unless the two are proton and neutrons, because of the Pauli principle. The more pairs of unlike nucleons, the greater is the space-exchange binding. The number of such pairs is maximized if the neutron and proton number are equal. Per pair of unlike interacting nucleons, we can expect a binding from this source which will be very roughly proportional to the probability that two nucleons find themselves within a given interaction volume. For nuclei large compared to this interaction range, this probability is inversely proportional to the total nuclear volume, and hence proportional to $1/A$. On the basis of such arguments, made in a more detailed fashion (see Blatt and Weisskopf, *Theoretical Nuclear Physics*, Chapter VI, John Wiley & Sons, New York, 1952), but chiefly in a semi-empirical spirit, a symmetry binding term is added, of form $(N - Z)^2/A$.

It is a striking fact that almost no nuclei with odd Z and odd N are stable (beyond $A = 14$); this suggests a term to represent the energy of the last unpaired particle, which can be estimated from the energy differences in successive β-decays for a given value of A. With these last two essential terms added, the binding energy in Mev may be written (cf. page 3):

$$E_B = 15.568A - 17.226A^{2/3} - 0.698Z^2/A^{1/3}$$

$$- (931.16/4A)(N - Z)^2 + \begin{cases} \mp 34/A^{3/4}; & Z \text{ odd, } A \text{ even} \\ & Z \text{ even, } A \text{ even} \quad (19.3) \\ 0; & A \text{ odd} \end{cases}$$

where the coefficients are determined by seeking the best possible fit to the observed values. This is the very useful *semi-empirical formula* [see Green and Engler, *Phys. Rev. 91*, 40 (1953)].

Formula 19.3 gives for every value of A a range of binding energies depending on the nuclear charge Z. If we maximize the binding energy for a given A by setting

$$\partial E_B(N, Z) \Big/ \partial Z \Big|_{A = N+Z = \text{const}, Z = Z_A} = 0$$

the resulting value of Z, called Z_A, marks the center of the stable valley in the nuclear energy surface in which the naturally occurring nuclei all lie. Since the actual values of Z are integers, and Z_A is not so restricted, exact agreement cannot be expected, but Z_A ought to lie closest to those integer values of Z for which the nuclei of a given mass number are most stable against β-decay. This is experimentally confirmed; indeed, this is one of the criteria employed to select the constants in equation 19.3. The value obtained is

$$Z_A = A/(1.985 + 0.01488A^{2/3}) \qquad (19.4a)$$

It is sometimes convenient to write the mass defect itself in terms of this variable, when it becomes

$$M(Z, A) - A = 16.10A + 17.226A^{2/3}$$
$$- 46.955[Z_A - (Z - Z_A)^2/Z_A] \text{ Mev} \quad (19.4b)$$

using the constants of equation 19.3, but omitting the pairing energy term.

These formulas give correct masses within a few Mev over very wide ranges of A or Z. They overlook all sorts of individual effects, the presence of which is often the sign of interesting features of nuclear structure, (cf. Fig. 1). In the discussion of a process like fission, where large changes in A and Z occur, formulas like the above are indispensable.

The semi-empirical formula gives no information about any other properties of nuclei than their energies and the Z/A ratio. It is attractive to consider the same model, a charged uniform liquid drop, in estimating the properties of the excited states of nuclei. The frequencies of the surface waves in a liquid drop follow the formula

$$\omega_l{}^2 = (\sigma/\rho)(l/R)^3 \qquad l \geq 2 \qquad (19.5)$$

where ω_l is the frequency of a surface wave with l crests around the circumference of the drop, σ is the surface energy per unit area, and ρ and R the nuclear mass density and radius. From the rough values $R = r_0 A^{1/3}$ and $4\pi r_0{}^2\sigma = 15$ Mev, with $r_0 = 1.2 \times 10^{-13}$ cm, the drop vibrational energies become $\hbar\omega_l \cong 22 l^{3/2} A^{-1/2}$. The position and character of the first couple of excited states have been observed for many nuclei. The symmetries (parity and J) of these states are usually those of the lowest two vibrations of a drop, but the energies show a very marked periodic change with A, superimposed on a slow fall. The values from the drop model are too high by an order of magnitude for most of the heavier nuclei. Improved classical calculations (taking into account the Coulomb energy, for example) do not bring better agreement.

B. THE FERMI GAS

A more or less opposite extreme among physical models is one which regards the nucleus as a gas of non-interacting nucleons moving freely about within a spherical potential well of the proper diameter, with depth adjusted so that the Fermi energy raises the highest-lying nucleons up to the observed binding energies. This amounts to an analogy with the free-electron model of a metal. Like that model, it gives useful results for problems where the momentum distribution, rather than the energies or the spatial distribution of the bound nucleons, is wanted.

The well is filled separately with nucleons of each type, allowing just two particles of a given type, with opposed spins, to each cell in phase space of volume $(2\pi\hbar)^3$. The Fermi energy, E_F, is defined by

$$E_F = p_F{}^2/2M$$

where p_F is the limiting momentum, below which all the states are filled. For a spherical well of radius $1.2A^{1/3} \times 10^{-13}$ cm filled with n nucleons, we obtain the value

$$E_F = 54(n/A)^{2/3} \text{ Mev} \qquad (19.6)$$

where n may be Z for the protons or $N = A - Z$ for the neutrons. The well depth is chosen to give the highest-lying neutron state the observed binding energy, usually near 8 Mev. If the nucleus is a fairly heavy one, the neutron number N will be appreciably larger than Z. The wells for neutron and proton gas must then differ, since for the over-all stability of the nucleus, the energy of the highest-lying filled proton state and that of the highest neutron state must be equal (neglecting the small n-p mass difference.)   But E_B depends on $n^{2/3}$ and hence will be much smaller for the fewer protons than for the neutrons. The depth of the well acting on the protons is greater than $E_F(Z)$ only by the binding energy for the last proton, again some 6 to 8 Mev. Thus the well depth for the proton gas will be considerably less than that for the neutrons, which is physically to be explained by the fact that the neutrons feel only the specific nuclear forces, whose net effect is attractive, but the protons feel in addition the repulsive Coulomb potential of their mutual electrostatic inter-

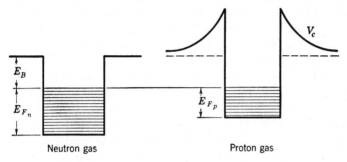

Neutron gas   Proton gas

Fig. 19.   The nuclear square wells for the neutrons and protons in a nucleus:
Fermi gas model.

actions.   The situation is illustrated in Fig. 19.   For a nucleus like Pb^{208}, with $Z = 82$, $N = 126$, $E_B \cong 6$ Mev, the bottom of the neutron well lies 44 Mev, and that for the protons, 34 Mev, below the energy zero.

This model makes plain the importance of the zero-point energy in nuclear matter and the typically high velocities of nucleons in nuclei.   Many experimental results confirm this point.   For example, the threshold for meson production by protons is lower in heavier nuclei than in hydrogen, because in the laboratory system some individual nucleons of the nucleus have velocities

$$v/c = (2E_F/Mc^2)^{1/2} \sim (2 \times 30/1000)^{1/2} \sim \tfrac{1}{4} \qquad (19.7)$$

which is evidently far from negligible.   The model also suggests that nucleon collisions will not often transfer small amounts of momentum to the nucleus, because the nucleon momentum states near the origin are filled.   Much momentum must be transferred, or the collision cannot occur.   Nuclear reactions show such effects, as we will see in Chapter XX.

C. THE SHELL MODEL

SHELL EFFECTS

The Fermi gas model is the simplest form of a wide class of models for many particle systems.   These models may be called single-particle models, for they treat the interacting system as a collection of independent single particles, each of which moves in a potential which is in fact determined by the average motion of all the other particles.   Atoms are treated best by this model (Hartree model), at least when somewhat extended to take care of the Pauli principle. For the atomic electrons, interacting through a long-range smooth Coulomb force, and with a well-defined center of force, the nucleus, to account for most of the potential, this model is immediately attractive and works as well as one might guess.   But for the short-range nuclear forces, with no particular center of force, the model appears hard to justify.   Nevertheless, because of its simplicity, the Hartree model was tried from the early days of nuclear physics. But only in 1949 (M. Mayer, H. Jensen, et al.) was the special scheme hit upon which makes the independent particle model so successful that with its aid we can predict most of the properties of the first few states of nearly every individual nuclear species.

The atomic shell effects show up most obviously in the closed-shell structure of the noble gases, whose high stability is apparent.   Like-wise for nuclei, though perhaps not so markedly, the special stability of particular numbers of neutrons, protons, or both, is easy to see and has been pointed out since 1934 (Elsasser).   The stability of the α-particle and of O^{16} can be seen by a glance at their binding energies compared to those of the neighboring nuclei, and similar, less quantitative arguments point to the special stability of nuclei for which either N or Z (or indeed both) have the values 2, 8, 20, 28, 50, 82, and 126.   These are jocularly called "magic" numbers, and their effects can be found by careful examination in a wide variety of nuclear properties.   As one example, the contour map for α-energy (Fig. 20) plainly displays the specially tight binding of the "doubly magic" nucleus Pb^{208} (containing 126 neutrons and 82 protons).

A few more lines of evidence for the magic numbers are listed here.

The number of stable isotopes for a given value of Z is greatest for $Z = 50$, and the number of stable nuclear species having a given neu-tron number $N = A - Z$ is greatest for $N = 82$.   The absolute abundances of nuclear species in nature are not fully understood, but it appears that elements like Zr (50 neutrons), Sn (50 protons), Ba (82 neutrons), and Pb (82 protons, 126 neutrons) are more abundant than their neighbors. The binding energy of the last neutron is

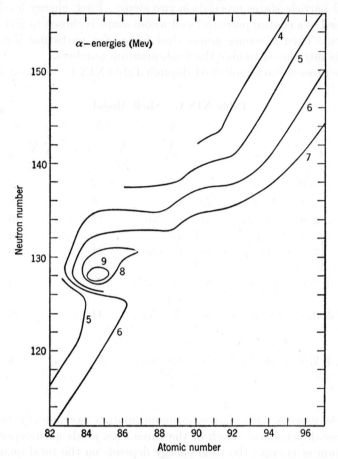

FIG. 20.   Contour map of α-particle emission energies.   Notice the high peak, denoting specially tight binding in the "doubly magic" residual nucleus. (126 neutrons, 82 protons).

so small for the fifty-first neutron in Kr^{87} and for the eighty-third neutron in Xe^{137} that these nuclei emit neutrons when excited by the β-decay of a parent radioactive fission product and are the two most prominent emitters of delayed neutrons among the products of fission. The neutron absorption cross section is abnormally low for just those nuclei with $N = 50$, 82, or 126, e.g., for Y^{89}, Ba^{136},

Bi^{209}. The stable nuclei which end the four natural radioactive chains either have $Z = 82$ (Pb^{206}, Pb^{207}), or $N = 126$ (Bi^{209}), or both (Pb^{208}).

Construction of the wave functions. The construction of the individual particle states proceeds in two steps. First, energy levels are assigned in a central potential well whose shape is chosen to give good results. Then a strong non-central force of a particular sign and type is introduced to give the final quantum numbers.

The process can be followed through Table XIXA. We consider a

Table XIXA.   Shell Model

1	2	3	4	5	6
N	l	nl	nl_j	$\sum\limits_{j(N)} (2j + 1)$	$\sum\limits_{0}^{N} \sum\limits_{j(N)} (2j + 1)$
0	0	$1s$	$1s_{1/2}$	2	2
1	1	$2p$	$2p_{3/2}, 2p_{1/2}$	6	8
2	2, 0	$3d, 2s$	$3d_{5/2}, 2s_{1/2}, 3d_{3/2}$	12	20
3	$\begin{cases} 3 \\ 3, 1 \end{cases}$	$4f$ $4f, 3p$	$4f_{7/2}$ $3p_{3/2}, 4f_{5/2}, 3p_{1/2},$ $5g_{9/2}$	8 22	28 50
4	4, 2, 0	$5g, 4d, 3s$	$5g_{7/2}, 4d_{5/2}, 4d_{3/2},$ $3s_{1/2}, 6h_{11/2}$	32	82
5	5, 3, 1	$6h, 5f, 4p$	$6h_{9/2}, 5f_{7/2}, 5f_{5/2},$ $4p_{3/2}, 4p_{1/2},$ $7i_{13/2}$	44	126
6	6, 4, 2, 0	$7i, 6g, 5d, 4s$	$7i_{11/2}, 6g_{9/2}, 6g_{7/2},$ $5d_{5/2}, 5d_{3/2},$ $4s_{1/2}, 8j_{15/2}$	58	184

particle moving with simple harmonic motion isotropically bound, in three dimensions. Each of the three axes yields an independent quantum of energy; the total energy depends on the total quantum number, $N = n_x + n_y + n_z$, and this number is listed in the first column of Table XIXA. The ground state corresponds to pure zero-point energy in each coordinate; $N = n_x + n_y + n_z = 0$; $E_0 = \frac{3}{2}\hbar\omega_0$. With the high symmetry of this potential, it is possible to express the wave function of any state also in spherical polar coordinates, as a linear combination of the several degenerate Cartesian wave functions for a typical level. The parity of a given state determines the odd or even character of the required orbital angular momentum, or l value, which belongs to each oscillator state. The degree of degeneracy gives the rest of the information needed. For example, if $N = n_x + n_y + n_z = 1$, there are only three possibilities for the quantum numbers; either n_x, n_y, or n_z equals unity, and the other two must be zero. There are just $2l + 1 = 3$ degenerate substates for this energy level, and they must have $l = 1$. These three can be chosen to correspond to the angular momentum substates with $l = 1$ and the z component of momentum $m = \pm 1, 0$.

But the harmonic oscillator well is most unrealistic. Its high degeneracy is artificial. We remove it by flattening out the bottom of the oscillator well, a step approaching the equally artificial extreme shape, the square well. The result of any such modification is to lift the degeneracy, splitting apart the states of various l and given N. As long as the well remains spherically symmetric, the $2l + 1$ substates of a given l will remain degenerate. The splitting will tend to reduce most the energies of the states with high angular momentum, because the corresponding particle orbits spend most time at the outer portions of the well, where the flattening has the greatest effect on the steeply rising harmonic potential. If we introduce a radial quantum number, n, equal to the number of nodes in the radial part of the wave function, we can write the third column as shown, where the states are displayed in the notation nl, l being indexed as usual in spectroscopy, writing $s, p, d \cdot \cdot \cdot$ for $l = 0, 1, 2$ $\cdot \cdot \cdot \cdot$. The states are listed in order of increasing energy (distance from the bottom of the well). States arising from a given N value are no longer equal in energy. However, we may expect the energy spread between states arising from a given N to be less than that between the states of differing N. Each degenerate oscillator state has split into a group, or shell, of states in the new well.

Now for the non-central potential. We assume that each particle feels a strong spin-orbit force, proportional to the expectation value of $\mathbf{l} \cdot \mathbf{s}$ for the particle, where $\mathbf{l} = \mathbf{r} \times \mathbf{p}$ and $\mathbf{s}$ is the spin operator. The strength of this force evidently grows with $|l|$. We assume it is of such sign and shape that of the two states coming from a given l, now split, which have total angular momentum $j = l \pm \frac{1}{2}$, the state of higher j (spin and orbital momentum parallel) is lower in energy, i.e., more tightly bound. For the first two N values, as one can see in column 4 of the table, we assume that the spin-orbit energy is small compared to the splitting between the several N values, and there is no need to indicate the separate j states. But for the high values, from $l = 4$ up, the spin-orbit energy becomes large enough to lower the energy of the low-lying member of the pair coming from a given l, that with $j = l + \frac{1}{2}$, until it is closer to the states coming from the next lower N value than to those arising from its own value of N. This can be followed throughout column 4. The values $l = 2$ and 3 occupy an intermediate position: The state $3d_{5/2}$ is definitely lower than $3d_{3/2}$, but it still forms part of the same shell. For the state $4f_{7/2}$, the l value, $l = 3$, is high enough to lower the state below all the other $N = 3$ states, but not enough to make it join the group from $N = 2$. It forms a shell of its own, perhaps somewhat less well-marked than those for higher values of l. In column 5 is entered the number of nucleons in a shell, $\Sigma(2j + 1)$. Column 6 is the cumulative total of column 5 and indicates how many nucleons in all are required to fill all the shells up to a given one.

Now the assignment of quantum numbers to a nucleus is straightforward, though one or two further assumptions are needed. The neutrons and protons fill the shells quite independently. For any nucleon numbers the states of the individual particles are now fixed. The resultant nuclear state is given by very simple rules, which go beyond a pure independent-particle theory and can be thought of as arising from interactions among the particles in an unfilled shell. These rules are:

1. An even number of nucleons of a given kind (neutrons or protons) belonging to a definite value of j always pair off their angular momenta so that the resulting ground state has a total angular momentum, J, equal to zero. Higher states will have various even values of J. With an odd number of nucleons of a given kind with a given j, the nucleons pair off as far as possible, so that the resulting orbital angular momentum and spin direction are just that of the single odd particle.

2. When pairs of nucleons occupy orbits of various j, an additional binding energy of pairing tends to make such states lie below those of the same shell with different j. This results in an order of filling which may be altered from the order of levels in the table, showing occasional crossing of levels within a single shell. This extra "pairing" energy is greater for orbits of higher l.

By the use of the spin-orbit interaction energy described, with a well intermediate in shape between the oscillator well and the square well, we get the level order of Table XIXA. From those levels, and the simple rules above, which are based on strong empirical tendencies, an enormous number of correct predictions may be made. It is rather the consequences of the shell model than its admittedly *ad hoc* derivation which make it such an important way of describing the structure of nuclei.

PREDICTIONS OF THE SHELL MODEL

1. *Abundances and stability of the closed-shell nuclei.* We have already spoken about the marked stability of the "magic number" nuclei. The latest direct mass measurements (see Fig. 1) show marked breaks in the course of the mass defect curve at nuclei with $Z = 20, 28, 50$, and at those with $N = 20, 28, 50$. The number of nuclear species which are stable become markedly larger for $N = 20$, 28, 50, 82 than for nearby N values, and the same is true for $A = 20$. Similar, less marked, favoring occurs for $Z = 28$ and 50. Among the rare earths, where chemical processes in nature cannot much affect the original abundances, the isotopes with $N = 82$ are outstandingly abundant. The neutron binding energy is especially high for nuclei with $N = 50, 82$. All these properties, and those listed before on page 162, demonstrate the extra stability of closed-shell nuclei. The strong tendency to asymmetric fission by thermal neutrons seems to be a dynamic effect of some complexity, but again it depends on the marked stability of the closed nucleon shells, so that the most favored fragments are those with $N = 82$ and their complements.

2. *The spins of nuclear ground states.* All observed nuclei with even Z and even $N = A - Z$ are spherically symmetric in the ground state, with $J = 0$. This is the simplest line of evidence for rule 1 for pairing off the angular momenta of nucleons. But with this once assumed, the angular momenta for nuclei with Z odd, N even, or with Z even, N odd, follow from the model nearly uniquely. The occasional ambiguities involve perhaps two possibilities for the choice of the lowest state; with this amount of freedom, rather sparingly used, assignments can be correctly made for about a hundred and fifty such nuclei, with a handful of exceptions.

For example, from Table XIXA it follows that the lightest nucleus with spin $\%$ must occur when the neutron $5g_{\%}$ state begins to be filled. This is at 41 neutrons. The lightest nucleus with $N = 41$ is Ge^{73}, which indeed has a measured spin of $\%$. No lighter stable nucleus is known to have so high a spin.

The states of odd-odd nuclei are not uniquely determined by the established shell model rules, but the possibilities are limited by the states of the individual particles. Only five stable odd-odd nuclei are known: H^2, Li^6, B^{10}, N^{14}, V^{50}. Several long-lived radio-active nuclei of this type have measured spin values. For nearly all of these the shell model gives consistent but not unique predictions, if the configurations are chosen as close as possible to the shell-model predictions for the nearby odd-even nuclei.

3. *Magnetic moments of nuclei.*   The magnetic dipole moment of a nucleus can be finite only if $J \geq \frac{1}{2}$.   On the shell model, each odd-even nucleus has a spherically symmetric set of closed neutron and proton shells, surrounded by paired neutrons and protons, again with $J = 0$, and therefore no magnetic moment.   All the angular momentum J is assigned to the resultant spin and orbital motion of the one remaining odd nucleon, and with that J, all magnetic moment.

From this single-particle picture, the magnetic moment can be calculated, just as in the atomic Zeeman effect, by the formulas of the vector model.

The magnetic moment vector is the sum of two contributions, one from whatever current is produced by the orbital motion of the nucleon, one from its intrinsic magnetic moment.   For the magnetic moment we have:

$$\text{Odd } Z \text{ (proton contribution} \quad \boldsymbol{\mu} = \boldsymbol{\mu}_{\text{orb}}. + \boldsymbol{\mu}_{\text{int}} = \frac{e\hbar}{2Mc}[1 + \mu_p(2\mathbf{s})]$$
$$\text{only)}$$

$$\text{(19.8)}$$

$$\text{Odd } N \text{ (neutron contribution} \quad \boldsymbol{\mu} = 0 + \mu_n(2\mathbf{s}) \frac{e\hbar}{2MC}$$
$$\text{only)}$$

where the vectors $\mathbf{l}$ and $\mathbf{s}$ are the orbital angular momentum and spin operators, and the coefficients μ_p, μ_n the intrinsic magnetic moments of the two nucleons, in units of the nuclear magneton, $e\hbar/2Mc$ (see Chapter VIII).   The neutron orbital motion produces no electric current, and hence no contribution to the magnetic moment.   The measured magnetic moments correspond to energies of orientation in a magnetic field along which the total angular momentum $\mathbf{j} = \mathbf{l} + \mathbf{s}$ is quantized, while $\mathbf{l}$ and $\mathbf{s}$ precess about it.   The tabulated magnetic moment, μ, refers to the maximum value of the projected component of the moment along the magnetic field direction, i.e., to that obtained when $\langle \mathbf{j}_z \rangle = (M_j)_{\text{max.}} = j$.   From the vector model we have the relations:

$$(\mathbf{l} + \mathbf{s})^2 = \mathbf{j}^2 = \mathbf{l}^2 + \mathbf{s}^2 + 2\mathbf{l} \cdot \mathbf{s}$$

so that $\mathbf{l} \cdot \mathbf{j}/j^2$ and $\mathbf{s} \cdot \mathbf{j}/j^2$ may be easily found.   The magnetic moment is just

$$\langle \boldsymbol{\mu}_z \rangle_{\text{max.}} = \mu = \frac{(\boldsymbol{\mu} \cdot \mathbf{j})}{\langle \mathbf{j}^2 \rangle} j$$

or

$$\mu = \left(a_1 \frac{\mathbf{l} \cdot \mathbf{j}}{\langle \mathbf{j}^2 \rangle} + a_2 \frac{\mathbf{s} \cdot \mathbf{j}}{\langle \mathbf{j}^2 \rangle} \right) j$$

where the constants a_1 and a_2 can be read from equation 19.8, and of course

$$\langle \mathbf{j}^2 \rangle = j(j+1); \quad \langle \mathbf{l}^2 \rangle = l(l+1); \quad \langle \mathbf{s}^2 \rangle = s(s+1) = \tfrac{1}{2} \times \tfrac{3}{2} = \tfrac{3}{4}$$

The final formulas for the magnetic moments are called the Schmidt formulas, which we write in the compact form

Odd Z: $\mu = j\{[1 \mp 1/(2l+1)] \pm 2\mu_p/(2l+1)\}$ nuclear magnetons

Odd N: $\mu = j\{ \qquad [0] \qquad \pm 2\mu_n/(2l+1)\}$ nuclear magnetons

$$\mu_p = +2.79 \text{ nuclear magnetons;} \qquad \mu_n = -1.91 \text{ nuclear magnetons;}$$
$$j = l \pm \tfrac{1}{2}$$

These formulas define two curves, for μ vs. j, with the values $j = l \pm \frac{1}{2}$, for each class of odd-even nucleus. All measured values lie within the regions bounded by the curves (with the exception of the pair H^3, He^3). The values lie mainly in two broad bands roughly parallel to the two Schmidt curves, but not very well defined (Fig. 21). In a large number of cases the value lies nearer one of the curves than another, and in nearly all these cases, the l value so indicated is the shell-model value. The deviations from the Schmidt curves are under one nuclear magneton. These deviations are evidence of the approximate nature of the single-particle model, but the qualitative correctness of the picture cannot be doubted.

4. *Parity of nuclei.* With all the closed shells and the paired-off nucleons having space- symmetric wave functions, the parity of a nucleus on the shell model is just that of the orbital motion of the odd nucleon and is even or odd according to the character of l. Since l is determined by the magnetic moment (in the ideal case), the measured magnetic moments provide one check on parity. The other important determination of parity is provided by β-decay theory. As we shall see in Chapter XXI, the parity change in β-transitions, together with the spin change, determines the lifetime for a given energy release. The predictions of the shell model have made possible a very orderly classification of β-transitions, confirmed in an over-all way by the shapes of β-ray spectra. The parity predictions, and their confirmation by β-decay studies, have been generally unambiguous, and this is perhaps the most powerful method of getting the detailed order of orbital momenta within shells. The subject is a highly specialized one; a good review has been given by Mayer et al. [*Revs. Mod. Phys.* **23**, 315 (1951)]

5. *Excited states.* The properties of nuclear excited states which can be measured are in general not the same as the properties easily

found for the ground states. Magnetic moments are almost never measured, but spins, parity, etc., often can be inferred from various reactions of nuclei. The low-lying states of nuclei have shown very often the value of the single-particle model, which at sufficiently

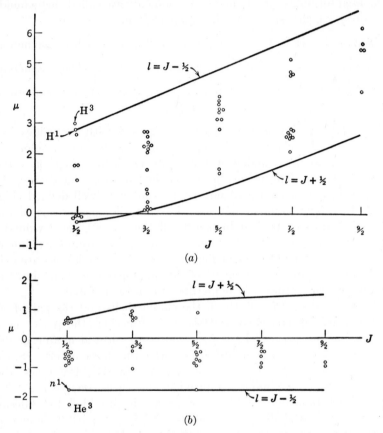

Fig. 21. The Schmidt curves for odd-even nuclei: (a) curves and experimental points for odd proton nuclei; (b), curves and experimental points for odd neutron nuclei. Note that although all values of J are exact half-integers, the plotted points have been spread horizontally to avoid crowding.

high excitation, however, would become much less useful because the number of states is so great as to require statistical treatment.

Nuclear Isomerism. An excited nuclear state which endures long enough to have a directly measurable lifetime is called an *isomeric state*. Such a state decays by radioactivity which is empirically different from that of the ground state but must be assigned to the same values of Z and A. In a few cases several isomeric states are present. It is clear that the notion is entirely an empirical and somewhat arbitrary singling-out of particular excited states of a nuclear system. It is striking that of the sixty or seventy isomers of life $T_{\frac{1}{2}} \geq 1$ second known, all occur in "islands" of the periodic table, grouped just below the "magic numbers" 50, 82, and 126. Here the two lowest levels available for the odd nucleon have very different angular momenta, and consequently the lowest excited state of the nucleus is required to have a sizable difference in spin from the ground state. Now radiation of photons which carry off a large spin is slowed down by the familiar multipole factor, $(R/\lambda)^{2\Delta l}$, where Δl is the spin difference. If the energy is not too large, a slow emission, and hence an isomer, should be observed. This point of view has been brilliantly confirmed. In the nuclei with Z just below 50, and also those with N below 50, dozens of isomers are known, all decaying by magnetic 2^4-pole radiation, exactly what would be expected from the selection rules for transitions in which one nucleon jumps between $p_{\frac{1}{2}}$ and $g_{\frac{9}{2}}$ orbits, which differ by four units of spin and have opposite parity. Table XIXA shows that here it is just these two orbits which are competing for the odd nucleon. A review of the very complex experimental material is given by Goldhaber and Hill [*Revs. Mod. Phys.* **24**, 179 (1952)].

The occurrence of similar isomeric states in a series of nuclei which differ by the successive additions of *pairs* of nucleons is well marked, for example, in Te^{121}, Te^{123}, Te^{125}, and even heavier odd Te isotopes, all of which show the three lowest states $s_{\frac{1}{2}}$, $d_{\frac{3}{2}}$, $h_{11\frac{1}{2}}$, with varying energy positions, but the same order.

Electric Dipole Radiation. All the states within a shell have the same parity except for one single state which has been pushed down from the higher oscillator level by the spin-orbit splitting. But this state has a j value larger by two or more units than any other level in the shell. Electric dipole radiation requires a parity change but can permit a spin change of not more than one unit. This radiation type, in general the simplest and most probable, cannot occur between levels of one shell, and therefore not between low-lying states of nuclei.

Long before the shell model had been proposed in its present form, it had been pointed out that most of the experimentally observed radiative transitions between low-lying nuclear levels are quadrupole (or higher multipole) transitions, with correspondingly low transition probabilities and long lifetimes of the excited levels. Only for energies high enough to permit transitions between one shell and the shells lying higher in energy can dipole radiation occur. Dipole radiation of this type has actually been seen in a few special cases in light nuclei and has been suggested as the origin of the strong photoeffect found in all nuclei in the region of 15 to 25 Mev (see Chapter XX).

Radiative Neutron Capture. A quite direct method of studying some fairly highly excited states is the measurement of $\sigma(n, \gamma)$, the cross section for radiative neutron capture, an important process for most nuclear species. The levels studied are levels of the compound nucleus, i.e., the nucleus which is formed when a neutron is absorbed by the initial target nucleus. They lie above the ground-state energy by about the binding energy of the neutron, some 6 to 8 Mev, for the neutron kinetic energies used are small compared to that figure. The theory and the experimental results found in the study of the sharp resonance maxima and the smoother features of this cross section will be described in Chapter XX. It is relevant here that from such studies evidence, both direct and indirect, is found that the energy levels are more widely spaced in compound nuclei which are formed by adding a neutron to a closed-shell nucleus than in any other compound nuclei. Direct evidence comes from measurement of the spacing of well-resolved and distinct resonance peaks. For Pb^{208}, a "doubly magic" nucleus, this spacing is of the order of tens of kilovolts; for other "normal" nuclei of similar atomic mass, it is about 10 ev. The other evidence comes from the average cross section for the radiative capture of neutrons with kinetic energy of the order of 100 kev, where in general individual resonance levels cannot be resolved. It can be shown that this capture is inversely proportional to the spacing between energy levels (equation 20.30). Capture is observed to be roughly a hundred times less for magic nuclei than for their neighbors; otherwise the capture cross section is represented by a rather smooth function of A.

To explan this spectacular reduction in level density, two factors may be considered. First, the simplest consequence of a tightly bound shell is that the next neutron added is less strongly bound than the average, and hence the nucleus is not so highly excited as is an average nucleus after neutron capture. Since level densities always increase rapidly with excitation energy, this reduced binding energy is bound to show up as a reduced level density and a lower cross section. But an additional specific reduction in level density, even at a given excitation energy, is probably present, for nuclei with one neutron beyond a closed shell compared to the average nucleus, and may amount to a factor of the order of magnitude of 10.

This will be discussed briefly under "Model 3" in Chapter XX, Section E.

Similar, though less pronounced, reductions in level density are observed in neutron capture by even-even nuclei, compared to that by nuclei of odd A. These form evidence for the "pairing" energy, i.e., the fact that an odd nucleon is less strongly bound than one of a pair of nucleons in the same level (see also equation 19.3).

D. THE COLLECTIVE NUCLEAR MODEL

The surprising success of the independent-particle model, with strong spin-orbit coupling, is made a little more acceptable by its occasional failures, as for example the deviations of magnetic moments from the Schmidt curve. Recently another model has been introduced which may go a long way to improve the whole picture. This is the collective model (A. Bohr), which is a kind of reasonable dynamical compromise between the liquid-drop model and the extreme single-particle model. It is clear that the well in which the nucleons move is not a given and fixed field of force, but one co-determined by the total motions of all the nucleons present. Taking it as a fixed well, as the single-particle models do, is thus inadequate. The drop model is too classical and glosses over the important effects of single nucleons. The collective model describes the nucleus as being made up of a more or less stable core of nucleons formed into closed shells, with the extra nucleons moving in the potential of the core, but then includes the deformation of the core caused by the interaction of core with the outside nucleons. This deformed core amounts to a modification of the field in which the nucleons move. The model is evidently much more advanced in principle than is either the drop or shell model, and its formal working out is considerably more complicated. We shall list a few of the results which this point of view has so far achieved.

1. *Deviations from the Schmidt curves.* The shell model misses the values of most nuclear magnet moments by a considerable amount. In the collective model, two distinct effects are plainly present which will modify the Schmidt values:

a. The rotation of the odd nucleon will react back on the core. The core will be distorted from spherical symmetry, and a kind of surface wave will run around it, which corresponds to a current produced by the rotation of the core more or less as a whole. Since the angular momentum of the core will be wholly orbital (spins cancel in pairs) and the effective charge to mass ratio is just Z/A the magnetic moment contributed will be about $Z/A \times (e\hbar/Mc)l_{core}$.

This is smaller for a given amount of angular momentum than the contributions of magnetic moment which enter the Schmidt formula either for the proton orbital motion or for the anomalous intrinsic moments of neutron or proton, and the result will be to retain the magnetic moment values well within the Schmidt curves.

b. The surface distortions of the core will in turn influence the motion of the odd nucleon, and the result will be to mix into the wave function of the odd nucleon other single-particle wave functions than that predicted by the simplest shell model theory. This may have an effect in either direction on the resultant moment; it will vary from the nucleus, moreover, depending on just which orbitals are involved.

On the whole, this model goes a long way to explain the individual deviations from the Schmidt curves, but it does not explain them all. Further work is needed. It seems also that the possible effect of transient meson currents, which is certainly responsible for the pushing of the H^3, He^3 values outside of the Schmidt region (Chapter VIII), may be present in heavier nuclei as well. A few tenths of a nuclear magneton may in special cases be contributed by such effects.

2. *Electric quadrupole moments (ground states).* The electric quadrupole moments of many nuclei imply the lack of spherical symmetry of the charge distribution. The quadrupole moment is defined by the expression

$$ Q = e \int d\tau \, \psi^* \left(\frac{3Z^2}{r^2} - r^2 \right) \psi $$

as in the case of the deuteron. In the pure shell model the value of Q must be attributed to the influence of centrifugal force on the last odd proton, giving a negative Q depending on J, but very roughly $\sim eR^2$. For an odd-neutron nucleus, only the slow rotation of the core (the reaction against the motion of the odd neutron) comes in; since the charge to mass ratio is only $\sim \frac{1}{2}$, and the relative rotational speed only $1/A$, the Q values are smaller by amount $\sim 1/2A$ than for an odd proton. No such effects are actually found. In particular, Q values are mainly positive, tend to increase with A quite rapidly, though they fluctuate through zero at closed shells, and have similar values for odd-N and odd-z nuclei alike. The very large values reached for some heavy nuclei, $Q \sim 20eR^2$, can in no way be accounted for as an effect of single-particle motion, or of rotation of the closed shells as a whole. Here the collective model has its most convincing successes, ascribing the Q values to a surface deformation of the nuclear core, and getting big values from the contributions of many protons, even with only rather small geometrical deformations. Closed-shell cores are more stable and deform less under the interactions with the odd nucleons. The observed tendency for large deviations from the Schmidt magnetic moments to be associated with large electric quadrupole moments is a rather strong physical argument for the qualitative picture. Further evidence for departure from spherical symmetry is found in the study of α-decay of the heaviest nuclei.

Radiative transitions with $\Delta l = 2$, and no change in parity, must be assigned to electric quadrupole radiation. Here what is measured is the lifetime of the transition, and the off-diagonal quadrupole moment (like Q, but with wave functions ψ_i and ψ_j corresponding to two different states, rather than an expectation value) can be inferred from this. The topic is discussed in the next section.

3. *Excited states in even-even nuclei.* The energies of the first excited states in even-even nuclei have been measured for a wide range of nuclei. They show a remarkably systematic behavior, generally falling slowly with increasing A, but having very large maxima at closed shell nuclei. This can be interpreted nicely only on the collective picture: indeed these low levels are not due to single-particle excitation, which would involve breaking up the interaction of paired nucleons and would cost too much energy. Instead, the rotation of the deformed core is responsible. The core rotates, not like a rigid body, but with only the surface deformation carrying the angular momentum. The effective moment of inertia is given by the surface energy and the amplitude of the distortion, not by the mass and size of the core as a whole. The closed shell cores are not easily distorted in this way, and the first excited states there correspond instead to a quite different motion, more a vibration of the core than a rotating surface disturbance. In a number of nuclei, a series of excited states has been found whose energies are proportional to $J(J + 1)$ as expected for a rotator. Since the nuclear deformation is expected to be symmetric with respect to reflection in the origin, only even J states, all with even parity, are allowed. In the decay of the isomeric state with high spin in Hf^{180}, for example, there are found five successive levels whose energy ratios fit the symmetric rotator energies within 1 or 2 per cent.

The energy levels for a symmetric rotator satisfy the familiar relation

$$E(J) = \frac{\hbar^2}{2I} J(J + 1) \qquad J \text{ even, parity even}$$

where J is the angular momentum of the state and I is the moment of inertia. In the observed rotational levels of nuclei, the energy differences are larger than if the whole nucleus were involved in the rotation, which would give a larger value of I than does the surface wave motion of the core. Rigid rotation of the nucleus, for the lowest state with $J = 2$, gives an energy of excitation about 30 kev, $A \cong$ 200, while the energies observed are 100 kev or more. The energy required to excite the surface waves depends of course on the surface deformation energy of the nucleus.

Since the first excited states of this type, found in even-even nuclei, all have $J = 2$ and even parity, and the ground state always has $J = 0$ and even parity, the transitions between them are due to electric quadrupole moments. They are measured both by γ lifetimes, as mentioned above, and lately by observing the excitation of these states after the near passage of a proton, which can excite them by its Coulomb field. It is typical to find that the quadrupole moments responsible for such transitions are many times those which could be due to the transition of a single proton and must be ascribed to the collective motion of many protons, as expected, and as already observed in the mean quadrupole moments of the ground states of odd-even nuclei.

The study of such nuclear details by the collective model is evidently only beginning; many refinements of the model are to be expected in the near future.

XX. NUCLEAR REACTIONS
AND SCATTERING

In this chapter we are again concerned with the heavier nuclei, with the practical problem of predicting cross sections for nuclear reactions, particularly those involving heavier nuclei the quantum states of which are not known precisely.

The most characteristic feature of collisions involving heavier nuclei is that many alternative results of the collision exist. A neutron, for example, may be elastically scattered, inelastically scattered, or captured with the subsequent emission of γ-rays, charged particles, or more neutrons. It is necessary to cast the theory of scattering into a form general enough to handle such a situation.

A. ELASTIC AND TOTAL CROSS SECTIONS

We write again the fundamental formula for the scattering cross section:

$$\frac{d\sigma}{d\Omega} = \left| \frac{1}{2ik} \sum (2l + 1)P_l(\cos\theta)(1 - \eta_l) \right|^2$$

$$\sigma = \int_{\text{sphere}} d\Omega(d\sigma/d\Omega) \qquad (20.1)$$

in which we have expressed the phase shift term $e^{2i\delta_l}$ by writing $\eta_l = e^{2i\delta_l}$; η_l is the measure of the amplitude and phase of the outgoing wave, relative to the unit amplitude and zero phase angle of the incoming wave, which gives the 1 in the formula above. As we saw earlier, if $\eta_l = 1$ for all l (which is the same as zero phase shift δ_l for all l), there is no scattering cross section at all; the outgoing and incoming partial waves combine to give the incident plane wave at all points far from the scatterer, with no additional waves at all. Now the presence of any processes which end in removing particles from the outgoing wave can be represented by letting the number η_l have a modulus less than unity. Then the outgoing wave will have a smaller amplitude than the incoming one, and some amount

177

of the incoming current is "lost." Here only outgoing waves which are coherent with the incoming beam, having exactly the same factor $e^{iEt/\hbar}$, e.g., and can therefore interfere with it, contribute to true elastic scattering processes. Every other wave function must be regarded as represented only by the change in the magnitude of η_l, and not as making any contribution at all to the outgoing scattered wave. This extends to processes like (1) true particle absorption, (2) re-emission of a particle of some other kind, (3) or even re-emission of the original incoming kind of particle but at a different energy (or with different spin orientation, or with any other internal coordinate definitely changed). Such incoherent processes may in some cases include events very hard experimentally to distinguish from the true elastic scattering. The cross section for all these incoherent processes together, which we will call the reaction cross section, σ_r, will be given by subtracting the intensity (proportional to $|\eta_l|^2$) of the outgoing coherent wave from that of the incoming wave, and integrating the difference over a large sphere surrounding the target. This net current is the amount which is "switched" from the entering wave function into some other incoherent wave; the current so found leads in the usual way to a cross section. Separating the various partial waves, which contribute separately when the differential cross section is integrated over all angles, we obtain:

$$\sigma_{\text{tot.}} = \sigma_{\text{el.}} + \sigma_r = \sum_l (\sigma_{\text{el.}}{}^{(l)} + \sigma_r{}^{(l)})$$

$$\sigma_{\text{el.}}{}^{(l)} = \pi\lambda^2(2l + 1)|1 - \eta_l|^2 \qquad (20.2)$$

$$\sigma_r{}^{(l)} = \pi\lambda^2(2l + 1)(1 - |\eta_l|^2)$$

$$\sigma_{\text{tot.}}{}^{(l)} = 2\pi\lambda^2(2l + 1)[1 - \text{Re}\,(\eta_l)]$$

These relations are quite general. Note that they imply that every absorption process must be accompanied by elastic scattering, for $\sigma_{\text{el.}}{}^{(l)}$ cannot vanish unless $\eta_l = 1$, and then $\sigma_r{}^{(l)}$ vanishes also. This relation is the origin of the so-called shadow scattering. Consider the very simple case when the wavelength of the incident beam is small compared to the radius of the obstacle, and we can use classical trajectories with good accuracy. Take a completely "black" obstacle, of radius R. Such a center will absorb completely all particles which strike it. This means that for those partial waves whose l value is $l \leq l_{\text{max}} \cong R/\lambda$, the value of η_l is 0. For all other partial waves, the scatterer will have no effect, and $\eta_l = 1$. Then the cross sections will be given, in this approximation, by the sum:

$$\sigma_{\text{tot.}} = \sum_{l \leq l_{\text{max.}}} 2\pi\lambda^2(2l + 1) \cong 2\pi R^2$$

$$\sigma_r = \sigma_{\text{el.}} \cong \pi R^2 \tag{20.3}$$

and the total cross section, in the classical limit, goes to twice the geometric area of the black obstacle.

The elastic scattering by a black obstacle, which is not expected from the most naive picture of the process, may be thought of as the result of ordinary wave-optical diffraction. For in the classical limit such an absorbing nucleus can be regarded as a black sphere of radius R which casts a shadow. This is described in the language of wave optics by saying that just enough light is scattered in the forward direction to cancel the incident beam. This would mean a cross section for shadow scattering of πR^2. Furthermore, to cancel the incident beam behind the sphere, this shadow scattering must be of the same energy, i.e., it represents elastic scattering. According to an elementary wave-optical argument, the shadow scattering will be mostly confined to an angle λ/R from the forward direction.

In the case of light and macroscopic obstacles, for which $\lambda \ll R$, the shadow scattering is not easily measurable, since the shadow extends practically to infinity. In the nuclear case with particles of a few Mev, λ/R is, say, $\frac{1}{3}$ or $\frac{1}{5}$, so that the umbra or region of complete shadow extends only a short distance back of the nucleus, certainly not as far back as the measuring apparatus. Thus it is possible to make measurements outside the main beam but still at small enough angles to it to obtain the elastic shadow scattering. The existence and general features of shadow scattering have been confirmed experimentally.

For obstacles which are not black, but partly transparent, or "gray," and for other than the classical limit, shadow scattering is still present but not equal in cross section to the geometrical area.

B. RESONANCES AND THE DISPERSION FORMULA

The most striking feature of nuclear reaction cross sections is the frequent occurrence of high, narrow peaks in the cross section expressed as a function of energy. These peaks are called resonance peaks and are found most strikingly for slow neutrons in nuclei of middle and high A, and for protons and α's on light nuclei, $A \lesssim 30$. The first theory of this process was developed by Breit and Wigner. The result is analogous to the theory of optical dispersion, so that the main formula obtained is often called the dispersion formula. We shall derive it as a consequence of the theory of scattering in a natural approximation.

For simplicity consider only the case in which neither centrifugal or Coulomb forces are present, i.e., $l = 0$, and neutrons are incident. Then the cross section for S-wave neutron scattering is given by formula 10.9:

$$\sigma^{(0)} = 4\pi\lambda^2 \sin^2 \delta_0$$

in terms of the phase shift δ_0. Introduce as in equation 10.10 the scattering length $a(k)$, by the usual relation (Fig. 9):

$$k \cot \delta_0 = -1/a(k) \tag{10.10}$$

The phase shift can again be expressed in terms of the outgoing amplitude η_0:

$$\eta_0 = e^{2i\delta_0} = (\cos \delta_0 + i \sin \delta_0)^2$$

$$= \frac{[-1/a(k) + ik]^2}{k^2 + 1/a^2} \tag{20.4}$$

$$= \frac{1 - ika}{1 + ika}$$

From equations 20.2 the elastic and the reaction cross sections can now be put in terms of the scattering length or, better, its reciprocal $1/a(k)$:

$$\sigma_{\text{el.}}^{(0)} = (\pi/k^2)\big|1 - \eta_0\big|^2 = 4\pi/\big|ik + 1/a(k)\big|^2$$

$$\sigma_r^{(0)} = (\pi/k^2)(1 - |\eta_0|^2) = 4\pi\lambda\{\text{Im}\,[1/a(k)]\}/\big|ik + 1/a\big|^2 \tag{20.5}$$

From these formulas, the generalization of the scattering length follows directly. If the length a is real, $\sigma_{\text{el.}}^{(0)}$ takes the familiar value from the effective range theory (equation 10.10), and $\sigma_r^{(0)} = 0$.

In the previous use of the scattering length, attention was directed solely to the low-energy limit of $a(k)$ as $k \to 0$. Now we want to study more general types of behavior of $a(k)$ with k, (or energy $E = \hbar^2 k^2/2M$), which can fully describe the whole behavior of scattering and reaction cross sections.

We first consider the simple case, with a real. Then $\sigma_{\text{el.}}^{(0)}$ has the same form as in the effective range theory (equation 10.10), and the reaction cross section $\sigma_r^{(0)} = 0$. It is interesting to examine the behavior of $\sigma_{\text{el.}}^{(0)}$ near its maxima, which occur whenever $1/a(k) = 0$. Suppose that there is an energy, E, for which

$$1/a(E_0) = 0$$

Then in the neighborhood of E_0 we may expand:

$$\frac{1}{a(E)} = 0 + (E - E_0) \frac{d}{dE}\left(\frac{1}{a}\right)\bigg|_{E_0} + \cdots \qquad (20.6)$$

We define a quantity Γ_s by the relation

$$\frac{d}{dE}\left(\frac{1}{a}\right)\bigg|_{E_0} = + \frac{2k}{\Gamma_s} \qquad (20.7)$$

and the cross section $\sigma_{\text{el.}}{}^{(0)}$ becomes, for energies close enough to E_0 so that the linear term in the expansion is adequate,

$$\sigma_{\text{el.}}{}^{(0)} = \frac{\pi\lambda^2\Gamma_s{}^2}{\Gamma_s{}^2/4 + (E - E_0)^2} \qquad (20.8)$$

This exhibits the familiar Lorentzian shape of classical optical or circuit-theory resonance. The quantity Γ_s, which is proportional to k [since $(d/dE)(1/a)\big|_{E_0}$ is a constant], is the full energy width of the resonance peak at half its maximum value, provided that $\Gamma_s/E_0 \ll 1$, so that the slow variation of k across the energy E_0 may be neglected. The choice of the factor $2k$ in the definition of Γ_s is clearly conventional, to give the familiar form to equation 20.8, and make Γ_s the width at half-maximum. The sign of Γ_s is immaterial in this case; in other cases we will show that the sign in equation 20.7 is a natural choice.

If at a given energy any reaction occurs, there the quantity $a(E)$ must be complex. To study the behavior of $\sigma_{\text{el.}}{}^{(0)}$ and $\sigma_r{}^{(0)}$ near their resonance maxima, which we expect to be near the zeros of $1/a$ from the simple case above, we must consider $1/a$ as an analytic function of a complex variable. We extend the energy E from the real axis, where it has a direct physical meaning, into the whole complex plane. Suppose that there is a value of $E = E_0$ at which $1/a(E_0)$ vanishes, as in equation 20.6, but now E_0 is in general complex, and this complex energy can be written

$$E_0 = \epsilon_0 - i\Gamma_r/2 \qquad (20.9)$$

We can again expand $1/a$ and drop all terms beyond the linear term, exactly as in equation 20.6, but instead of the simple definition (equation 20.7) we write the relation

$$\text{Re}\left[\frac{d}{dE}\left(\frac{1}{a}\right)\bigg|_{E_0}\right] = + \frac{2k}{\Gamma_s}; \qquad \text{Im}\left[\frac{d}{dE}\left(\frac{1}{a}\right)\bigg|_{E_0}\right] = k\alpha \qquad (20.10)$$

for the real and imaginary parts of the now complex quantity $(d/dE)(1/a)\big|_{E_0}$. From these relations we obtain, for real E,

$$\mathrm{Re}\left[\frac{1}{a(E)}\right] = +\frac{2k}{\Gamma_s}\left[E - \left(\epsilon_0 + \frac{\alpha\Gamma_r\Gamma_s}{4}\right)\right]$$

$$\mathrm{Im}\left(\frac{1}{a}\right) = k\left[\frac{\Gamma_r}{\Gamma_s} + \alpha(E - E_0)\right] \tag{20.11}$$

Writing the appropriate cross sections from equation 20.2, and neglecting the term proportional to $(E - \epsilon_0)$ in $\mathrm{Im}\,(1/a)$ (which is certainly justified not too far from resonance), we obtain

$$\sigma_{\mathrm{el.}}{}^{(0)} = \pi\lambda^2[\Gamma_s{}^2/\tfrac{1}{4}(\Gamma_s + \Gamma_r)^2 + (E - E_r)^2] \tag{20.12a}$$

$$\sigma_r{}^{(0)} = \pi\lambda^2[\Gamma_r\Gamma_s/\tfrac{1}{4}(\Gamma_s + \Gamma_r)^2 + (E - E_r)^2] \tag{20.12b}$$

with

$$E_r = \epsilon_0 + \Delta; \qquad \Delta = \alpha\Gamma_r\Gamma_s/4$$

The cross-section shape in equations 20.12 is very similar to that for pure scattering, equation 20.8. Two differences are important: the width of the resonance in the more complete case depends on the total level width Γ:

$$\Gamma = \Gamma_r + \Gamma_s$$

so that the possibility of a reaction widens the scattering peak, and the reverse. Moreover, the position of the maximum, E_r, is not unaffected by the possibility of reaction. The peak is shifted by Δ, an amount which is proportional to the reaction width. This level shift has been at least qualitatively observed. A strong capture resonance is found both for protons and for neutrons on C^{12} around 3 Mev. There is good evidence that the two levels, one in C^{13} and one in N^{13}, so formed are very similar and should be displaced in energy only by the Coulomb difference between these two mirror nuclei. An additional shift is found, which can be roughly ascribed to the fact that proton emission with a fairly large width Γ_r is possible for the N^{13} state, but neutron emission is energetically forbidden from the state in C^{13}.

Equations 20.12 are the famous Breit-Wigner dispersion formulas for a single S-wave resonance. We can expect them to fit experiment only rather near the resonance energy, so that the linear term of the expansion is adequate to represent the variation of $1/a$. In such a region, if other resonances are well separated in energy, the theory is quite generally satisfactory and fits a great many examples, some with high precision.

The interpretation of the complex energy E_0 is connected with the non-stationary nature of resonant states which decay into some reaction product. The usual Schrödinger separation of variables leads for an energy E_0 to a wave function with time factor $e^{-iE_0t/\hbar} = e^{-i\epsilon_0 t/\hbar} \times e^{-\Gamma_r t/2\hbar}$ showing a damping in time. This is the underlying reason for the requirement that Im $(1/a)$, essentially proportional to Γ_r, must be positive. The second relation (equation 20.11) also justifies the choice of the positive sign in equation 20.7 and makes Γ_s, like Γ_r, positive. In this way, the resonance phenomena can be defined completely by giving the generalized scattering length associated with the nucleus as a function of k. More often a different picture is employed. The nucleus is considered as a sphere of definite radius R, and the effect of scattering or reaction is broken up into two parts, which take place, respectively, within and outside of this region. The separation is not a physically verifiable one; it is just a formal way of describing the source of the disturbances which give rise to the outgoing amplitude η_0, which is all that can be measured. It has the great advantage, however, of emphasizing just what effects are specifically due to nuclear levels, and what are due simply to the presence of the nuclear matter within a volume of a definite size and shape. The function $1/a$ can be related to the specification of the wave function matching conditions between the outside region and the volume within the nuclear radius, and the resonance condition $1/a = 0$ then becomes the statement that the wave function has zero slope at the matching radius, $d\psi/dr \big|_R = 0$ (see below, equation 20.23).

To introduce the sphere radius R, we recall that the relative amplitude factor η_0 is the ratio of the amplitude of the outgoing wave to that of the incoming wave. In all scattering and reaction experiments, this is evaluated by measurements made asymptotically far away from the center of scattering. But it may be referred to the surface of a sphere within which all unknown interactions take place, if a correction is made for the known variation of the wave functions with distance, in the external region where only known forces act. Then the scattering length a which appears is a property of the nuclear interior only. We will write the wave function [actually the radial function $r\psi(r)$] in the form

$$r\psi = \begin{cases} u_0(r) = u_+(\infty)e^{+ikr} \\ u_i(r) = u_-(\infty)e^{-ikr} \end{cases}$$

for outgoing and incoming waves, respectively, where the constant amplitudes are indicated by the factors $u_+(\infty)$ and $u_-(\infty)$. From the definition of η_0, we have

$$\eta_0 = \frac{u_+(\infty)}{u_-(\infty)} = \frac{u_{\text{out}}(R)e^{-ikR}}{u_{\text{in}}(R)e^{+ikR}} = \eta_0(R)e^{-2ikR} \qquad (20.13)$$

by which we have defined the quantity $\eta_0(R)$ as the analog of η_0, but referring now to the ratio of the outgoing and incoming amplitudes *at the nuclear surface*, and in no way depending on the external forces. We can thus define a quantity $a_R(k)$:

$$\eta_0(R) = \frac{1 - ika_R(k)}{1 + ika_R(k)} \qquad (20.14)$$

exactly as we defined η_0 in equation 20.4, but now $a_R(k)$ is the generalized scattering length referring to the nuclear interior alone.

The cross sections of equation 20.5 can now be written in terms of $a_R(k)$. The factor $\exp(-2ikR)$ in equation 20.13 does not affect the reaction cross section, which is the same function of $a_R(k)$ as of $a(k)$, but the scattering cross section becomes

$$\sigma_{\text{el.}}^{(0)} = 4\pi \left| \frac{(1 - \eta_0)}{2ik} \right|^2 = 4\pi \left| \frac{1}{2ik} \left[1 - e^{-2ikR} \frac{(1 - ika_R)}{(1 + ika_R)} \right] \right|^2$$

$$= 4\pi \left| \frac{e^{ikR} \sin kR}{k} + \frac{1}{ik + 1/a_R} \right|^2 \qquad (20.15)$$

where the two terms are called the potential and the resonance scattering amplitudes respectively. This formula is to be compared with the form of $\sigma_{\text{el.}}^{(0)}$ given by equation 20.5 in terms of $a(k)$ itself.

The behavior of equation 20.15 is of course exactly the same as that of equation 20.5, but now it is possible to see explicitly how the presence of the nuclear interaction volume affects the elastic scattering. The potential and resonance scattering amplitudes will in general interfere, and even rather simple forms for $a_R(k)$ will yield quite varied behavior for the cross section. The potential scattering has an explicitly given dependence on R and k; the resonance term contains the entire dependence of $\sigma_{\text{el.}}^{(0)}$ on the internal structure of the nucleus. If $a_R(k)$ vanishes, the nucleus behaves like a perfectly rigid sphere. The scattering cross section does not then vanish but becomes just the cross section for scattering by a spherical obstacle. It is this property which makes the formulation in terms of a definite sphere radius better suited for nuclear problems than is the over-all scattering length $a(k)$, which we have used until now especially for scattering by a single nucleon, where the interaction sphere is not so natural a model. At energies near 1 Bev, when $\lambdabar = 1/k$ approaches the nucleon Compton wavelength, $\hbar/Mc = 0.22 \times 10^{-13}$ cm, the model of an interacting sphere may again be plausible even for a single nucleon.

Several special cases of equation 20.15 are of interest. If we consider the low-energy limit, where the principal partial wave is the S-wave, then $kR \ll 1$. The maximum of $\sigma_{el.}^{(0)}$ will be reached when $1/a_R \to 0$, the usual condition for resonance. Then

$$\sigma_{el.}^{(0)} \to 4\pi \left| R + \frac{1}{ik} \right|^2 = 4\pi\lambdabar^2$$

as expected. Now at energies below a resonance a_R is negative, as can be seen from the linear approximation in equation 20.6. If $kR \ll 1$, and we are at an energy below resonance,

$$\phi_{el.}^{(0)} \cong 4\pi \left| R + \frac{1}{ik + 1/a_R} \right|^2$$

$$\cong 4\pi \frac{(1 + R/a_R)}{k^2 + 1/a_R^2} \tag{20.16}$$

and $\sigma_{el.}^{(0)}$ will be reduced by partial cancellation of a_R and R, while the resonance peak will follow as $E \to E_R$. This dip before a resonance peak has been observed in several cases. At higher energies, kR may approach $\pi/2, 3\pi/2, \cdots$. Here we can write, for $1/a_R \to 0$,

$$\sigma_{el.}^{(0)} \cong 4\pi \left| (e^{ikR} \sin kR - i)/k \right|^2 \tag{20.17}$$

and it is evident that at resonance $\sigma^{(0)}_{el.}$ may show a dip instead of a peak. This too has been observed in scattering from rather light elements (though with protons, where potential scattering includes Coulomb effects). Of course, there are intermediate cases, covering the whole range from peak through dip; the 180° shift of the phase of the resonance scattering amplitude as E goes through E_R adds to the rather slowly varying potential term in a way which depends on the phases and magnitudes of the quantities involved.

This whole formulation may be generalized to include Coulomb and centrifugal forces. The generalization gives very similar formulas, except that the phase kR and the simple term ika of equations 20.13 and 20.14 are replaced by more complicated functions, say $\alpha(R)$ and $iK(k)a$, where K may be complex. The relationships are analogous to those between the effective-range theory of neutron-proton and that of proton-proton scattering. The best method for generalization is to go back to the derivation of the partial-wave formula equation (20.1) itself (see Blatt and Weisskopf, Chapter VIII). The reciprocal scattering length $1/a_R$ turns out to be proportional to the logarithmic derivative of the wave function at the nuclear radius R.

C. OBSERVATIONS ON RESONANCES

Many nuclear resonances have been identified and studied in more or less detail. About three hundred have been examined in fair detail in the elements up to neon, mostly with charged particles; a similar number have been identified, but are less well known, in the elements up to A about 30 or 40; beyond this mass, nearly all of the several hundred known levels are observed in neutron capture and scattering with neutrons below perhaps 1000 ev.

The first experiments on neutron capture (Fermi and others, Moon and Tillman) used ingenious but rather complicated methods of studying self-absorption of various elements for the neutrons which induced radioactivity. At present the most satisfactory method is to determine the velocity of the neutrons by their time of flight to the detector. Pulsed neutrons are made either by modulating an ion or an electron beam before it strikes the target in which the neutrons are produced, or by using a fast mechanical rotary shutter in a beam of neutrons coming out of a pile. For very slow neutrons, a crystal spectrometer is often employed in the pile neutron beam. Many results of these measurements have been published by the Columbia cyclotron group (Rainwater and collaborators) in a series of papers in the *Physical Review* since 1947, and by workers at Brookhaven, Argonne, Oak Ridge, and Harwell. See the compilation by Hughes and Harvey, *Neutron Cross Sections*, Brookhaven National Laboratory, Upton, N.Y., 1955 (BNL-325).

The information about the resonances so obtained can best be described in a statistical manner, by giving the average spacing between levels, their "scattering width" Γ_s, their reaction width Γ_r, etc.

The average spacing, best obtained from nuclei for which a good many levels are observed, decreases generally and rapidly with increasing atomic weight. For slow neutrons, it is some tens of kev for light nuclei ($A < 30$), one or perhaps a few kev between $A = 50$ and 60, and of the order of 10 ev for $A \geqslant 100$, with many individual variations superposed (compare the shell model discussion Chapter XIX, Section C). The general increase in the density of levels with

A can be interpreted as due to the fact that the energy of excitation can be distributed in a greater variety of ways among many particles than among few.   This will be discussed in Section F of this chapter, where it will also be shown that the level density increases rapidly with the excitation energy of the nucleus, a conclusion which it is difficult to verify directly by experiment.   However, if this conclusion is accepted, one can explain why the level density does not increase much further for $A > 100$: slow neutron capture corresponds to an excitation energy of the compound nucleus equal to the neutron binding energy.   This binding energy decreases from $A = 100$ to 200, and the effect of this decrease of excitation energy just about compensates the effect of the increase of A on the level spacing as measured with slow neutrons.

Experimentally, Γ_n may be separately determined in two different ways.   First, in the common case, with $\Gamma_\gamma \gg \Gamma_n$, the capture cross section $\sigma_\gamma^{(0)}$ at exact resonance becomes

$$\text{Const.} \times \Gamma_n/E_r\Gamma \tag{20.18}$$

Here Γ is the width of the resonance at half-maximum; therefore, Γ_n can be determined from σ at resonance, Γ and E_r.   Second, the ratio of scattering to capture cross sections at resonance is Γ_n/Γ_γ, and Γ_γ is very nearly equal to Γ.   Unfortunately, in order to get the scattering cross section at resonance it must be disentangled from the potential scattering.

The width Γ of a nuclear level is related to the decay lifetime of the nuclear level, as indicated in Section B above:

$$|\psi_i|^2 \sim [\exp\,(-\Gamma t/2\hbar)]^2$$

The mean lifetime τ is given by the relation $\tau = \hbar/\Gamma$, and numerically

$$\tau = \frac{6.6 \times 10^{-16}}{\Gamma \text{ ev}} \text{ second} \tag{20.19}$$

For most of the slow neutron radiative capture levels, the width is about 0.1 ev, implying a lifetime $\sim 10^{-14}$ second, quite long compared to the time for a nucleon to cross the nuclear volume.   The width can be decomposed into two parts, as in equations 20.12, a scattering width Γ_s and a reaction width Γ_r, the former being usually denoted by Γ_n for neutrons.   The reaction width may in turn be further decomposed into partial widths according to the various reactions which may take place.   In the case of slow neutrons, the only reaction which can take place energetically (apart from elastic scattering) is usually γ-ray emission. (Major exceptions are Li^6 and B^{10}; they emit α-particles under slow neutron bombardment.) In this case, then, $\Gamma_r \cong \Gamma_\gamma$, the γ-ray width, and

$$\Gamma = \Gamma_\gamma + \Gamma_n \tag{20.20}$$

As we shall show below, the neutron width is proportional to v, the neutron velocity, for slow neutrons, whereas Γ_γ is independent of v. Therefore at sufficiently low neutron energy, the γ-ray width will always be larger than the neutron width. For nuclei of $A \geqslant 100$ which do not have closed neutron shells, this condition is satisfied usually up to neutron energies of several kev, i.e., throughout the region normally investigated by neutron velocity selectors. The observed level width Γ of about 0.1 ev then represents essentially Γ_γ. When $\Gamma_\gamma \gg \Gamma_n$, capture is far more likely than scattering, which is experimentally observed for medium-weight and heavy nuclei with slow neutrons.

On the other hand, for lighter nuclei (and magic nuclei) the reverse is true. For instance, in Mn^{55} there is a strong resonance at 345 ev neutron energy with $\Gamma_n = 20$ ev and Γ_γ only about 1 ev. Generally, nuclei of $A < 60$ have mainly scattering resonances. The relatively large neutron width for lighter (as for magic) nuclei is directly related to the large level spacing found in such nuclei (see equation 20.32). Neutron widths have been statistically investigated for a large number of levels. The mean values so found, and their fluctuations, seem consistent with the ideas of the optical or compound-nucleus model discussed in Section F below. The Γ_γ are remarkably constant, showing a tendency to increase somewhat at small A. In Section G the theory of γ-emission will be sketched.

In the region near zero energy, if no resonance lies nearby, the width for scattering, Γ_s, is proportional to v. This follows from the fact that Γ_s is proportional to the probability of neutron re-emission per second, and thus to the density of states for the scattered neutron in momentum space, $p^2(dp/dE) \sim p$. Thus the Breit-Wigner formula reduces to $\sigma_r{}^{(0)} \sim \lambda^2 v \sim 1/v$, since all specifically nuclear quantities are practically constant over the small energy range represented by $v \to 0$. This is the well-known $1/v$ law for the capture cross section at very low energy. It makes the number of capture processes per second per target atom, which is $\sigma_r v$, independent of the neutron energy distribution, and proportional only to the total neutron density. For very light nuclei, the resonance levels are widely spaced, and no level is likely to be found up to a considerable energy. For example, in the capture of neutrons by B^{10}, the $1/v$

law is valid to at least 100 kev, perhaps up to 1 Mev.   Absorption by B^{10} may therefore be used for a rough measurement of neutron velocities; it makes a very convenient standard of cross section as well, both because of the energy independence of the capture, and also because of the large magnitude of the cross section.

The spacing and arrangement of the neutron resonances supplies most of the information we have about the states of heavier nuclei. Beyond a kilovolt or so above the lowest neutron energy, the levels become, as we have seen, so closely spaced that they overlap, and individual resonances are no longer marked.   It is to be noted that the resonances studied in this way represent a random selection of

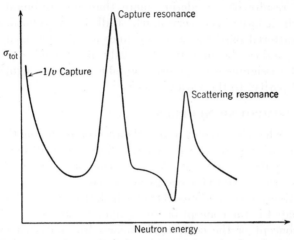

Fɪɢ. 22.   Typical experimental total neutron cross section for a heavy nucleus at low neutron energies, below say 10 ev.   The scattering resonance peak is preceded by a dip because of interference between resonance and potential scattering, as in equation 20.17.

those states of the nucleus near 8 Mev excitation energy, and that perhaps a million states of a nucleus of middle atomic weight lie below the region studied on such an enlarged scale of energy.   This implies that the levels ought to be randomly arranged in energy, and statistical evidence tends to support that idea.

For *protons*, capture resonances have been observed only for the very light nuclei.   The level spacings are of the order of 10 to 100 kev with an excitation energy of $\sim$10 Mev.   For heavier nuclei, the Coulomb barrier prevents capture resonances for protons because the excitation energies which result after a proton has been given sufficient energy to get over the Coulomb barrier are so high that the resonance levels overlap.   A few resonances have also been observed for α-particles, the reactions of which lead mostly to the emission of protons or neutrons, and other particles, like the deuteron and H^3, have also been used. The resonances of many nuclei, up to $A \cong 20$, are fairly well identified, all the way from the ground state up to 10 or 20 Mev excitation. An invaluable survey of all this mass of material on light nuclei is issued in frequent editions by Ajzenberg and Lauritsen; the latest version is found in the *Revs. Mod. Phys.* **27**, 77 (1955). See also K. Way *et. al.*, *Nuclear Level Schemes*, U.S. Atomic Energy Commission, 1955 (TID-5300) for elements from Ca to Zr.

The effect of spin on the dispersion (or Breit-Wigner) formulas and the results of considering more than one resonant state are topics which have been very much studied. Angular distributions of the scattered particles near resonance are the principal new data of such studies, beyond those already mentioned. Such results enable the assignment of quantum numbers, mainly angular momentum and parity, to the various levels.

D. THE COMPOUND NUCLEUS

So far we have given only a formal means of discussing the variation of the quantity $1/a_R$ with the energy and type of incoming particle and a little about the actual determination of quantities like Γ_s and Γ_r, which are related to the energy dependence of $1/a_R$ near resonance. One relatively successful model from which these quantities may often be estimated is the concept of the compound nucleus.

The concept of the compound nucleus was initiated by Bohr in 1935. In order to get a clear picture of this concept we shall examine the difference between nuclear collisions and atomic collisions.

For collisions between an atom and a particle of high or moderate energy, the Born approximation is valid because the incident particle passes right through the atom practically undisturbed. Slight deflections, inelastic collisions, and emission of radiation are progressively less likely processes. The reason that particles are likely to pass right through is that the atom is a loosely bound structure. Another way of saying this is that the interaction of atomic electrons with, say, an incident electron of several thousand volts is much smaller than the incident energy—which is precisely the condition for validity of Born's approximation.

Nuclear interactions, on the other hand, are of the order of 20 Mev, which is much greater than the kinetic energy of the incident particle normally used, i.e., several Mev or less. This is precisely the opposite of the conditions required for Born's approximation.

Here, the interaction energy is more important than the kinetic energy.

Another difference: An electron striking an atom can be regarded as interacting with the average "Hartree" field of the atom. This approximation is valid because the interaction with a single electron is much smaller than the average interaction with all the electrons. On the other hand, the short range and the saturation character of nuclear forces require that nucleons interact only with a small number of neighbors. Thus individual interactions will be of the same order of importance as the average total interaction—and it did not seem permissible to replace the nucleus by an average field.

It should be observed that the great success of the Hartree approximation, in the more recent form of the shell model with strong spin-orbit coupling, precisely contradicts the last idea. How the shell model, which applies particularly well to the nuclear states of low excitation, is to be reconciled at least in part with the compound-nucleus picture, which is meant mainly to apply to states of rather higher excitation energy, with $T \cong E_B$, will be presented in Section G.

The Bohr picture takes advantage of the large interactions and describes them in terms of a compound nucleus. The theory makes the following statements:

1. *Any particle which hits the nucleus is caught.* A new nucleus is formed called the *compound nucleus.* The reason for this is that an incident particle will interact with one or two nucleons, transferring much of its energy to them and thus to the nucleus, before penetrating it appreciably. Then it may no longer have sufficient kinetic energy to escape the attractive nuclear forces, and is therefore caught.

2. The *compound nucleus is long-lived* compared to the natural nuclear time. (This is the time for a neutron to cross the nucleus—

say 10^{-12} cm$/10^9 \dfrac{\text{cm}}{\text{sec}} \cong 10^{-21}$ second.) The reason for this is that the compound nucleus, which is in an excited state (excitation energy above the ground state = incident energy + binding energy of one particle), will live until this excitation energy, or a reasonable fraction of it, is concentrated again on *one* particle.

3. The final *break-up* of the nucleus is *independent of the mode of formation,* i.e., regardless of how the nucleus was formed there will be definite probabilities for decay into each of several possible residual nuclei. This can be explained in terms of the long lifetime of the compound nucleus during which complete statistical equilibrium is assumed to be established—thus the nucleus forgets how it was

formed; formation and disintegration can be regarded as independent events.

For example, the nucleus $_{30}\mathrm{Zn}^{64}$ can be formed as a "compound nucleus" in a highly excited state from any of the reactions:

$$_{28}\mathrm{Ni}^{60} + {_2}\mathrm{He}^4 \rightarrow {_{30}}\mathrm{Zn}^{64} \qquad \text{excited}$$

$$_{29}\mathrm{Cu}^{63} + {_1}\mathrm{H}^1 \;\; \rightarrow {_{30}}\mathrm{Zn}^{64} \qquad \text{excited}$$

$$_{30}\mathrm{Zn}^{64} + \gamma \;\;\;\; \rightarrow {_{30}}\mathrm{Zn}^{64} \qquad \text{excited}$$

$$_{28}\mathrm{Ni}^{61} + {_2}\mathrm{He}^3 \rightarrow {_{30}}\mathrm{Zn}^{64} \qquad \text{excited}$$

and indeed from many others. The compound nucleus can then decay back, reversing the reaction, into any one of the nuclei just mentioned, or also into others, with a definite probability for each which is the same for all modes of formation. The residual nuclei may also be left in excited states, with probabilities which are also independent of the manner of formation. The first two reactions listed were actually studied experimentally by Ghoshal [*Phys. Rev. 80*, 939 (1950)], who found that the cross-section ratios for the various products emitted from the compound nucleus for a given energy of excitation were the same, within about 10 per cent, independent of the model of formation. Other examples have been observed, and also some exceptions.

Formation of compound nucleus. By assumption 1 of the Bohr picture the cross section for formation of the compound nucleus is equal to the reaction cross section of equation 20.12*b*. With assumption 2, this implies that the eventual concentration of all the energy of excitation on a single particle, one of the same type as that incident, moreover, is so unlikely that it can be neglected. Elastic reaction processes are assumed absent, and any elastic processes observed correspond to collisions in which the incident particle did not enter the nuclear interaction volume but was scattered by the external potential, or reflected at the nuclear boundary. Naturally, this can be accurate only when there are many possible states lying below the excited level of the compound nucleus into which it can decay. If only a few such states exist, elastic re-emission is more likely; such elastic re-emission can, of course, interfere with the potential scattering. This assumption restricts the compound-nucleus picture to nuclei with medium or high A, and excitation energies of at least several Mev. For energies of excitation which go beyond several tens of Mev, the nucleon collision mean free path even in nuclear matter begins to rise with energy, and the nucleus (unless perhaps it is very heavy) can no longer be considered "opaque" (failure of assumption 1). But between a few and 30 or 40 Mev, for nuclei that are not too light, the compound-nucleus picture seems plausible.

One rather direct test of the assumptions is provided by the use of neutrons of about 15 Mev. For such fast neutrons, with $\lambda \ll R$ ($\lambda = (4.55/E_{\text{Mev}}^{1/2})10^{-13}$ cm for nucleons of kinetic energy E Mev), the classical geometrical path is followed by incident neutrons with sufficient accuracy, since the uncertainty in position of the neutron is only λ. The reaction cross section for such neutrons is observed to be πR^2, and the total cross section, including the shadow scattering, $2\pi R^2$ (see Chapter XX, Section A).

At lower energies, the classical approximation is no longer valid. Neither can it be expected to hold for protons, because of the Coulomb barrier, which becomes negligible for the heavier nuclei only at energies so high that the assumption of "blackness" is doubtful. For such cases, the contributions from the various partial waves may be directly summed, with the theory of potential barrier penetration used to estimate their effects. The reaction cross section experimentally found for charged particles of around 8 to 12 Mev on nuclei of middle or higher A fit satisfactorily with the theoretical sum of partial waves.

Let us consider the simple case, s-wave neutrons, but no longer merely the classical limit. Then, from equation 20.5, and assumptions 1 and 2, we have

$$\sigma_{\text{comp.}}{}^{(0)} \cong \sigma_r{}^{(0)} = \frac{4\pi\lambda\ \text{Im}\ (1/a_R)}{|ik + 1/a_R|^2}$$

The compound-nucleus picture now leads to a choice of $1/a_R$. Since the entry of the particle into the nucleus implies no re-emission, the reaction cross section must be as large as possible. Therefore $1/a_R$ is pure imaginary, and we write:

$$1/a_R(k) = iK(k) \tag{20.21}$$

where $K(k)$ is a reciprocal length, an unknown function of k. Now we have

$$\sigma_{\text{comp.}}{}^{(0)} = \pi K^2\ \frac{4kK}{(k + K)^2} \tag{20.22}$$

It is possible to interpret K, and thus to estimate it on physical grounds. To do this we recall relation 20.13. The quantity $\eta_0(R)$ is determined by the properties of the nuclear interior, but it is defined only in the external region, $r > R$. Indeed, η_0 is not continuous across the nuclear boundary R. On physical grounds, there can be no source or sink of particles at the radius R, and hence the particle current must be continuous right across the matching radius R. This implies, as usual, the continuity of both the radial wave function, $r\psi = u_0(r) + u_i(r)$ and of its radial derivative $d(r\psi)/dr \equiv (r\psi)' = u_0' + u_i'$. The ratio of these last two quantities, which is also continuous, may always be written with ψ in the external region:

$$\frac{(r\psi)_{r=R}}{(r\psi)'_{r=R}} = \frac{u_0(R) + u_i(R)}{u_0'(R) + u_i'(R)}$$

$$= \frac{u_0(R) + u_i(R)}{ik[u_0(R) - u_i(R)]} \tag{20.23}$$

and with the relation 20.14, this becomes

$$\frac{(r\psi)_{r=R}}{(r\psi)'_{r=R}} = \frac{[\eta_0(R) + 1]}{ikR[\eta_0(R) - 1]} = \frac{i}{ik \cdot ka_R} = \frac{1}{k^2 a_R} \tag{20.24}$$

so that

$$1/ka_R = k(r\psi)/(r\psi)' = kR/f_0$$

where we have introduced the dimensionless quantity $f_0(k)$ proportional to the logarithmic derivative of the wave function at the nuclear radius, which is commonly found in the literature. Proportional to our generalized scattering length, $1/a_R(k)$, $f_0(k)$ may also be used to describe any s-wave scattering or reaction cross section.

In general, it is not possible to evaluate ψ within the nucleus. But if for some simple model it is possible to write down ψ within the interaction volume, then $1/a_R$ (or f_0) can be determined directly from the properties of $\psi_{int.}$. In the present case we can assume that within the volume bounded by R the particle wave function is a simple spherical s-wave with constant wave number, but entirely incoming; no outgoing wave exists within the nuclear region. This is a plausible physical picture for the implications of the "black" compound nucleus. On this assumption (corresponding to a square-well potential with the outgoing wave wholly suppressed), we write, for the inside wave function, when $r < R$,

$$r\psi = u_0 + u_i \to 0 + \text{const. } e^{-iKR}$$

where $K(k)$ is the wave number for the incoming nucleon inside R, and thus

$$\frac{(r\psi)_{int.}}{(r\psi)'_{int.}} \to \frac{(r\psi)_{r=R}}{(r\psi)'_{r=R}} = \frac{e^{-iKR}}{-iKe^{-iKR}} = \frac{i}{K} \tag{20.25}$$

Now the ratio on the left of equation 20.25 is continuous through the radius R and can therefore be set equal to the same quantity evaluated in terms of the outside wave function alone, from equation 20.24:

$$\frac{1}{f_0} = \frac{1}{R}\frac{r\psi}{(r\psi)'} = \frac{i}{KR} = \frac{1}{k^2Ra_R}$$

and this gives the desired form, cf. equation (20.21):

$$1/a_R(k) = ik^2/K(k)$$

This model of the compound nucleus (called the continuum theory) leads to a cross section for formation of the compound nucleus:

$$\sigma_{comp.}^{(0)} = \pi\lambda^2[4kK/(k + K)^2] \qquad (20.26a)$$

with K the wave number of the nucleon within the nucleus, where it is taken as moving in a uniform potential with depth V_0, so that

$$K^2 = K_0^2 + k^2; \qquad \hbar^2K_0^2/2M = V_0$$

The motion is of course, not fully described by such a potential, for the outgoing wave was taken as entirely absent. This choice does lead to the desired limiting values. If $\lambda \to 0$, we have from equation 20.22

$$\sigma_r^{(0)} \to \pi\lambda^2 \qquad (20.26b)$$

as expected, for the geometrical value $\sigma_r \cong \pi R^2$ can be attained only if the maximum possible value $(2l + 1)\pi\lambda^2$ holds for all those particles whose angular momentum allows them to strike the nuclear target.

At low energy, $k/K_0 \ll 1$, the form of equation 20.22 becomes

$$\sigma_r^{(0)} = 4\pi/kK_0 \qquad (20.26c)$$

just the $1/v$ law expected for low-energy neutron capture. The factor $4kK/(k + K)^2$ in equation 20.22 may be recognized as the wave-transmission probability for a wave striking a region of discontinuity in particle velocity; it is a kind of reflection from the nuclear surface, which of course can interfere in the scattering cross section with the potential scattering.

How far these ideas of the compound nucleus have to be modified we shall see in later sections.

Disintegration of compound nucleus. The probability that the compound nucleus will disintegrate in a particular way is related to the cross section for the corresponding inverse capture process with some factors containing the density of initial and final states.

This follows from considering a statistical equilibrium condition between the compound nucleus and all the possible states of all the residual nuclei into which it can disintegrate (similar to Chapter XII, p. 81). In equilibrium, the number of nuclei present in a small energy range between E and $E + dE$ will be proportional to the density of states $\rho(E)$ in that energy range, and to a Boltzmann factor. Since energy is conserved in the total system, the Boltzmann factors cancel out and the condition for equilibrium takes the form

$$\rho_A W_{A \to B} = \rho_B W_{B \to A} \qquad (20.27)$$

where ρ_A and ρ_B are the densities of initial and final states of the system at corresponding energies, and the W's represent probabilities for the direct and inverse processes.

For our process, A is the excited compound nucleus with a density of states $\rho_A(E_A) = 1/D_A$, where D is the average separation between neighboring states, at an energy E_A above the ground state of A. (Each state is counted according to its statistical weight.) $W_{A \to B}$ is the probability of disintegration of the compound nucleus into a *definite* state of the residual nucleus B with energy E_B above its ground state, with the emission of a particle (say neutron) of energy E. $W_{B \to A}$ is the probability that nucleus B will capture this particle of energy E and produce a compound state of excitation E_A. Finally, $\rho_B(E_B)$ gives the number of states between E and $E + dE$ available for the outgoing particle, viz.,

$$\rho_B = \frac{4\pi p^2}{v(2\pi\hbar)^3} \qquad (20.28)$$

with p and v the momentum and velocity of the outgoing particle. We now use the relation between the capture probability and the capture cross section, which is

$$W_{B \to A} = \rho \sigma_f(E) \qquad (20.29)$$

for one neutron in a box of unit volume moving with velocity $v = (2E/m)^{1/2}$, and the relation between the excitation energies E_A and E_B,

$$E_B = E_A - E - B$$

where E is the energy of the outgoing particle and B its binding energy in the unexcited nucleus A.

Using all the relations just given, and setting $l = 0$ in equation 20.2 (other l give very similar results), we now have a relation by means of which the disintegration probability $W_{A \to B} \equiv \Gamma_B/\hbar$ can be computed in terms of the cross section for formation of the compound nucleus by the inverse capture reaction,

$$(1/D_A)(\Gamma_B/\hbar) = \rho_B v \sigma_c{}^{(0)} \tag{20.30}$$

and $\sigma_c{}^{(0)}$ is given by the expression

$$\sigma_c{}^{(0)} = \pi\lambda^2\xi_B \tag{20.31}$$

where ξ_B is the probability of forming the compound nucleus once the incident particle reaches the nuclear surface.   Then

$$(1/D_A)(\Gamma_B/\hbar) = \rho_B v \, \pi\lambda^2\xi_B$$

or, inserting equation 20.28 and simplifying,

$$\Gamma_B/D_A = \xi_B/2\pi \tag{20.32}$$

This important equation relates the disintegration probability Γ_B, leading to a definite state of the residual nucleus, to the level spacing D_A.   For high energies, ξ_B approaches 1; for low energies it is proportional to the velocity v of the emitted particle.   Both D_A and Γ_B can be deduced from experiment; D_A and ξ_B can also be estimated from various statistical models for heavy nuclei.

Formula 20.32 leads to a valuable physical interpretation of the level spacing D_A.   A collection of highly excited states near E_A could be used to construct a wave packet representing the particle moving in an orbit inside the excited nucleus.   If the nucleus is capable of decay, the packet can be used to represent the motion of a particle which has just entered the nuclear matter and must move about for a long time until it again reaches the surface of the nucleus with the same energy.   The time for recurrence of the configuration is determined by the closest spacing in frequency for components of the wave packet, and for equally spaced levels $\sim 2\pi\hbar/D$.   Now formula 20.32 says that the lifetime of the decaying state is just equal to the probability of penetration through the surface, multiplying the time of recurrence of the favorable configuration.   If the compound state is to be well defined, showing resonance phenomena, then $\Gamma_B(E_A) \ll D_A$, and the particle must knock at the door often before leaving.   If it can leave essentially every time it attains the right configuration, then $\Gamma_B \sim D_A$, and the compound state is poorly defined in energy.

The disintegration probabilities $\Gamma_B/\hbar$ are also related to the widths of the resonances observed in these reactions: since the total decay probability is

$$\Gamma/\hbar = (1/\hbar) \sum_B \Gamma_B. \tag{20.33}$$

the time dependence of the wave function is of the form

$$e^{-iEt/\hbar}e^{-\Gamma t/2\hbar} = e^{-i(E-\frac{1}{2}i\Gamma)t/\hbar} \qquad (20.34)$$

(Note that the absolute *square* of the wave function gives the occupation of the state and decays according to equation 20.19.) Equation 20.34 has a Fourier transform the absolute square of which is

$$\frac{1}{(E' - E)^2 + (\Gamma/2)^2}$$

Thus Γ has the same dimensions as E and gives the width at half-maximum of the level, or resonance line. The quantity Γ_B represents a *partial level width*, i.e., the contribution to Γ arising from the disintegration into a definite end state B.

It will be seen that these direct deductions about the meaning of decay times and corresponding level widths are exactly the same as those which arose from the general ideas of the scattering theory, in the paragraphs following equation 20.9.

Since the compound nucleus must eventually decay, the cross section for a reaction ending in state B is given by the cross section for forming the compound nucleus, times Γ_B/Γ. Thus

$$\sigma_{fB} = \sigma_f \Gamma_B/\Gamma \qquad (20.35)$$

and for fast particles:

$$\sigma_{fB} = \pi R^2 \Gamma_B/\Gamma \qquad (20.36)$$

In the discussion of the compound-nucleus formation, an estimate was given for ξ_B in the case of s-wave neutron capture. The result, from equation 20.22, is

$$\xi_B = 4k\mathrm{K}/(k + \mathrm{K})^2$$

This has at least the proper behavior for large energy, since

$$4k\mathrm{K}/(k + \mathrm{K})^2 \rightarrow 4k^2/(2k)^2 = 1$$

for energies such that $k \gg \mathrm{K}_0$. A rough estimate of K_0 can be obtained from the low energy limit, the $1/v$ neutron capture region, formula 20.26c:

$$\sigma(n, \gamma) \cong \sigma_r^{(0)} = 4\pi/k\mathrm{K}_0 \cong 500/(\mathrm{E}_{\mathrm{ev}})^{\frac{1}{2}} \text{ barns} \qquad (20.37)$$

where the numerical value holds roughly for average nuclei (not magic nuclei) in the region of some tens or hundreds of kev neutron energy, where many experimentally unresolved resonance levels are studied, but the energy remains low enough so that $k \ll \mathrm{K}_0$. From this result, K_0 turns out to correspond to a value of V_0 (equation 20.26a) about what might be expected, around 35 Mev.

When the energy of excitation gets well above the binding energy of a nucleon, many alternatives (often called channels) are available for the disintegration of the compound state. The widths become the sum over a large number of partial widths, corresponding to the emission of many types of particles, and to emission into various excited states of the residual nucleus. Then the total width will be very large compared with D, and equation 20.30 and those which follow from it have to be modified. They lack a factor $\rho_{Bnucl.}\ dE_B$, the number of states of the final nucleus (in equation 20.30 decay to a single definite level was considered), and this factor determines the energy distribution of the emitted nucleons. (Compare Section E, especially the last paragraphs.)

Energy distribution and type of emitted particles. From equation 20.32 we see that Γ_B is almost the same for any final state B, since the sticking probability ξ_B is a slowly varying function of the energy of the outgoing particle. This information is useful in predicting the energy distribution of the emitted particles. For example, if we consider the inelastic scattering of neutrons

$$Z^A + n \to Z^{A+1} \to Z^A + n$$

and make use of the fact that the density of states in the *residual* nucleus increases rapidly with excitation energy, then we see that the residual nucleus will most likely be left in a fairly high excited state and the emitted neutron will come out with low energies.

The fact that emitted neutrons come out with greatly reduced energies has been experimentally confirmed for many nuclei. The main condition for this conclusion is that the incident energy be high enough so that the residual nucleus B possesses a great many levels with an excitation energy less than the incident kinetic energy E_0, in order that the statistical considerations used may be valid. Given high-enough kinetic energy for the neutron, this will be fulfilled for any target nucleus. For most target nuclei, a neutron energy of 1 to 2 Mev is sufficient, but for "magic" nuclei such as lead, or for very light nuclei, there are few excited levels at low energy, and therefore inelastic scattering becomes predominant only at several Mev. The emission of charged particles such as protons requires the penetration of a potential barrier. This penetration probability is similar to that given in the theory of α-decay and is quite small unless the emitted protons have energy nearly equal to, or greater than, the barrier height B. Thus, in a rough way, we may say that the protons must leave with a minimum energy B. This would leave the residual nucleus at a lower energy than if neutrons were emitted. Since the density of residual nucleus states decreases rapidly with decreasing energy, the probability for proton emission will be much smaller than that for neutron emission because of the fewer number of states available, especially if the nuclear charge is high and the available energy low.

The emission of γ-rays will in general be small compared to heavy-particle emission when the latter is energetically possible because the coupling of the nucleus with the radiation field involves the small factor $e^2/\hbar c = 1/137$.

One type of compound nucleus disintegration has been omitted. This is fission. For the heaviest nuclei, with $A \geq 220$ or so, the fission mode of decay has a partial width quite comparable in many cases with the neutron widths. The study of fission is a specialized topic.

E. DENSITY OF NUCLEAR ENERGY LEVELS— NUCLEAR TEMPERATURE

The density of nuclear energy levels increases rapidly as a function of energy. To see how this comes about, a model which is only a crude approximation is used. We consider the nuclear particles as independent of each other, and suppose each of them has a set of equally spaced energy levels spaced by an energy difference Δ. Then, the excited states of the system will also be spaced by the interval Δ and will have a greater statistical weight, the greater the excitation energy, because of the greater number of ways of dividing the energy among the particles. When an interaction among the particles is then introduced, there will be splitting of each energy level; and the statistical weight of an energy level of the non-interacting system is a measure of the energy level density in the same region of the spectrum, after the interaction has been introduced.

To calculate the level density a model of the nucleus must be used. Three models will be mentioned. [For more details see *Revs. Mod. Phys.* 9, 69 (1937).]

1. *Free particles in a box the size of the nucleus.* The level spacing D is proportional to $\exp(-\sqrt{E})$, where E is the excitation energy of the nucleus. For $A = 120$, $E = 8$ Mev, we get $D \sim 10$ ev, which is about what is observed.

2. *Free particle in a box, with correlations.* Bardeen has pointed out that the free-particle model must be modified to be in accord with the assumption of exchange forces. The result gives a level

spacing depending on excitation energy in about the same way as before, but the level spacings are somewhat wider: $D \sim 100$ ev for $A = 120$, $E = 8$ Mev.

3. *Shell model.* Because of its success in explaining the low-lying states of a nucleus, this is probably the best model for the density of excited states as well. Bloch [*Phys. Rev. 93*, 1094 (1954)] has made an analytic calculation of the level density of this model. The density for a given excitation energy shows periodic fluctuations with A, being high near the middle of an incomplete shell, low for complete shells. The Bardeen effect is incorporated in this model but is very nearly compensated on the average by the high statistical weight of an individual-nucleon state in a shell of high angular momentum, $2j + 1$. Thus on the average the level spacing turns out to be about the same as in the simple model 1.

These models give a level spacing which is a decreasing function of the energy of the form $\exp[-f(E)]$, where $f(E)$ is a slowly variable function of the energy.

If the density of states, $\rho(E) = 1/D$, of *any* system is given as a function of energy, then an entropy can be defined as $S = k \log \rho(E)$, and a temperature as $\partial S/\partial E = 1/T(E)$. Each of the three models mentioned will therefore define a nuclear temperature as a function of excitation energy. It turns out that for 10 Mev excitation energy, kT is of the order of 1 Mev, i.e., $T = 10^{10\circ}$ K.

The most satisfactory simple treatment of nuclear thermodynamics [Blatt and Weisskopf, pp. 371ff.] avoids a model and supposes level density

$$\rho(E) = 1/D = C \exp (2 \sqrt{aE}) \qquad (20.38a)$$

where the constants are determined from experiment: from the observed position of the low excited levels, about 1 Mev, and from the spacing of observed slow neutron resonance levels near $E \sim 8$ Mev (binding energy of neutron in nucleus), C and a can both be found; this gives:

For light nuclei, $A \sim 40$; $C = 0.4$ level per Mev; $a = 1/$Mev

medium nuclei, $A \sim 120$; $C = 0.02$ level per Mev; $a = 8/$Mev

heavy nuclei, $A \sim 230$; $C = 0.005$ level per Mev; $a = 12/$Mev

$$(20.38b)$$

These values must be taken as a very rough guide only. For excitations below 1 Mev, they are particularly unrealistic. Setting the level density below 1 Mev to be independent of E, equal to the value given by the formulas at 1 Mev, is better.

Any of the level density functions lead approximately to a Boltzmann distribution for inelastically scattered neutrons. If the incident energy of the neutrons is E_0 and the energy of the emitted neutrons is W then the excitation energy of the residual nucleus is $E_0 - W$. Supposing that the level density of the residual nucleus is $\exp[+f(E)]$ and expanding,

$$f(E) = f(E_0) - f'(E_0)W + \cdots$$

we get a level density

$$\exp f(E) = \exp f(E_0) \times \exp(-f'W) \qquad (20.39)$$

Therefore, setting $f' = 1/kT$ (which is exactly the expression demanded by $\partial S/\partial E = 1/T$) gives a Boltzmann distribution for the level density of the residual nucleus as a function of W and therefore for the kinetic energies of the emitted neutrons. A more careful consideration gives a probability of emission proportional to $W \exp(-W/kT)$, and this shape is roughly found in experimental data.

Experimental data exist for inelastic scattering from a wide variety of targets, both for incident neutrons at energies near 14 Mev, and for protons at higher energies [Gugelot, *Phys. Rev.* 93, 425 (1954)]. The experiments are not very precise, but they suggest that the overall agreement with the simple theory does not extend to details like the variation of T with A. The thermodynamics of the nucleus is not fully described as yet, even if the reactions proceed under favorable conditions along the lines here described.

The whole compound-nucleus theory is approximate in character, and a good many deviations from its predictions are observed even under apparently satisfactory conditions for applying the various approximations made. It has been regarded as a clue to the major processes involved, but it does not describe the full complexity of the observed situation.

F. THE OPTICAL MODEL

The concept of the compound nucleus is so different from the ideas behind the shell model that it can come as no surprise that the results of the compound-nucleus theory too are not always reliable. The statistical nature of the compound-nucleus theory implies that its predictions are at best averages, and gloss over the differences between specific nuclei.

The total neutron cross section for neutrons between about 0.1 Mev and a few Mev energy is the most instructive case in point. At these energies for middle and heavy nuclei many levels are involved, and the spacing is so close that particular resonances cannot be experimentally resolved, even if they could be defined in theory. The total neutron cross section $\sigma_{tot.} = \sigma_e + \sigma_r$ would decrease smoothly with increasing energy on the assumptions of the compound nucleus theory. At low energies, where $\sigma_{tot.} \cong \sigma_{r_1}$, we expect

$$\sigma_r \cong \sigma_r^{(0)} \cong 4\pi/kK \tag{20.26c}$$

and at high energies

$$\sigma_{tot.} \cong 2\pi R^2 \tag{20.40}$$

for the total cross section, since the classical approximation must hold, and the nucleus is assumed "black." Experimentally the results are very different; $\sigma_{tot.}(E)$ has a complicated set of maxima and minima, whose shapes and energies shift in a systematic way with increasing A.

Figure 23 presents the situation graphically. The experimental total neutron cross sections are, of course, averaged over the resonance peaks. For the higher mass number, the averaging is done by the experimental apparatus itself, which cannot resolve the peaks; for low A the average was performed in drawing the profiles. The experimental data, which are both accurate and extensive, are due to several groups, especially the work of Barschall and co-workers in Wisconsin. Most of the data are obtained by direct transmission measurements of the effect of the sample on a neutron beam of very well-defined energy, with energies in the range from 50 kev to 3 Mev or more. The neutrons are generally produced by exciting an endothermic reaction in a thin target with a proton or deuteron beam of highly precise energy obtained from an electrostatic generator. The general success of the theory is striking. Similar good agreement is shown with the angular distributions of elastic scattering, which are known at 1 Mev for a wide range of A.

The basic assumption made is that the incoming wave is *not* all absorbed by a black nucleus. Instead, the nucleus is considered as a gray sphere, partly absorbing and partly refracting the incoming wave. The portion of the wave which is transmitted interferes, naturally, with shifted phase, with the incoming wave, and the complicated broad maxima result. The shift in the curves with A simply corresponds to diffraction by successively larger spheres. The "clouded crystal ball" model is then a complete analog to physical

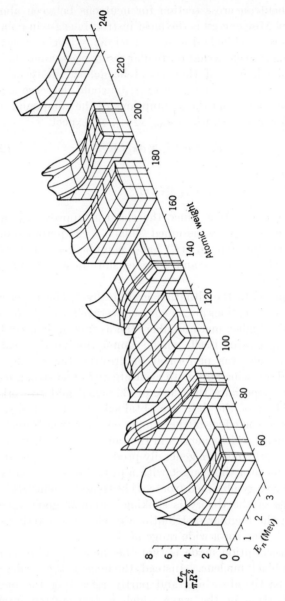

Fig. 23.   Experimental neutron total cross sections, vs. incident neutron energy, averaged over resonance peaks, for many elements.   [Okazaki, Darden, and Walton, *Phys. Rev. 93*, 461 (1954).]

optics.   The nucleus is replaced by a spherical region of fixed refractive index (an attractive potential well) and a given opacity.   To make the calculations at least for not too large values of kR, so that only a few l values come in, it is necessary only to modify slightly the assumptions of the "black" or compound nucleus theory.

Again we employ the model of the nuclear interior which we have used before—a spherical well of constant potential depth and radius R.   Within the well, as in equation 9.5a or equation 20.25, the s-wave function is given by

$$r\psi = A \sin Kr$$

where A is a constant, and K the effective wave number, from equation 20.25.   We now form the quantity

$$\frac{(r\psi)_R}{(r\psi)'_R} = \frac{A \sin KR}{AK \cos KR} = \frac{\tan KR}{K}$$

and can therefore write

$$\frac{1}{a_R(k)} = k^2 \frac{(r\psi)}{(r\psi)'} = k^2 R \frac{\tan KR}{KR} \qquad (20.41)$$

If the nucleus is taken as simply a potential well, able only to scatter the nucleon elastically, without any reactions of any kind, we know that $1/a$ must be pure real.   In equation 20.21, we represented the "black" compound nucleus by a pure imaginary value for $1/a_R$. To represent now the partial opacity and partial transparency of the present model, the "gray" or "cloudy" sphere, we have only to make $1/a_R$ complex.   The wave equation for a complex potential will have solutions with the same form as those for a real potential, but with a complex K.   We write then

$$K^2 = K_0{}^2 + k^2; \qquad K_0{}^2 = (2M/\hbar^2)V_0(1 + i\zeta) \qquad (20.42)$$

where V_0 is the depth of the equivalent nuclear well.   Here ζ measures the effect of the incoherent processes which lead to a reaction; it is a kind of damping or frictional term.   Remarkably good fit is obtained, as the Figs. 23 and 24 indicate, with this very simple assumption for the potential well, which employs three parameters, only one of which, ζ, is not already fairly well determined from other information.   The model can be refined to correspond to a less-artificial well shape.   It seems certain that this model tells a major part of the story.   The damping term ζ is only 3 to 5 per cent for neutrons of 1 to 2 Mev.

From the particle point of view the model allows a partial connec-

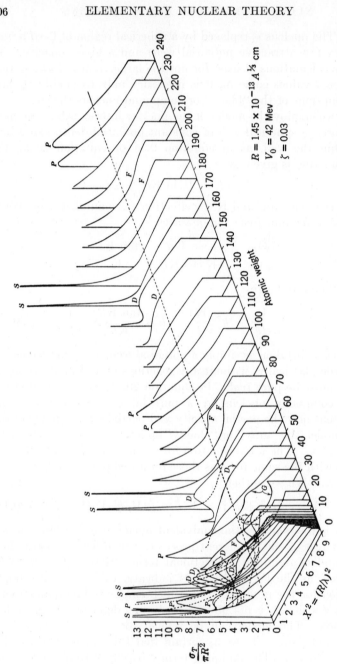

FIG. 24. Theoretical average total cross sections for neutrons, computed from the optical model of nuclei. These curves are to be compared with the experimental values in Fig. 23. [Feshbach, Porter, and Weisskopf, *Phys. Rev. 96*, 448 (1954).]

tion of the apparently contradictory compound nucleus and shell model concepts. Here the particle may traverse nuclear matter and yet remain in a given quantum state, just as presumably the nucleons do while describing the well-defined orbits of the Hartree model. Eventually the nucleon changes its state incoherently; it is amalgamated with the nuclear matter as a whole, transferring its energy to a complex model of motion involving not one but many particles. It forms a compound-nucleus state. In this way the imaginary part of the potential equation (20.42), the opacity, may be regarded as a damping of the single-particle orbits of nucleons in nuclear matter. This damping is small near the ground state, where the shell model works so well, increases with excitation energy, and decreases again when at very high energies the nucleon collision cross sections finally begin to drop, so that the nucleon has a chance to cross the whole nucleus without a single collision. The nucleus becomes there nearly transparent. At 10 or 11 Mev excitation, the mean free path before an incoherent collision in nuclear matter is about 20×10^{-13} cm, with the parameters of equation 20.42.

For low energies, up to 5 Mev or so, the method of partial waves is more or less tractable, though tedious. For high energies, above 50 Mev or so, the same model can be computed by semi-classical methods based on the optical theory of Fraunhofer diffraction [Fernbach, Serber, and Taylor *Phys. Rev.* 75, 1352 (1949)]. Intermediate energies have been attacked by machine computation. The optical model gives an excellent description of the total neutron cross section for just about all energies from a few to 200 Mev or more, for all nuclei, using a simple spherical well of correct radius and a V_0 and ζ which vary with energy but remain independent of A. Proton scattering also has been treated in part. How V_0 and ζ, which fix the refractive index and opacity, are related to the fundamental interactions of nucleons is still little known.

It turns out that a surprisingly good account of the magnitude and energy variation of the opacity is given by an extremely simple, and almost inconsistent model. The nucleons of the nucleus are treated as wholly independent, moving as an ideal Fermi gas in the nuclear potential well. Then an incoming nucleon is considered as being incoherently scattered if it makes any collision with any other nucleons, using the observed cross sections for free nucleons. At low energies, the collisions are greatly reduced in number by the exclusion principle, which makes a collision with small momentum transfer, which is the major contributor to the cross section at low energy, impossible unless the nucleon struck lies near the Fermi energy. For nucleons of lower initial momenta there are no vacant levels in the well into which they and their collision partner can be scattered. This effect greatly reduces the opacity at low energies. At high energy, the cross section for free nucleon collision has decreased considerably. The maximum comes about at 15 Mev of kinetic energy, where the nucleus is observed to be nearly black. This picture, too, is evidently capable of great refinement.

All these models are to be regarded as efforts to account for the average behavior of the resonance levels, ways to obtain the correct parameters, especially the Γ_n, for the Breit-Wigner formula. For the actual cross sections are nothing but the sum of Breit-Wigner peaks, perhaps overlapping, and not the comparatively featureless curves of Fig. 24. The smooth wide maxima and minima in those curves are the reflections of the effects of independent-particle levels on the actual widths and spacing of the very numerous resonance peaks of the actual many-nucleon system hidden beneath that gross structure. The elucidation of the relationship is not complete.

G. HIGH-ENERGY REACTIONS

For energies above, say, 50 Mev, the nucleon collision cross section begins to fall strongly with E, and the wavelengths are short enough to permit semi-classical treatment. The low cross-section implies that nuclear matter is semi-transparent. Optical-model calculations give good fits to the total cross section, and even to angular distributions of elastically scattered nucleons.

Nuclear reactions at such energies are complex. They are frequently called "spallation" when studied by radiochemical methods, or "stars" when observed in photographic emulsion or cloud chambers. Both names emphasize the fact that not one or two but many product particles emerge, roughly $(E/10 \text{ Mev})$ nucleons coming out. The most successful way of handling the phenomenon is to break it again into two parts. The incoming nucleon and the nucleons in the nucleus are thought of as initially interacting with some collision cross section, perhaps modified from that of free nucleons because the Pauli principle will forbid low-momentum transfers to most nucleons in the degenerate Fermi gas which is nuclear matter. The collision products—the recoil nucleon and its partner—are followed classically, through collision after collision, using the best cross sections available and carrying out the work numerically, repeating the calculation over and over again with properly randomized choices (Monte Carlo method) for the nature and position of the successive collisions. Most of these nucleons will escape from the nucleus in a "nuclear cascade," showing some tendency to go into the forward hemisphere because of the transfer of forward momentum from the incoming nucleon. Some collision partners will accumulate less energy than needed to leave the nuclear well. This total energy is then thought of as giving a second stage: exciting the residual nucleus, which behaves like any compound nucleus and finally is de-excited by the processes of ordinary nuclear reactions. These emitted nucleons will be isotropic. The whole process is roughly confirmed by experimental results. The production of mesons, both those able to escape the nucleus and those which are reabsorbed, is an obvious and important omission, especially for incident energies about 200 Mev or more, but could in principle be treated the same way.

H. EMISSION AND ABSORPTION OF γ-RAYS

Whenever an excited nucleus is left with too little energy to emit a nucleon, it will lose excitation energy by radiation. This means that the final steps of almost all nuclear reactions involve radiation of a few Mev. Photon beams may also induce reactions, and these photonuclear processes can be observed up to very high energies. We have discussed the special case of the deuteron radiative processes in Chapter XII.

Multipoles. A more general account of nuclear radiative processes is based on the multipole expansion. This procedure, familiar in classical radiation theory, separates the radiation from any system of charges and currents into distinct types, classified by their angular distributions. In quantum theory, this corresponds to sorting the emitted quanta by the amount of angular momentum radiated by the system. Since the total angular momentum of the whole system must be conserved, the multipole classification is directly related to the possible J values of the initial and final nuclear states. The classification is into multipole radiation of two types, electric and magnetic, which differ in parity, for each of the possible integer values of angular momentum radiated. We are already familiar with the electric and magnetic dipoles. In general there are electric and magnetic 2^L poles for each positive integer L. These are usually indicated by the symbols EL or ML, so that $E1$ stands for electric dipole; $E2$, electric quadrupole; etc. In general, the electromagnetic radiation field of a system contains all the multipoles, and without a further condition they would be of little use. The further condition is the familiar classical restriction

$$(R/\lambda_\gamma) \ll 1$$

where R is a typical radius of the charge-current system, λ_γ the radiated wavelength/2π. Since for a γ-ray of energy E Mev,

$$\lambda_\gamma = 197/E_{\text{Mev}} \times 10^{-13} \text{ cm}$$

and the multipole expansion converges as a power series in R/λ, only the lowest multipole order L allowed by the symmetries of the system can make an appreciable contribution, for γ-rays up to quite high energy.

The strength of the electric multipole of a given order can be expected to exceed in strength the magnetic multipole of the same order by the factor c/v, where v is a velocity of the charged particles in motion. This is familiar in the usual classical magnetic dipole case, a current loop. More quantum-mechanically, the ratio v/c can be estimated roughly:

$$\langle v \rangle/c \cong \hbar/M\lambda_{\text{part.}}c \cong \hbar/MRc$$

where R again is the radius of the current system. The presence of intrinsic magnetic moments coming from spin somewhat modify the usual classical treatment of currents of moving charges alone, but the modification is small in all relevant cases, except that the intrinsic moments tend to increase the magnetic multipole strengths by a factor of a few. All this is discussed at length in Blatt and Weisskopf, Chapter XII.

The selection rules for radiative transitions of every multipole order can be stated in this way:

Multipole Type	Total Angular Momentum Change	Parity Change
EL	$J_i + J_f \geqslant L \geqslant \lvert J_i - J_f \rvert$	$(-1)^L$
ML	Same	$(-1)^{L+1}$

Here J_i and J_f are initial and final values of total angular momentum of radiating systems. For example, if a nucleus makes a transition between two states such that $\Delta J = 1$, and the parity changes, then $E1$ will be the dominant radiation, with the higher contributions EL reduced by a factor $(R/\lambda_\gamma)^{2L-2}$ in intensity. But if $\Delta J = 1$, and the parity remains unchanged, then $E1$ is forbidden, and the transition will proceed via the magnetic dipole ($M1$) radiation, with intensity reduced by about $(v/c)^2$. The electric quadrupole, $E2$, is allowed as well. The $E2$ intensity is reduced compared to a normal $E1$ emission by the factor $(R/\lambda_\gamma)^2$, but it may be of the same order of magnitude as the $M1$ emission, or in special cases even larger. Depending on the parity change then, for a given ΔJ, one will expect either an electric multipole emission or a mixture of the electric and magnetic multipoles of next higher order. The values of the multipole moments here roughly estimated may vary greatly from such general estimates, and can be found exactly only from the detailed wave functions of any given system.

It is to be noted that no radiative transitions exist for $L = 0$; that is, no monopole radiation exists. If $J_i = J_f = 0$, ordinary radiation is wholly forbidden. A few such transitions have actually been observed to proceed by production of electron-positron pairs, or by direct ejection of an orbital electron. Here the monopole interaction with charged particles is responsible. Such $0 \to 0$ transitions can also take place by simultaneous emission of two quanta. By a similar argument, if $J_i = J_f = \frac{1}{2}$, no multipole order higher than the dipole ($E1$ or $M1$) can contribute, and so on.

It is possible by rather specialized techniques to determine the order of a multipole radiative transition without any reference to the lifetime of decay, and thus to verify any theory from which decay rates are calculated. One such method is the study of internal conversion coefficients, both the absolute intensity of orbital electron ejection and the ratio of electrons ejected from several atomic shells. Another depends on finding the angular distributions of the radiation, fixing some axis of the multipole in space by observing correlation between successive γ-emissions, or with a β-electron, or perhaps with a direction of an external aligning magnetic field. A great deal of classification of nuclear states has been done by the study of transitions by these methods.

The probability of emission of radiation per second $w_{L,M}$, can be written in terms of the multipole moment P_{LM} for the general case in this way:

$$w_{L,M} = \frac{F(L)}{\hbar(\lambda_\gamma)^{2L+1}} |P_{LM}|^2$$

For P_{LM}:

(electric) $$Q_{LM} = \int d\tau \psi_f^* \left(\sum_\alpha e_\alpha r_\alpha^L Y_L^M(\Omega_\alpha) \right) \psi_i$$

$$(20.43)$$

(magnetic) $$M_{LM} = \int d\tau \psi_f^* \left\{ \sum_\alpha \frac{e_\alpha}{M_\alpha \dot{c}} \left[\frac{1_\alpha}{(L+1)} + \mu_\alpha S_\alpha \right] \right\} \psi_i \cdot \nabla(r_\alpha^L Y_L^M)$$

where the summation goes over all the particles of the system, each with position $\mathbf{r}_\alpha$, charge e_α, and mass M_α, and with magnetic moment μ_α (in Bohr magnetons). The operator $\mathbf{l}_\alpha = \mathbf{r}_\alpha \times \mathbf{p}_\alpha$, and $\mathbf{S}_\alpha = (\hbar/2)\mathbf{\delta}_\alpha$. The integral $\int d\tau$ implies also a sum over the spin coordinates; the initial and final wave functions are ψ_i, ψ_f; and the Y_{LM} are normalized spherical harmonics. The function

$$F(L) = 8\pi(L+1)/L[1 \times 3 \times 5 \cdots (2L+1)]^2$$

and the orientation of the multipole is given by the magnetic quantum number M. The familiar dipole cases are included in Chapter XII. For example,

$$Q_{1,0} = \left(\frac{3}{4\pi}\right)^{1/2} \int d\tau\psi_f{}^* \left(\sum_\alpha e_\alpha z_\alpha\right) \psi_i$$

which can be compared with equation 12.2. The general case has a different normalization, coming from the choice of the spherical harmonics as the basis, rather than the Cartesian components of the tensors involved.

It is evident that the magnetization currents included in M_{LM} are only those arising from the orbital motion of the nucleons and from their magnetic moments. Any further currents, arising from the exchange of charged mesons, have not been considered in the formation of M_{LM}. These are in fact present, but cannot be directly handled with the fundamental assumption that the nucleus consists of neutrons and protons alone. The point has been discussed in Chapter VIII.

Radiative widths. Most of the detailed study of nuclear radiative transitions has fixed on transitions following radioactive decay, in which the residual nucleus after a β-decay (or perhaps an α-decay) has an excitation energy of some 2 or 3 Mev at most. A great many transitions have been identified as to their multipole type. Where individual levels can be studied, and only a few low-lying levels, including the ground state, contribute to the decay, a direct application of formula 20.43 is possible. The experimental data show that only very rarely are $E1$ transitions observed. High-multipole orders have been recognized, especially in the long-lived isomeric states already discussed in Chapter XIX, going up to $M4$. The special significance of the $E2$ transitions for the collective model was pointed out earlier (p. 175). The magnitude of the radiative widths

$$\Gamma_\gamma(i_{LM} \to f) = \hbar w_{LM}$$

is given in most cases (excluding the special $E2$ values) high by an order of magnitude on the assumption of the independent particle model: that a single nucleon changes its state, with estimated value of the electric moment taken as the maximum under such an assumption, namely

$$Q_{LM}{}^{\text{i.p.m.}} \cong eR^L$$

and the magnetic moment given just by 2 to 3 $(\hbar/MRc)Q_{LM}$. The deviations are real, but certainly not large. Their prediction requires consideration of the more complex relations between the collective motion and the independent-particle model. The great reduction of the $E1$ transitions is a consequence of the shell model, which requires that a change in J of one unit be accompanied by no change in parity within a given configuration. But the few Mev here involved can lead only to states which belong to the same configuration as does the ground state.

The next natural energy range for somewhat detailed study is the energy amounting to the binding energy of a neutron. For this energy, the total width of radiative transitions from a given level is known, because it enters the Breit-Wigner formula (equation 20.12). The total radiative width is in the neighborhood of 0.1 ev for most of the heavier nuclei, as already pointed out in Section C of this chapter. Such a width is due to the radiation into a great many lower-lying levels. From this complex spectrum it is often possible to isolate a few transitions, like those all the way down to the ground state, which contribute appreciably to the total radiation. The total radiation of course includes cascades of successive γ-rays as well as the photons emitted in the actual neutron capture itself. Where spins can be more or less fixed for the ground states of target and residual nucleus, with s-wave thermal neutrons known to enter, the multipole moment of these high-energy capture γ's can sometimes be determined. It appears that the dipole transitions, both $E1$ and $M1$, (depending on parity), are by no means uncommon. This implies that the restriction to a single configuration is no longer in force, as indeed the excitation of 8 Mev or so would lead us to expect.

The estimates of equation 20.43 lead to rough values for the radiative width for the dipole radiation:

$$\Gamma_\gamma{}^{\text{i.p.m.}} = \begin{cases} 0.047E_\gamma{}^3R \text{ ev.} & (E1) \\ 0.021E_\gamma{}^3 \text{ ev.} & (M1) \end{cases} \qquad (20.44)$$

where R is the nuclear radius in 10^{-13} cm, E_γ the energy in Mev. For the lighter nuclei, say with $A < 30$, the observed γ-ray width is in many cases not less than the values of formula 20.44 by as much as an order of magnitude, suggesting that the independent-particle model without much mixing of configurations is still pretty good for these excitations of the light nuclei. But for heavy nuclei, the ratio $\Gamma_\gamma^{\text{i.p.m.}}/\Gamma_\gamma^{\text{obs.}}$ for the particular ground-level transitions observed [Kinsey and Bartholomew, *Phys. Rev. 93*, 1260 (1954)] is reduced by a factor of 10^5 or more. Since no strong transitions to particular states were found with high-multipole orders, and since in the complex neutron capture spectrum the bulk of the radiation usually competes reasonably well with the ground-state dipole transition, it is likely that most of the total radiative width is in fact contributed by dipole transitions ($E1$ and $M1$), some to the lowest lying states, but more to states well above the ground, to which in these heavy nuclei many configurations may contribute, just as many may contribute to the resonance level in which neutron capture occurs. No shell model considerations then reduce the dipole intercombination of the capture level with the many levels lying below.

The estimate of the radiative width by dipole radiation can be made roughly by observing that the high-lying capture level would, in an independent-particle model, be highly degenerate, since the excitation could be shared in many ways among the nucleons. The same is true for a more or less close-lying group of levels near the ground state. For each of the lower levels, there is a particular level of the higher set which can be reached by increasing the energy given to one single nucleon. Only such levels of the upper set will make transitions down, since radiative transitions imply single-particle quantum jumps. But in reality the upper and lower sets are split by the deviations from strict independent-particle levels. Roughly speaking, we can expect that on the average every one of the upper group of states will now intercombine to the same extent with some level of the lower set. Then it will follow that

$$\Gamma_\gamma^{\text{obs.}}(i \to f) \sim \Gamma_\gamma^{\text{i.p.m.}}(i \to f)/\text{No. of combining states}$$

$$\sim \Gamma_\gamma^{\text{i.p.m.}} D(E)$$

so that the average width of a given resonance capture level should be proportional to the level spacing $D(E)$ of the compound nucleus at the given excitation energy E. The constant can be set very roughly by taking literally the prediction of the independent particle model from equation 20.44. Summing over possible final states f, the result for a typical radiative width turns out to be about

	$E1$	$M1$	$E2$
$A = 190$: $\Gamma_\gamma(\text{ev})$	20 ev	0.2 ev	0.02 ev

which is a couple of hundred times too large, if $E1$ is in fact the main contributor. How far this effect is due to a special reduction of the dipole moments, and how far to the various inaccuracies in our estimates, and especially in the level densities, is uncertain.

It is interesting that closed-shell nuclei, with considerably reduced level densities, show much higher relative transition probabilities to the ground states, nearly 100 per cent being reached in lead isotopes 207 and 208.

Photonuclear effect. Once the particle threshold is reached, it is possible to study radiative transitions by observing the ejection of protons and neutrons (rarely other products) by γ-rays, as well as by the capture reaction. The photoeffect has been very much studied; we have already discussed the special case of the deuteron (Chapter XII).

In nearly all nuclei, there is a strong absorption of γ-rays showing quite a well-defined and more or less narrow peak with energy, centered at around 20 Mev in the lighter nuclei, decreasing smoothly to about 15 in the heaviest ones, and uniformly about 6 Mev wide at half-maximum. Some evidence exists from angular distribution that this so-called "giant resonance" is in fact an electric dipole absorption peak. But the strongest evidence for the dipole nature of the peak, now accepted, is provided by the sum rule for photon absorption.

A very general quantum-mechanical result (known as the Thomas-Reiche-Kuhn sum rule in atomic physics) gives for the integrated electric dipole photoabsorption cross section:

$$\int_0^\infty \sigma_{\text{abs.}}{}^{E1}(E_\gamma)\, dE_\gamma = \frac{\pi^2}{137}\left(\frac{\hbar}{Mc}\right)^2 Mc^2 \frac{NZ}{A} = 0.058\,\frac{NZ}{A}\ \text{Mev-barn}$$

This must be satisfied according to quantum theory for any system of N neutrons and Z protons independent of its dynamical make-up. Actually there is a modest increase (30 to 50 per cent) allowed because of the presence of meson exchange currents, which shows up even when only the nucleon motion is considered, provided that Majorana exchange forces act between proton and neutron. Since the low-energy electric dipole transitions are so strongly reduced, as we have seen, and yet the sum must be exhausted, the cross section must rise. It can be shown very generally that it will fall at high energies, unless the potentials involved in the structure are highly singular. Actually the peak itself exhausts most of the area allowed by the sum rule for dipole transitions, which makes its identification certain, since the higher multipoles have much smaller sums. The cross section at the peak is about

$$\sigma_{\max.}^{E1} \cong 0.2(A/100)^{1.5} \text{ barn}$$

Just why this rather narrow peak uses up most of the dipole sum is not yet clear; independent-particle model considerations can account for the narrowness of the peak, and the sum rule then fixes its height. But, directly interpreted, such a theory gives much too low a peak energy. The suggestion that two-particle interactions within the nuclear matter, corresponding to close collisions of nucleons, are important in increasing this energy is probably correct.

The ejected nucleons seem in part to come from a direct photo-effect, showing a characteristic forward peak in angular distribution, but in part from decay of compound-nucleus states, for there is also a strong isotropic component. The presence of low-energy protons, in numbers exceeding the amount that evaporation theory could allow to cross the Coulomb barrier, also implies that the process goes in part directly, not through a compound nucleus mode of decay.

At energies well above the peak, say from 30 to a couple of hundred Mev, the photoeffect seems to proceed by interaction between the γ-ray and two nucleons (neutron-proton pair, for a net electric dipole moment) which are in close collision within the nuclear matter. Such high momentum transfers as are required by high-energy γ-ray absorption are not probable for a system whose wave function is wholly described by the independent-particle model, with the nucleons moving in a well the size of the nucleus. Absorption by such transient "deuterons" (in positive energy states within the nucleus) fits the facts much better. The two nucleons can leave the nucleus without further collisions, or, more frequently, one will initiate a nuclear cascade on its way out.

XXI. β-DISINTEGRATION

In Chapter VI, experimental evidence was given for the hypothesis of the production of neutrinos of rest mass 0 and spin ½ in β-decay processes. This assumption made possible the conservation of energy and spin. The first detailed theory of the process was given by Fermi [Z. Physik 88, 161 (1934)]. A still valuable summary was given by Konopinski [Revs. Mod. Phys. 15, 209 (1943)], and a more up-to-date review by Konopinski and Langer [Ann. Rev. Nuclear Sci. 2, 261 (1953)].

Fermi introduced a new interaction between the nucleon and the two light particles, electron and neutrino. His interaction was chosen in analogy with the interaction between charges and electromagnetic field in quantum electrodynamics. (This analogy was also used in the Chapter XXVIII in connection with the meson theory of nuclear forces.) The heavy particles are to act as sources and sinks of the light particles.

If the Hamiltonian of the interaction between the proton, neutron, and electron-neutrino fields is H, then the number of transition processes per unit time is

$$(2\pi/\hbar)\left|\int\psi_{\text{fin.}}{}^{*}H\psi_{\text{in.}}\,d\tau\right|^{2}\cdot\rho(E) \tag{21.1}$$

where $\rho(E)$ = the number of final states of the system per unit energy interval.

$\psi_{\text{in.}}$ = initial state of the system
= $u_{\text{in.}}$ = initial state of the nucleon.

$\psi_{\text{fin.}}$ = $u_{\text{fin.}}\cdot\psi_{\text{elec.}}\cdot\varphi_{\text{n.}}$ = final state of the system
= (final state of nucleon) · (final state of electron) · (final state of neutrino).

Fermi's assumption for H was essentially

$$\int\psi_{\text{fin.}}{}^{*}H\psi_{\text{in.}}\,d\tau = g\int u_{\text{fin.}}{}^{*}\psi_{\text{elec.}}{}^{*}\varphi_{\text{n.}}u_{\text{in.}}\,d\tau \tag{21.2}$$

(neglecting relativistic corrections which are important only if the *heavy* particle has high velocity), where $\psi_{\text{elec.}}$ and $\varphi_{\text{n.}}$ are to be evaluated at the position of the nucleon, and therefore the integral is over the coordinates of the nucleon alone. This is similar to the

217

case of electrons and light: a charge can interact with a light quantum only when they are at the same place. The constant g which determines the strength of the interaction must be found from experiment. It has the dimensions erg $\cdot$ cm^3, since $\psi_{\text{elec.}}$ and $\varphi_{\text{n.}}$ are to be normalized per unit volume.

Note that we use $\psi_{\text{elec.}}{}^*$, but $\varphi_{\text{n.}}$ (without a star). This corresponds to the emission of an electron but the absorption of a neutrino. However, this absorbed neutrino can be taken from a state of negative energy which corresponds to the emission of an "antineutrino." Owing to the absence of charge and magnetic moment, an antineutrino is equivalent to a neutrino. The formulation (equation 21.2) is therefore equivalent to the emission of an electron and a neutrino, and it is a mathematical convenience to have formally one particle absorbed and one created. The positron emission would be described by $\psi_{\text{elec.}}\varphi_{\text{n.}}{}^*$.

Since the neutrino has very little interaction with anything, its wave function may be taken as a plane wave. If $\mathbf{p}_{\text{n.}}$ is the momentum of the emitted antineutrino, then $-\mathbf{p}_{\text{n.}}$ is that of the absorbed neutrino of negative energy, and

$$\varphi_{\text{n.}} = V^{-\frac{1}{2}} \exp\left(-i\,\mathbf{p}_{\text{n.}} \cdot \mathbf{r}/\hbar\right) \qquad (21.3)$$

where V is the volume of a box in which the wave function is normalized. The factor $V^{-\frac{1}{2}}$ may be omitted if a unit volume is used for the normalization. $\psi_{\text{elec.}}$ should be a Coulomb wave function; but if Z, the charge number, is small, the Coulomb energy of the electron can be neglected in comparison with its kinetic energy and a plane wave can be used for the electron wave function. The number of final states per unit energy is

$$p(E) = \frac{\text{(Volume element of momentum space of electron)}}{(2\pi\hbar)^3}$$

$$\times \frac{\text{(Volume element of momentum space of neutrino)}}{(2\pi\hbar)^3}$$

$$= [(p_{\text{elec.}}{}^2\, dp_{\text{elec.}}\, d\omega_{\text{elec.}})(p_{\text{n.}}{}^2\, dp_{\text{n.}}\, d\omega_{\text{n.}})/(2\pi\hbar)^6]\, dE_{\text{n.}} \qquad (21.4)$$

where $d\omega_{\text{elec.}}$ and $d\omega_{\text{n.}}$ are elements of solid angle, and $(2\pi\hbar)^3$ is the volume of phase space occupied by a single state of a particle.

The result for the transition probability of an electron into $dE_{\text{elec.}}$ and solid angle $d\Omega/4\pi$ (integration over all directions of the neutrino has been carried out) is

$$\frac{G^2}{2\pi^3} \frac{mc^2}{\hbar} \left| \int u_{\text{fin.}}^* \, u_{\text{in.}} \, \exp\left[-i(\mathbf{p}_{\text{n.}} + \mathbf{p}_{\text{elec.}}) \cdot \frac{\mathbf{r}}{\hbar} \right] d\tau \right|^2$$

$$\times \, \epsilon(\epsilon^2 - 1)^{\frac{1}{2}}(\epsilon_0 - \epsilon)^2 \, d\epsilon \, \frac{d\Omega}{4\pi} \quad (21.5)$$

with $G = (g/mc^2)(\hbar/mc)^{-3}$, $\epsilon = E_{\text{elec.}}/mc^2$, $\sqrt{\epsilon^2 - 1} = p_{\text{elec.}}/mc$, $\epsilon_0 = E_{\text{avail.}}/mc^2$. A plane wave has been substituted for the electron wave function.

Just as in the theory of atomic transitions, there will be selection rules for β-decay processes. If $p_{\text{elec.}}$ and $p_{\text{n.}}$ are both of the order of magnitude mc, as is usually the case, the exponent $(\mathbf{p}_{\text{n.}} + \mathbf{p}_{\text{elec.}})$ $\cdot \mathbf{r}/\hbar$ will be of the order of magnitude:

$$\frac{R}{\hbar/mc} \approx \frac{4 \times 10^{-13} \text{ cm}}{3.86 \times 10^{-11} \text{ cm}} \sim \frac{1}{100} \quad (21.6)$$

(R = nuclear radius; medium-weight nuclei have been chosen.) Thus, $\exp\left[i(\mathbf{p}_{\text{n.}} + \mathbf{p}_{\text{elec.}}) \cdot \mathbf{r}/\hbar\right]$ will be nearly 1, and the matrix element in equation 21.5 reduces to $M = \int u_{\text{fin.}}^* \, u_{\text{in.}} \, d\tau$, i.e., to an expression depending only on the state of the nucleon before and after the transition. M is determined by the nuclear wave functions. In particular, the orthogonality of the nuclear wave functions for states of different angular momentum I gives the selection rule:

$$M \neq 0 \text{ implies } \Delta I = 0 \quad (21.7)$$

Such transitions are called allowed. Transitions for which $M = 0$ are called forbidden; in this case the exponential in equation 21.5 must be expanded in a power series; the order of the forbidden transition is the number of the first term in this power series which gives a non-vanishing result for the matrix element. Because of the estimate (equation 21.6), the probabilities should decrease by a factor of about 10^4 with each order.

A. ALLOWED TRANSITIONS

The only dependence of the allowed transition probability on the electron energy is through the volume element in momentum space. The energy spectrum of electrons is therefore

$$N(\epsilon) \, d\epsilon \sim \epsilon \, \sqrt{\epsilon^2 - 1}(\epsilon_0 - \epsilon)^2 \, d\epsilon \quad (21.8)$$

Since ϵ_0 is unknown, the experiments have to yield a value of ϵ_0, while giving a check on the theoretical spectrum. This is easily done by making a "Kurie plot." In this plot, the quantity

$$F(\epsilon) = \sqrt{N(\epsilon)/\epsilon(\epsilon^2 - 1)^{\frac{1}{2}}} \qquad (21.9)$$

(as observed) is plotted against the energy ϵ. According to equation 21.8, $F(\epsilon) \sim \epsilon_0 - \epsilon$; therefore the plot should yield a straight line which cuts the ϵ axis at ϵ_0.

The first measured spectrum which confirmed this prediction closely was that of In^{114}, a specially suitable case measured by Lawson and Cork [Phys. Rev. 57, 982 (1940)]. Until quite recently, most experimental spectra showed far too many electrons at low energies. Most of this distortion is now known to be due to electron scattering in the material and backing of the source, which was far more important than first realized, especially because the sources often tend to be non-uniformly spread over the supporting material. Such errors even led to now-discarded modifications in the theory [Konopinski and Uhlenbeck, Phys. Rev. 48, 7 (1935)] which were widely accepted at one time.

A typical very carefully measured spectrum of allowed type is shown in Fig. 25 [Phys. Rev. 77, 801 (1950)]. This plot is entirely straight from the end point at 223 kev down to under 15 kev electron energy. The source was known to be uniformly about 10 $\mu g/cm^2$ in thickness, whereas in the earlier work a few milligrams per square centimeter was taken to be a thin source. Many other allowed spectra are now known to agree with theory for the full reliable range of the experimental data. In a few cases, like those of N^{13} and Cu^{61}, there were discrepancies which could not be removed by eliminating the effects of electron scattering. These turned out to be the consequences of a complex mode of decay of the parent nucleus. Several β-decays take place simultaneously, each leading to a different energy level of the residual nucleus. The spectrum is then the sum of simple spectra of different intensities and end points.

The three simplest β-active nuclei are the neutron itself, H^3, and He^6. All three have measured spectra fitting the allowed shape very well, though the techniques of measuring differ greatly. The fundamental β-decay, that of the neutron, is discussed more fully two sections below.

Coulomb field and atomic electrons. In expression 21.8 for the electron energy spectrum no account has been taken of the Coulomb field. The correct spectrum has a greater electron density at low energies. There is no zero for $\epsilon = 1$ because the factor $\sqrt{\epsilon^2 - 1} \sim v$

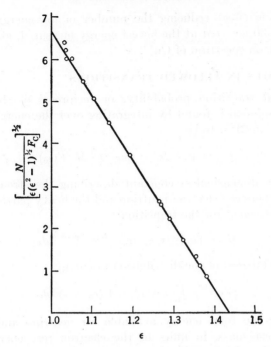

FIG. 25. Kurie plot for a typical allowed β-decay spectrum (Pm^{147}). F_C is the Coulomb correction mentioned in the text, p. 220. The total electron energy in units of mc^2 is plotted on the horizontal axis. (Langer, Motz, and Price, Phys. Rev. 77, 798 (1950).)

(velocity) in the density of states is canceled by a $1/v$ in the charge density of electrons at the nucleus. The resulting electron spectrum is shown in Fig. 26.

For positrons, fewer of low energy should be expected than the number given by expression 21.8 because of the repulsion of the positrons in the Coulomb field. The Coulomb wave function of the electron in expression 21.2 has a factor exp $(-2\pi Ze^2/\hbar v)$, which lowers the transition proba-bility considerably for low velocities.

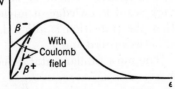

FIG. 26. Energy distribution of β-rays with effect of the atomic Coulomb field.

The Coulomb correction is well-confirmed by experiment; indeed the actual plot in Fig. 25 includes a Coulomb factor. Even the deviations from a pure Coulomb field caused by the electrostatic screening of the nucleus by the innermost electrons of the atom have a measurable effect reducing the number of low-energy positrons emitted by 30 per cent at the lowest energy measured, about 25 kev in the positron spectrum of Cu^{64}.

B. LIFETIMES IN ALLOWED TRANSITIONS

The total transition probability, or reciprocal of the lifetime, for β-ray emission is found by integrating over the energy distribution (equation 21.5) to be

$$1/\tau = (G^2/2\pi^3) \cdot (mc^2/\hbar)|M|^2F(\epsilon_0) \tag{21.10}$$

Here G is a dimensionless constant describing the strength of the interaction between electron-neutrino and the heavy particles. M is the matrix element for the transition:

$$M = \int u_{\text{fin.}}^*(\mathbf{r})u_{\text{in.}}(\mathbf{r})e^{-i(\mathbf{p_n.}+\mathbf{p}_e)\cdot\mathbf{r}/\hbar}\,d\tau \tag{21.11}$$

$F(\epsilon_0)$ is the integral of the distribution in energy

$$F(\epsilon_0) = \int_1^{\epsilon_0} \epsilon \sqrt{\epsilon^2 - 1}\,(\epsilon_0 - \epsilon)^2\,d\epsilon \tag{21.12}$$

where ϵ_0 is the total energy available for neutrino and electron, including rest mass, in units of the electron rest energy. $F(\epsilon_0)$ varies rapidly with ϵ_0, being approximately equal to $(1/30)\epsilon_0^5$ for $\epsilon_0 \gg 1$ and to $0.216(\epsilon_0 - 1)^{7/2}$ for ϵ_0 nearly unity. Thus τ decreases rapidly with increasing ϵ_0, but not as fast as in the case of α-decay, where the transition probability is proportional to an exponential of the energy. In Chapter II it was pointed out that in natural α-decay a factor of 2 in energy is equivalent to a factor of 10^{-20} in lifetime.

The matrix element M is in general not known because we have very scant knowledge of nuclear wave functions. Even if we know that the transition is allowed, we can in general say only that $|M|$ is between zero and 1.

The most fundamental β-decay is that of the neutron:

$$n \rightarrow H + \beta^- + \nu \tag{21.13}$$

The matrix element for this reaction should be exactly unity, as the wave function for a single proton ought to be the same as that of a single neutron. Measuring the lifetime of this reaction should give an exact value of G. However, this reaction is hard to observe, as the neutrons are removed much more rapidly by other means (capture, diffusion) than by the above reaction as long as any matter is present.

In an elegant experiment [Robson, *Phys. Rev. 83*, 239 (1951)] a strong thermal beam from a nuclear chain reactor was passed through an evacuated space, and the decay protons and electrons were counted in appropriate spectrometers. An excellent fit was obtained to the allowed spectrum shape for the electrons, the end point expected from known masses was confirmed to 10 kev or so, and the half-life was measured as

$$T_{1/2} = 770 \pm 140 \text{ seconds}$$

In some cases more complicated than the neutron we can guess the value of M to better than order of magnitude. For allowed transitions ($\Delta I = 0$), we have

$$M \approx \int u_{\text{fin.}}{}^* u_{\text{in.}} \, d\tau \qquad (21.14)$$

M will be near unity when the wave functions $u_{\text{fin.}}$ and $u_{\text{in.}}$ are nearly alike. Such is the case for β-transition between mirror nuclei (Chapter II) (for which also the selection rule $\Delta I = 0$ is likely to be fulfilled. Such mirror transitions, and a few others between nuclei less simply related, have empirically a high probability, and are called allowed and favored transitions. A few examples are given in Table XXIA.

Table XXIA. Allowed and Favored Transitions

Reaction	$T_{1/2}$ (sec)	ϵ_0	$F(\epsilon_0)T_{1/2}$ (sec)
Mirror nuclei:			
$n \rightarrow H^1 + \beta^-$	~ 750	2.53	1200
$H^3 \rightarrow He^3 + \beta^-$	3.93×10^8	1.036	1020
$C^{11} \rightarrow B^{11} + \beta^+$	1230	2.88	3900
$Mg^{23} \rightarrow Na^{23} + \beta^+$	11.6	6.51	3200
$Sc^{41} \rightarrow Ca^{41} + \beta^+$	0.87	10.6	2500
Others:			
$He^6 \rightarrow Li^6 + \beta^-$	0.823	7.85	820
$O^{14} \rightarrow N^{14} + \beta^+$	76.5	4.5	3300
$F^{18} \rightarrow O^{18} + \beta^+$	6720	2.24	3700

From equation 21.10 the product of lifetime and energy integral $\tau F(\epsilon_0)$, is equal to a constant times the nuclear matrix element $|M|^2$. Both factors can be obtained directly from experiment, and the product (using the half-life $T_{1/2}$ instead of τ) is tabulated as a test of the constancy of the matrix element $|M|^2$.

The product $FT_{1/2}$, although not precisely a constant, is strikingly near to it, considering that the half-life varies by a factor about 10^9. Putting aside the non-mirror cases for the moment, it seems reasonable that $FT_{1/2}$ is somewhat smaller for the first two than for the last three mirror nuclei, for in a nucleus containing only three particles we would expect $u_{\text{fin.}}$ and $u_{\text{in.}}$ to be more nearly alike than in the heavier nuclei, so that $|M|$ would be closer to unity in the light nucleus.

Most of the remaining variation in the value of $|M|^2$ arises from simple and calculable statistical weight factors, like those resulting from the fact that the experiments, of course, detect β-decay to all of the $(2J + 1)$ variously oriented substates of angular momentum component M belonging to a given nuclear energy level with total angular momentum J. When such factors are taken into account, the values of $|M|^2$ for a nuclear transition between single states are constant within about 20 per cent in the cases considered here.

For nuclei of intermediate mass, the effect of the Coulomb repulsion already produces a considerable excess of neutrons over protons. From the point of view of the shell model, this clearly means that the quantum levels occupied by neutron and proton are generally quite different. Their wave functions will therefore overlap relatively little; even if the shell model wave functions are not precise, such a difference must be expected. Thus, even for allowed transitions, smaller matrix elements are expected for intermediately heavy nuclei than for light, mirror nuclei. This is borne out well by the data for some sixty transitions whose $FT_{1/2}$ values lie in the range $\sim 10^5$. These are called allowed, but not favored, transitions. In Table XXIB some examples are given. There is no systematic

Table XXIB.   Allowed But Not Favored Transitions

Reaction	$F(\epsilon_0)T_{1/2}$ (sec)
$S^{35} \rightarrow Cl^{35} + \beta^-$	1.0×10^5
$Ca^{45} \rightarrow Sc^{45} + \beta^-$	4×10^5
$Mo^{91} \rightarrow Nb^{91} + \beta^+$	6×10^5
$In^{114} \rightarrow Sn^{114} + \beta^-$	3×10^4
$Er^{169} \rightarrow Tm^{169} + \beta^-$	2×10^5

Source: Mayer et al., *Revs. Mod. Phys. 23*, 315 (1951).

trend for $FT_{1/2}$; in particular, it does not seem to increase as A goes to the highest values, above 200. A few of the naturally radioactive nuclei, like RaC'' and Pb^{209}, appear to have low $FT_{1/2}$ values in the allowed group but cannot be allowed transitions in the sense of the theory, because they involve violations of the selection rules for allowed transitions.

There are a number of well-known cases, such as that of C^{14}, which from the shape and the known or surmised initial and final values of spin (and parity) ought to be normal allowed transitions, but have $FT_{1/2}$ values around 10^8. This implies that the wave functions $u_{\text{fin.}}$, $u_{\text{in.}}$ are nearly orthogonal, although they correspond to the same values of all the well-known constants of the motion. Several lines of evidence point to the conclusion that these cases are simply examples of accidental cancellation between several matrix element contributions. It is not unlikely on a purely statistical basis that among so many known β-activities one or two should show such effects [see Jancovici, Talmi *Phys. Rev. 95*, 289 (1954)].

Assuming $|M| \approx 1$ for the lightest mirror nuclei, G can be calculated from Ft. The result is

$$G \approx 10^{-11} \qquad (21.15)$$

This corresponds to $g \approx 10^{-48}$ erg · cm³. The smallness of this coupling between electron-neutrino and the heavy particle is what makes β-decay take place so slowly compared to other nuclear reactions, except some α-radiations with high Coulomb barriers. It is safe to say that β-rays are in general not emitted during nuclear collisions but that the collision is first completed, and only then the residual nucleus may emit β-rays, a long time afterward. The only known exception is the reaction

$$H + H \rightarrow d + \beta^+ + \nu \qquad (21.16)$$

But even this reaction is extremely improbable: at the center of the sun, with a density about 100 g/cm³ and a temperature of 15×10^6 °K., an average proton will "live" for about 10^{10} years before undergoing reaction 21.16 [see Salpeter, *Phys. Rev. 88*, 547 (1952)]. Slow as it is, this reaction presents the best opportunity for β-decay during a nuclear collision. It is probably the major contributor to the energy radiated by the sun.

C. LIFETIMES IN FORBIDDEN TRANSITIONS

The second term in the Taylor expansion of the exponential in the matrix element (equation 21.11) will give a non-vanishing integral when $\Delta I = \pm 1$, which transition was forbidden in the first approximation. Similarly, $\Delta I = \pm 2$ transitions become possible with the third term in the expansion, and so on. For $\epsilon_0 = 2$, the argument of the exponential averages about 1/100 over the range of the heavy-particle wave function, so that $|M(\Delta I = \pm 1)|^2$ might be expected to be about 10^{-4} times $|M(\Delta I = 0)|^2$. Actually, the true wave function for an electron in the Coulomb field varies faster than the plane-wave approximation used in equation 21.11, and the factor 10^{-4} becomes about 10^{-2} for medium and heavy nuclei. This correction does not help the higher forbidden transitions so much as the first.   Higher ϵ_0 makes all forbidden transitions more probable. Table XXIC quotes experimental data for forbidden transitions

Table XXIC.   Half-Lives in Forbidden Transitions

Emitter	$T_{1/2}$ (sec)	ϵ_0	$T_{1/2}F(\epsilon_0)$ (sec)
First Forbidden Transitions			
S^{37}	300	9.4	1.2×10^7
Y^{91}	4.9×10^6	4.04	4.8×10^8
Cs^{137}	1.1×10^9	2.01	4.1×10^9
RaE^{210}	4.3×10^5	3.28	10^8
Second Forbidden Transitions			
Be^{10}	8.5×10^{13}	2.08	5×10^{13}
C^{36}	1.4×10^{12}	2.39	3×10^{13}
Third Forbidden Transition			
K^{40}	3.4×10^{16}	3.66	10^{18}

Source: Mayer et al., *Revs. Mod. Phys.* *23*, 315, 322 (1951).

The key to the modern understanding of the Fermi theory was given when the shapes of the spectra of two forbidden transitions were measured (Y^{91}, Cs^{137}) and it was found that the Kurie plot did not give a straight line, but that a simple modification of it did. If we expand the exponential in equation 21.11 and consider only the second term of the expansion (a first forbidden case), the integral M becomes

$$(\mathbf{p}_\text{n.} + \mathbf{p}_e) \cdot \int u_\text{fin.}^*(\mathbf{r}/\hbar)u_\text{in.} \, d\tau \qquad (21.16a)$$

Averaging the first factor (to be justified in the next paragraph) over all directions of emission of electron and neutrino, we get for the energy spectrum of the first forbidden transition.

$$N_1(\epsilon) \, d\epsilon \sim (p_\text{n.}^2 + p_e^2)N(\epsilon) \, d\epsilon = [(\epsilon^2 - 1) + (\epsilon_0 - \epsilon)^2]N(\epsilon) \, d\epsilon \qquad (21.17)$$

where $N(\epsilon)$ is the allowed spectrum, equation (21.8).   (Note that the integral in equation 21.16a does not depend on energy.)   The experimental result is plotted in Fig. 27, together with the theory.   In such forbidden cases the $FT_{1/2}$ values also should be corrected for the shape of the energy spectrum.

D. FERMI AND GAMOW-TELLER SELECTION RULES

The selection rule $\Delta I = 0$ for allowed transitions is not always adhered to.   Consider the reaction:

$$He^6 \rightarrow Li^6 + \beta^- + \nu \qquad (21.18)$$

Li^6 can be thought of as an α-particle plus a deuteron. The α-particle has $I = 0$, and the deuteron has $I = 1$. We expect, therefore, that Li^6 has $I = 1$, in agreement with experiment. In the same picture, He^6 is an α-particle plus two neutrons. In the ground state, the double neutron should have spin zero (cf. Chapter XV), so that the same argument gives $I = 0$ for He^6. An additional argument for

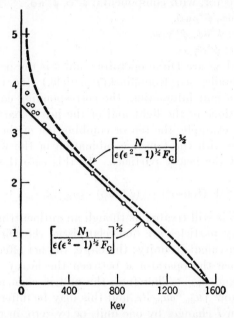

Fig. 27. Example of a β-decay spectrum for first-forbidden transition (in Y^{91}). The data are plotted both in standard Kurie plot form for allowed transitions (dashed line) and in the corrected form appropriate for first-forbidden transitions (solid line). N_1 and N are related by a factor: $N_1 = N/[(\epsilon^2 - 1) + (\epsilon_1 - \epsilon)^2]$ (cf. equation 20.17). The kinetic energy of the electron, $T = (\epsilon - 1)mc^2$, is plotted on the horizontal axis in kev. (Wu and Feldman, *Phys. Rev.* 76, 696 (1949).)

this is that all nuclei containing even numbers of neutrons and protons have zero spin as far as they have been investigated. Thus $\Delta I = 1$, and the transition should be forbidden. But the experimental lifetime of the reaction shows that it is allowed and favored. At least fifteen more cases of allowed transitions are believed to have a spin change of one unit, on the basis of a combination of experimental and theoretical arguments from the shell model. So there can be allowed transitions with $\Delta I = 1$.

Gamow and Teller first showed how this can come about. They

said that in considering possible interactions, one ought to include all relativistically invariant combinations of the four wave functions, $u_{\text{in.}}$, $u_{\text{fin.}}$, $\psi_{\text{elec.}}$, and $\phi_{\text{n.}}$. For *two* wave functions, let us say ψ and ϕ, there are five combinations which are covariant under Lorentz transformations:

Scalar: $\psi^*\beta\phi$ (Fermi theory).

Polar four vector, with components: $\psi^*\phi$, $\psi^*\alpha\phi$.

Tensor: $\psi^*\beta\sigma\phi$, $\psi^*\beta\alpha\phi$.

Axial vector: $\psi^*\sigma\phi$, $\psi^*\gamma_5\phi$.

Pseudoscalar: $\psi^*\beta\gamma_5\phi$.

where β, α, and γ_5 are Dirac operators and σ is the usual spin operator. (For details, see Konopinski's article.) To obtain a relativistically invariant interaction, the corresponding combinations of the wave functions of the light and of the heavy particles must be multiplied; for example, the tensor combination of the light-particle wave functions with the tensor combination of the wave functions $u_{\text{in.}}$ and $u_{\text{fin.}}$ of the heavy particles. In this case the Hamiltonian becomes

$$V \text{ (tensor)} = (\psi^*\beta\sigma\phi) \cdot (u_{\text{fin.}}^*\beta\sigma u_{\text{in.}}) \qquad (21.19)$$

(The transition is still treated as though an antineutrino is emitted.) Since the heavy particles are non-relativistic, the Dirac operator β for them is equivalent to unity; therefore, the net effect of equation 21.19 is to place the operator σ between the heavy particle wave functions $u_{\text{in.}}$ and $u_{\text{fin.}}$. Therefore, the matrix element for allowed transitions is now $\int u_{\text{fin.}}^*\sigma u_{\text{in.}} \, d\tau$, and this may be different from zero if the total spin I changes by one unit, or by zero, in the transition. Thus $\Delta I = \pm 1, 0$ can be "allowed" for the tensor interaction.

The axial vector interaction gives the same selection rule as the tensor,

$$\Delta I = 0, \pm 1 \qquad (21.20)$$

The other three possible interactions lead in the same way to selection rules for an allowed transition. We list the selection rules for the five types of interaction, in allowed transitions:

For S and V: $\Delta I = 0$ Parity cannot change

For T and A: $\Delta I = 0, \pm 1$ Parity cannot change; no $0 \to 0$ transition

For P: $\Delta I = 0$ Parity must change

The rules which hold for T and A are called the Gamow-Teller selection rules, those for S and V, the Fermi selection rules. The pseudoscalar case is in some ways special, since it depends on small relativistic terms in the nucleon wave function, which are not fully known. The experiments demonstrate that Gamow-Teller rules must apply in most cases.

With this decided, we can justify the very simple modification of shape for the first forbidden spectrum. For the T or the A interaction, the first forbidden spectrum arises from integrating over all directions of emission the expression:

$$\left|(\mathbf{p_n} + \mathbf{p}_e) \cdot \int d\tau u_f^* \mathbf{r} \partial u_i\right|^2$$

where the integral is a tensor. In general, this will lead to a rather complicated function of the angles, and the integrated result will not be simple. But if the only contribution from the integral factor is spherically symmetric, the correction will be given by

$$\text{Const.} \times \int d\Omega_e \left|\mathbf{p}_e + \mathbf{p_n}\right|^2 = \text{Const.} \times (p_e^2 + p_n^2) \sim (E^2 - 1) + (E_0 - E)^2$$

which is the factor needed to correct the observation. Such a simplification will occur here if the angular momentum change is $\Delta I = 2$, as a consequence of the familiar relations among spherical harmonics. In general, for any transition in which ΔI is greater by 1 than the degree of forbiddenness, a similar simplification will occur. The good agreement between experiment and this correction factor, in just the cases where it should apply, is in itself sufficient to verify the need for Gamow-Teller selection rules.

When several interaction types are present in comparable amounts, interference terms arise in the spectral shapes. A study of these interferences (first made by Fierz) shows that the simple allowed spectral shape could not occur if there were present both types of Gamow-Teller interaction (A and T) or both types of Fermi interaction (S and V). Later work has extended the argument to the first forbidden spectrum shapes, which would no longer agree with experiment if interference terms between S and A, or between T and V, were appreciable. This limits the choice to that between the mixture VA and the mixture ST. A very direct means has been used to establish that in the pure Gamow-Teller decay of He^6, where neither V nor S can occur, the responsible interaction is in fact the tensor. This is learned by a study of the distribution in angle of the outgoing decay electron with respect to the direction of the recoil nucleus (cf. Chapter VI). The observed angular distribution fits well with the prediction of the tensor theory and disagrees with that from A. Similar experiments for a transition partly of Fermi type (Ne^{19}

decay) has confirmed the prediction that there S, rather than V, is present. The neutron decay angular distribution is spherically symmetrical, implying presence of both S and T in a particular ratio.

The over-all conclusion is that the interaction consists of a mixture of S and T, with strengths such that $0.5 \gtrsim G_S^2/G_T^2 \gtrsim 1.5$, with an unknown, though probably small, amount of P.

It is noteworthy that reaction 21.16, which is responsible for most of the sun's energy, corresponds to a change from an initial two-proton state which at low energy is almost pure orbital S-wave, and therefore necessarily has $I = S = 0$ (because the two protons must obey the Pauli principle), to the final deuteron ground state, with $I = 1$. Thus the spin changes by one unit; the reaction can be allowed, and of importance in the stars, only because there is an interaction of the Gamow-Teller type.

E. ELECTRON CAPTURE

In this type of β-transition an atomic orbital electron is absorbed by a nuclear proton, changing the proton into a neutron, and resulting in the emission of a neutrino. The neutrino alone carries off the full energy of the transition and is therefore monoenergetic. Examples of electron capture are given in Chapter III, and an experiment which measures the recoil momentum given to the nucleus by the outgoing neutrino is described in Chapter VI.

The theory of electron capture has been worked out and agrees as well with the observed lifetimes as the ordinary cases of β-emission. The ratio of electron capture to positron emission for two given nuclear states between which both modes of transition are energetically possible has been found to check the theory closely. This is a test of the theory independent of the details of nuclear structure, for the nuclear matrix element cancels out of the ratio. A few cases have been observed in which electrons from other than the innermost K shell are captured. Since the density of such outer electrons near the nucleus is low compared to that of the K electron, such capture is much less probable, and observed usually only when the higher binding energy of the K electron energetically prevents its capture.

The transition rate for K capture is evidently proportional to the density of atomic electrons near the nucleus. It has been possible to observe an effect on the lifetime of the K capture of Be^7 depending on the state of chemical combination of the beryllium atom. In Be metal the lifetime is a little shorter than in the fluoride, presumably because in the metal the atomic electrons are somewhat more tightly packed than in the salt. This is one of only two known cases (the other is a Tc internal-conversion electron emitter) in which a nuclear lifetime has been even slightly influenced by chemical means.

F. NEUTRINO AND ANTINEUTRINO

The reactions of β-transition may be summarized as shown:

$$\beta^- \text{-decay} \qquad n^* \to \beta^- + p^* + \nu_1 \qquad (a)$$

$$\beta^+ \text{-decay} \qquad p^* \to \beta^+ + n^* + \nu_2 \qquad (b) \qquad (21.21)$$

$$\text{Electron capture} \qquad p^* + \beta^- \to n^* + \nu_2 \qquad (b')$$

where the asterisk denotes that the nucleon may not be free, but bound into a nucleus. Reactions b and b' are fully equivalent, and as we have seen may in fact compete for the decay of one and the same nuclear state. There is evidently a particular relationship between the role of the electron and that of the positron in these two reactions; the emission of a positron in reaction b is fully equivalent to the absorption of a negative electron in reaction b'. The electron and positron differ, of course, in other respects; their electric charge and magnetic moments are equal in magnitude but opposite in sign. Two spin ½ particles so related are said to be particle and the corresponding antiparticle: the Dirac theory predicts that such a pair will exist for every type of spin ½ elementary particle. The creation of such a pair by γ-rays is well known of course for electrons and positrons.

If the spin ½ particle, the neutrino, has this property, then it too will have a counterpart, the antineutrino. In that case, the neutral particle ν_1, emitted in ordinary β^--decay (which we will call the neutrino) can be absorbed in the reaction:

$$p^* + \nu_1 \to n^* + \beta^+ \qquad (21.22)$$

since this is exactly the reaction obtained from reaction b by considering the absorption of a neutrino ν_1, to be equivalent to the emission of an antineutrino, ν_2. But a neutrino could *not* be absorbed to induce a β^--decay; for that, the reaction must read instead

$$n^* + \nu_2 \to \beta^- + p^* \qquad (21.23)$$

obtained from reaction a in the analogous way; an incident *antineutrino* is required.

The neutrino capture experiment described in Chapter VI is designed to observe positron emission induced by neutrinos, ν_1, from fission product decays, which are exclusively β^--decays, and hence produce the proper particles, ν_1. If the Dirac theory applies to neutrinos as we have described it, a β^+-decay could *not* be induced by the flux of pile neutrinos. This effect is observable, and would directly check the statement that neutrino and antineutrino, which have neither charge nor magnetic moment, are yet distinct particles.

It was pointed out a long time ago by Majorana that the general theory of elementary particles does not demand such a distinction between particle and antiparticle if they are electrically neutral. In the alternative theory he proposed

$$\nu_1 \equiv \nu_2 \qquad (21.24)$$

and the neutrino flux from a chain reactor would induce equally well either β^-- or β^+-decay. Majorana suggested another, less direct, experimental distinction between his and the Dirac alternative for the relation between the particles ν_1 and ν_2. This is the process of double β-decay.

In most nuclei a double β-emission, in which two electrons or positrons are emitted at once, and the nuclear charge changes by two units, is energetically possible. The over-all observable reaction for such a process is

$$2n^* \rightarrow 2p^* + 2\beta^- \qquad (21.25a)$$

or

$$2p^* \rightarrow 2n^* + 2\beta^+ \qquad (21.25b)$$

with neutrinos disregarded. Let us consider the double β^--emission for definiteness. The reaction can be thought of as passing through an intermediate step:

$$2n^* \rightarrow n^* + p^* + \beta^- + \nu_1 \rightarrow \begin{cases} 2p^* + 2\beta^- + 2\nu_1 \\ 2p^* + 2\beta^- + \text{no neutrinos} \end{cases} \quad (21.26)$$

and it can be seen that two alternatives exist for the second step, either the *emission* of a second neutrino ν_1, or the *absorption* of the first. This is entirely analogous to the equivalent alternatives of positron emission or electron capture of reaction b′ (equation 21.21). Now the over-all process will at best be very slow, since its rate is proportional to the fourth power of the small constant G. But the rate of the transition by the alternative which corresponds to the real emission of two neutrinos is considerably smaller than for the other, because much more phase space is available in the possible intermediate states than for the actual emission of neutrinos.

Plainly the possibility of the two-neutrino alternative depends on the lack of a distinction between ν_1 and ν_2 so that a β^- can occur either with emission or absorption of a neutrino. If the Majorana theory applies, and $\nu_1 \equiv \nu_2$ the double β-decay will have a lifetime several powers of 10 shorter than if $\nu_1 \not\equiv \nu_2$, and the reaction $n^* + \nu_1 \rightarrow p^* + \beta^-$ is impossible. For typical cases, like the reaction $Zr^{96} \rightarrow Mo^{96} + 2\beta^-$, some 3 or 4 Mev of energy are available for the transition, and the predicted lifetime is $\sim 10^{14}$ years on the Majorana theory, and $\sim 10^{21}$ years on the Dirac theory. The experiments are not fully conclusive, although those depending on a search in old minerals for the expected decay product and the latest experiments in which the decay electrons were directly sought now agree in favoring the longer time.

SOME NUMERICAL RELATIONS

A. WAVELENGTHS

$$\lambda = \hbar/p = \hbar/(2M_0)^{\frac{1}{2}} \times 1/E_{\text{kin.}}^{\frac{1}{2}} \quad \text{(non-relativistic)}$$

$$= \hbar c /\beta E_{\text{tot.}} \cong \hbar c/E_{\text{tot.}} \quad \text{(relativistic)}$$

λ	Non-relativistic	Relativistic
Proton	$\dfrac{4.553 \times 10^{-13}}{E_{\text{kin.}}^{\frac{1}{2}} \text{ (Mev)}}$ cm	$\dfrac{0.1972 \times 10^{-13}}{\beta E_{\text{tot.}} \text{ (Bev)}}$ cm
π-Meson $_\pm$	$\dfrac{11.81 \times 10^{-13}}{E_{\text{kin.}}^{\frac{1}{2}} \text{ (Mev)}}$ cm	$\dfrac{197.2 \times 10^{-13}}{\beta E_{\text{tot.}} \text{ (Mev)}}$ cm
Electron	$\dfrac{1.951 \times 10^{-8}}{E_{\text{kin.}}^{\frac{1}{2}} \text{ (ev)}}$ cm	$\dfrac{197.2 \times 10^{-13}}{\beta E_{\text{tot.}} \text{ (Mev)}}$ cm
γ-Ray		$\dfrac{197.2 \times 10^{-13}}{E \text{ (Mev)}}$ cm

B. AREAS

$$1 \text{ barn (b)} = 10^{-24} \text{ cm}^2; \quad 1 \text{ millibarn (mb)} = 10^{-27} \text{ cm}^2$$

$\pi\lambda^2$	Non-relativistic	Relativistic
Proton	$\dfrac{651.2}{E_{\text{kin.}} \text{ (Mev)}}$ mb	$\dfrac{1.222}{\beta^2 E_{\text{tot.}}^2 \text{ (Bev)}}$ mb
π-Meson $_\pm$	$\dfrac{4.378}{E_{\text{kin.}} \text{ (Mev)}}$ b	$\dfrac{1222}{\beta^2 E_{\text{tot.}}^2 \text{ (Mev)}}$ b
Electron	$\dfrac{1196}{E_{\text{kin.}} \text{ (Mev)}}$ b	$\dfrac{1222}{\beta^2 E_{\text{tot.}}^2 \text{ (Mev)}}$ b

C. COULOMB RADII AND ENERGIES

$$a_0 = \hbar^2/me^2 \qquad Ry = e^2/2a_0$$

$$= \left(\frac{\hbar}{mc}\right)\bigg/\left(\frac{e^2}{\hbar c}\right) \qquad = \tfrac{1}{2}\alpha^2 mc^2$$

	a_0	Ry
Electron	0.5292×10^{-8} cm	13.61 ev
π-Meson	0.1937×10^{-10} cm	3.717 kev
μ-Meson	0.2555×10^{-10} cm	2.818 kev
Proton	0.2880×10^{-11} cm	24.00 kev

D. FERMI ENERGY

Assume n identical spin $\frac{1}{2}$ particles of mass M in a square well of radius R. Then:

$$E_F = \left(\frac{3}{8\pi}\right)^{\frac{2}{3}} \frac{h^2}{2^{\frac{1}{3}}} \frac{n^{\frac{2}{3}}}{MR^2}$$

If M is the proton mass and $R = r_0 A^{\frac{1}{3}} \times 10^{-13}$ cm, where A is the mass number, then

$$E_F = \frac{76.52}{r_0^2} \left(\frac{n}{A}\right)^{\frac{2}{3}} \text{Mev}$$

If $r_0 = 1.2$,

$$E_F = 53 \left(\frac{n}{A}\right)^{\frac{2}{3}} \text{Mev}$$

E. PHYSICAL CONSTANTS (correct to one or two in the last decimal place given)

Electronic charge: $\qquad\qquad e = 4.803 \times 10^{-10}$ esu

Planck's constant/2π: $\qquad \hbar = 1.054 \times 10^{-27}$ erg-sec

Proton mass: $\qquad\qquad\quad M_p = 1.672 \times 10^{-24}$ g $= 938.2$ Mev

π-Meson mass$\pm$: $\qquad\qquad M_\pi = 2.49 \times 10^{-25}$ g $= 140$ Mev

μ-Meson mass: $\qquad\qquad M_\mu = 1.89 \times 10^{-25}$ g $= 106$ Mev

Electron mass $\qquad\qquad\quad m = 9.108 \times 10^{-28}$ g $= 0.511$ Mev

Proton-electron mass ratio: $M_p/m = 1836.2$

Speed of light in vacuum: $\qquad c = 2.998 \times 10^{10}$ cm/sec

Bohr magneton: $\qquad \dfrac{e\hbar}{2mc} = 0.9273 \times 10^{-20}$ erg/gauss

$\qquad\qquad\qquad\qquad\qquad = 5.789 \times 10^{-9}$ ev/gauss

Nuclear magneton: $\qquad \dfrac{e\hbar}{2M_p c} = 5.050 \times 10^{-24}$ erg/gauss

$\qquad\qquad\qquad\qquad\qquad = 3.152 \times 10^{-12}$ ev/gauss

π-Meson magneton: $\qquad \dfrac{e\hbar}{2M_\pi c} = 3.40 \times 10^{-23}$ erg/gauss

$\qquad\qquad\qquad\qquad\qquad = 2.12 \times 10^{-11}$ ev/gauss

μ-Meson magneton: $\qquad \dfrac{e\hbar}{2M_\mu c} = 4.48 \times 10^{-23}$ erg/gauss

$\qquad\qquad\qquad\qquad\qquad = 2.80 \times 10^{-11}$ ev/gauss

APPENDIX

TABLE OF NUCLEAR SPECIES

EXPLANATION OF THE TABLE

Column 1: Z. Atomic number of the element. The name and chemical symbol of the element appear on the same line as its atomic number.

Column 2: A. Mass number of the isotope. All isotopes are grouped under the element to which they belong.

Column 3: Stability. If the isotope occurs in nature, a number is entered in this column which gives the percentage abundance of this isotope in the natural element. If the isotope does not occur in nature, no percentage is listed. Wherever the type of radioactive disintegration has been observed, a symbol occurs denoting the nuclear process. The symbols used are:

I Isomeric transition (emission of γ-rays or conversion electrons).

K Electron capture.

β^-, β^+ Negative, positive β-particle emission.

α α-Particle emission.

n, p Emission of neutrons, protons. Delayed neutron emitters are designated both by marking the parent isotope n and the daughter I_n.

f Spontaneous fission. This process is observed for most nuclei above $Z = 85$ or so, but it is very slow compared to other instabilities. The entry f appears in the table for only those few heaviest nuclei in which the spontaneous fission rate exceeds the rate of decay by any other process.

When radioactive decay types are known which have not been assigned definitely to a mass number, the entry is omitted. There are a few exceptions, in the elements above $Z = 95$. Parentheses indicate that the enclosed quantity is uncertain. In general, uncertain assignments of various kinds are omitted.

Column 4: The measured spin of the ground state, in units of $\hbar$.

Column 5: The mass excess, $M(A, Z) - A$, in units of Mev. All values refer to the *atomic* mass, including the Z electrons.

Column 6: Estimated standard deviation of the mass defect, in units of Mev.

Column 7: W_n. Binding energy of the last neutron, in units of Mev. These are calculated values wherever possible from H to Zn; elsewhere they are measured values. An asterisk on a pair of W_n values means uncertainty as to which isotope of the pair each belongs to.

Main References

For activities: Hollander, Perlman, and Seaborg, *Revs. Mod. Phys. 25*, 469, (1953), and the series *Nuclear Abstracts.*

For spins: Klinkenberg, *Revs. Mod. Phys. 24*, 63 (1952).

For abundances: Bainbridge, in Segrè (Ed.), *Experimental Nuclear Physics*, Vol. I, John Wiley & Sons, New York, 1953.

For masses: The masses up to about ^{15}P are based on measurements of nuclear disintegration energy; those from about S to Xe, on accurate mass-spectrographic work. From Ce to Th, the masses are based on mass-spectrographic work of much less precision and may be expected to have errors as high as 1.5 Mev. From Pb to the end of the table, the relative values are obtained in radioactive decay work, likely to be in error about ± 0.2 Mev between close neighbors which belong to a given radioactive series, but more between members of different series. The absolute values above Pb are based on the mass defect of Pb^{208} [after Goudsmit, *Phys. Rev. 85*, 630 (1952)] and are good to about ± 1.5 Mev at best.

Many of the mass measurements may be in error from unknown systematic causes. The errors cited are standard deviations estimated from the data, and cannot indicate the presence of additional systematic error. It is to be expected, however, that high precision will mean a low probability of large systematic error, and conversely.

Detailed references to the sources used for these mass tables and a late compilation of all relevant data (but *no* explicit mass tables) are to be found in a series of articles in the *Revs. Mod. Phys. 26*, 327–472 (1954).

A complete table of masses in a form similar to this one has been published by A. Wapstra and J. R. Huizenga, *Physica* 21, 367 (1955). His values are in substantial agreement with those given here, though above $A = 40$ there are a number of important disagreements.

Table of Nuclear Species

Mass-energy conversion:
  1 electron mass $= 0.51098$ Mev
  1 atomic mass unit $= \frac{1}{16}$ mass of O^{16} $= 931.14$ Mev
  H^1 atomic mass (proton $+$ electron) $= 1.00814$ atomic mass unit $=$ 938.72 Mev

These factors have an error of less than 2 units in the last place given.
[See DuMond and Cohen, *Revs. Mod. Phys.* 27, 363 (1955)]

Table of Nuclear Species (Continued)

Z	A	Stability	Spin	Mass Excess (Mev)	Error	W_n (Mev)
0. Neutron, n						
	1	β^-	½	8.369	0.003	
1. Hydrogen, H						
	1	99.985	½	7.584	0.003	
	2	0.015	1	13.720	0.006	2.23
	3	β^-	½	15.83	0.01	6.26
2. Helium, He						
	3	$10^{-5} - 10^{-4}$	½	15.81	0.01	
	4	$\sim$100	0	3.61	0.01	20.5
	5	n		12.88	0.08	
	6	β^-		19.40	0.04	2.0
3. Lithium, Li						
	4	p				
	5	p		13.17	0.15	
	6	7.5	1	15.85	0.02	5.5
	7	92.5 I	³⁄₂	16.97	0.02	7.2
	8	β^-		23.30	0.03	2.0
	9	β^-		28.1	1	3.6
4. Beryllium, Be						
	7	K		·17.83	0.02	
	8	α		7.31	0.03	18.9
	9	100	³⁄₂	14.01	0.03	1.7
	10	β^-		15.56	0.03	7.8
5. Boron, B						
	8	β^+		25.1	0.3	
	9	p		15.08	0.03	18.4
	10	18.7	3	15.00	0.03	8.4
	11	81.3	³⁄₂	11.91	0.02	11.5
	12	β^-		16.91	0.02	3.4
6. Carbon, C						
	10	β^+		18.9	0.1	
	11	β^+		13.89	0.02	13.4
	12	98.89	0	3.56	0.02	18.7
	13	1.11	½	6.96	0.02	6.0
	14	β^-	0	7.15	0.01	8.1
	15	β^-		13.3	0.5	2.2
7. Nitrogen, N						
	12	β^+		21.2	0.1	
	13	β^+		9.18	0.01	20.4
	14	99.635	1	7.00	0.01	10.6
	15	0.365	½	4.53	0.01	10.8
	16	β^-		10.3	0.5	2.6
	17	β^-		13.0	0.2	5.7

Table of Nuclear Species (Continued)

Z A	Stability	Spin	Mass Excess (Mev)	Error	W_n (Mev)
8. Oxygen, O					
14	β^+		12.1	0.1	
15	β^+		7.23	0.01	13.2
16	99.759	0	0	Standard	15.60
17	0.037	$\frac{5}{2}$	4.221	0.006	4.15
18	0.204	0	4.52	0.02	8.1
19	β^-		8.9	03.	4.3
9. Fluorine, F					
17	β^+		6.988	0.005	
18	β^+		6.19	0.02	9.2
19	100	$\frac{1}{2}$	4.15	0.01	10.41
20	β^-		5.91	0.02	6.61
10. Neon, Ne					
18	β^+		10.4	0.3	
19	β^+		7.40	0.01	
20	90.9		-1.14	0.02	16.9
21	0.257	$\geq \frac{3}{2}$	0.47	0.02	6.8
22	8.8		-1.53	0.02	10.4
23	β^-		1.65	0.02	5.2
11. Sodium, Na					
20	β^+		14.2	0.3	
21	β^+		3.99	0.04	
22	β^+	3	1.31	0.02	5.7
23	100	$\frac{3}{2}$	-2.74	0.02	12.4
24	β^-	4	-1.33	0.02	7.0
25	β^-		-2.1	0.3	
12. Magnesium, Mg					
23	β^+		1.35	0.02	
24	78.6		-6.86	0.02	16.5
25	10.1	$\frac{5}{2}$	-5.82	0.02	7.3
26	11.3		-8.56	0.03	11.1
27	β^-	$(\frac{1}{2})$	-6.63	0.03	6.4
28	β^-		-6.78	0.05	
13. Aluminum, Al					
24	β^+		7.2	0.5	
25	β^+		-1.57	0.09	
26	β^+		-4.54	0.03	
27	100	$\frac{5}{2}$	-9.24	0.03	12.8
28	β^-		-8.60	0.03	7.7
29	β^-		-9.4	0.2	
14. Silicon, Si					
27	β^+		-4.41	0.03	
28	92.3		-13.25	0.03	
29	4.7	$\frac{1}{2}$	-13.36	0.03	8.4
30	3.0		-15.61	0.03	10.6

Table of Nuclear Species (Continued)

Z	A	Stability	Spin	Mass Excess (Mev)	Error	W_n (Mev)
	31	β^-		-13.84	0.04	6.6
	32	β^-		-14.8	0.09	
15. Phosphorus, P						
	28	β^+				
	29	β^+		-8.39	0.03	
	30	β^+		-11.28	0.06	
	31	100	$\frac{1}{2}$	-15.32	0.04	12.1
	32	β^-		-14.88	0.04	7.9
	33	β^-		-16.61	0.04	10.1
	34	β^-		-14.8	0.3	
16. Sulfur, S						
	31	β^+		-9.9	0.1	
	32	95.1	0	-16.537	0.009	14.7
	33	0.7	$\frac{3}{2}$	-16.64	0.05	8.5
	34	4.2		-19.78	0.05	11.5
	35	β^-	$\frac{3}{2}$	-18.42	0.05	7.0
	36	0.016		-19.05	0.06	
	37	β^-				
17. Chlorine, Cl						
	32	β^+				
	33	β^+				
	34	$\beta^+ I$				
	35	75.4	$\frac{3}{2}$	-18.59	0.05	
	36	β^-	2	-18.76	0.06	8.57
	37	24.6	$\frac{3}{2}$	-20.80	0.05	10.4
	38	β^-		-18.54	0.06	6.1
	39	β^-				
18. Argon, A						
	35	β^+				
	36	0.337		-19.55	0.03	
	37	K		-19.98	0.05	8.8
	38	0.063		-23.36	0.04	11.8
	39	β^-				
	40	99.600		-23.33	0.14	
	41	β^-		-20.85	0.04	6.1
	42	β^-				
19. Potassium, K						
	38	β^+		-17.5	0.2	
	39	93.1	$\frac{3}{2}$	-22.29	0.03	13.2
	40	0.0119 $\beta^- K$ 1.31×10^9 yr	4	-21.84	0.07	7.7
	41	6.9 I	$\frac{3}{2}$	-23.37	0.04	10.1
	42	β^-	2	-22.36	0.09	7.4
	43	β^-				
	44	β^-				
	45	K				

Table of Nuclear Species (Continued)

Z A	Stability	Spin	Mass Excess (Mev)	Error	W_n (Mev)
20. Calcium, Ca					
39	β^+		−15.4	0.4	
40	97.0		−23.16	0.1	15.8
41	K		−22.9	0.2	8.4
42	0.64		−25.92	0.04	11.4
43	0.14	⁷⁄₂	−25.60	0.06	8.0
44	2.1		−28.64	0.06	11.4
45	β^-		−27.59	0.06	7.3
46	0.0033				
47	β^-				
48	0.18		−30.00	0.09	
49	β^-				
21. Scandium, Sc					
40	β^+				
41	β^+		−17.0	0.2	
43	β^+				
44	$I\ \beta^+\ K$				
45	100	⁷⁄₂	−27.84	0.05	
46	$I\ \beta^-$				
47	β^-				
48	β^-		−31.39	0.06	
49	β^-				
22. Titanium, Ti					
44	K				
45	$\beta^+\ K$				
46	7.87		−30.76	0.05	13.3
47	7.25		−31.03	0.09	8.6
48	73.9		−34.34	0.06	11.7
49	5.56	⁷⁄₂	−33.91	0.05	7.9
50	5.43		−36.53	0.04	11.0
51	β^-				
23. Vanadium, V					
46	β^+				
47	β^+				
48	$\beta^+\ K$		−30.29	0.06	
49	K				
50	0.24	6	−34.0	0.2	
51	99.76	⁷⁄₂	−36.76	0.05	11.1
52	$I\ \beta^-$		−35.70	0.06	7.3
53	β^-				
24. Chromium, Cr					
48	K				
49	β^+		−30.3	0.2	
50	4.3		−35.29	0.06	13.4
51	K		−36.01	0.05	9.1

Table of Nuclear Species (Continued)

Z	A	Stability	Spin	Mass Excess (Mev)	Error	W_n (Mev)
	52	83.8		−39.97	0.08	12.3
	53	9.5 I	$\frac{3}{2}$	−39.37	0.07	7.8
	54	2.4		−40.7	0.2	9.7
	55	β^-				
25. Manganese, Mn						
	50	β^+				
	51	β^+				
	52	$I\ \beta^+\ K$		−34.83	0.08	
	53			−38.77	0.07	12.3
	54	$I\ K$		−39.3	0.2	8.9
	55	100	$\frac{5}{2}$	−41.2	0.2	10.2
	56	β^-		−39.82	0.06	7.1
	57	β^-				
26. Iron, Fe						
	52	β^+				
	53	β^+		−34.6	0.2	
	54	5.8		−40.00	0.05	13.8
	55	K		−40.93	0.06	9.3
	56	91.7		−44.02	0.09	11.5
	57	2.2 I		−43.22	0.08	7.6
	58	0.3		−44.7	0.4	9.8
	59	β^-		−43.8	0.3	7.5
27. Cobalt, Co						
	54	β^+				
	55	$\beta^+\ K$		−37.47	0.06	
	56	β^+		−39.42	0.09	
	57	β^+	$\frac{7}{2}$			
	58	$I\ \beta^+\ K$				
	59	100	$\frac{7}{2}$	−45.4	0.3	10.2
	60	$I\ \beta^-$		−44.7	0.3	7.7
	61	β^-		−46.1	0.2	9.8
	62	$I\ \beta^-$				
28. Nickel, Ni						
	56	β^+				
	57	$\beta^+\ K$		−38.1	0.2	
	58	68.0		−43.34	0.09	11.7
	59	K		−43.97	0.08	9.0
	60	26.3		−47.5	0.3	11.9
	61	1.13		−47.4	0.2	8.7
	62	3.66		−49.53	0.08	10.5
	63	β^-		−47.18	0.06	6.0
	64	1.01		−48.84	0.07	10.0
	65	β^-		−45.99	0.06	5.5
	66	β^-				

Table of Nuclear Species (Continued)

Z A	Stability	Spin	Mass Excess (Mev)	Error	W_n (Mev)
29. Copper, Cu					
58	(β^+) (K)				
59	β^+				
60	β^+				
61	$\beta^+ K$				
62	β^+				
63	69.1	$\tfrac{3}{2}$	−47.25	0.06	10.8
64	$\beta^- \beta^+ K$				7.9
65	30.9	$\tfrac{3}{2}$	−48.09	0.06	9.8
66	β^-				
67	β^-				
68	β^-				
30. Zinc, Zu					
62	$\beta^+ K$				
63	$\beta^+ K$		−43.87	0.06	
64	48.89		−46.98	0.02	4.5
65	$\beta^+ K$		−46.71	0.06	8.1
66	27.82		−49.15	0.06	10.8
67	4.1 I	$\tfrac{5}{2}$	−48.2	0.4	7.4
68	18.5		−47.6	0.6	7.8
69	$I \beta^-$				
70	0.62		−50.2	1.6	9.2
71	β^-				
72	β^-				
31. Gallium, Ga					
64	β^+				
65	β^+				
66	$\beta^+ K$		−42.94	0.05	
67	K		−47.24	0.05	
68	β^+ (K)		−46.58	0.06	
69	60.2	$\tfrac{3}{2}$	−48.62	0.05	10.1*
70	β^-		−47.92	0.05	
71	39.8	$\tfrac{3}{2}$	−48.86	0.08	9.0*
72	β^-		−47.56	0.05	
73	β^-		−48.2	0.2	
32. Germanium, Ge					
66	(β^+)				
67	β^+				
68	K				
69	$\beta^+ K$		−45.27	0.04	
70	20.52		−49.94	0.06	
71	K		−48.60	0.08	
72	27.43 I		−51.57	0.06	
73	7.76	$\tfrac{9}{2}$	−49.64	0.04	
74	36.54		−51.53	0.05	

Table of Nuclear Species (Continued)

Z	A	Stability	Spin	Mass Excess (Mev)	Error	W_n (Mev)
	75	$I\ \beta^-$		-49.43	0.06	
	76	7.76		-50.67	0.05	
	77	$I\ \beta^-$		-48.43	0.05	
	78	β^-				
33. Arsenic, As						
	70	β^+				
	71	$\beta^+\ K$				
	72	$\beta^+\ K$		-47.21	0.05	
	73	K		-49.25	0.05	
	74	$\beta^-\ \beta^+\ K$		-48.84	0.09	
	75	100	$\frac{3}{2}$	-50.56	0.05	10.1
	76	$\beta^-\ (\beta^+)$		-49.46	0.05	
	77	β^-		-50.90	0.05	
	78	β^-				
	79	β^-				
34. Selenium, Se						
	70	β^+				
	72	K				
	73	$\beta^+\ K$		-46.57	0.05	
	74	0.87		-50.10	0.07	
	75	K		-49.67	0.04	
	76	9.0		-52.55	0.05	
	77	$7.6\ I$	$\frac{1}{2}$	$-(51.60)$	0.05	
	78	23.52		(-53.70)	0.05	
	79	$I\ \beta^-$	$\frac{7}{2}$	-52.31	0.05	
	80	49.8		-53.96	0.05	
	81	$I\ \beta^-$		-52.33	0.05	
	82	9.2		-53.22	0.05	9.8
	83	$I\ \beta^-$				
	84	β^-				
35. Bromine, Br						
	75	$\beta^+\ K$		-46.95	0.07	
	76	β^+		-47.96	0.07	
	77	$\beta^+\ K$		-50.24	0.07	
	78	β^+		-50.19	0.14	
	79	50.5	$\frac{3}{2}$	-52.47	0.05	10.6
	80	$I\ \beta^-\ \beta^+\ K$		-52.07	0.06	
	81	49.5	$\frac{3}{2}$	-53.70	0.05	10.0
	82	β^-				
	83	β^-		-54.39	0.06	
	84	β^-		-52.70	0.06	
	85	β^-				
	87	$\beta^-\ n$				
	88	β^-				
	89	$\beta^-\ n$				

Table of Nuclear Species (Continued)

Z	A	Stability	Spin	Mass Excess (Mev)	Error	W_n (Mev)
36. Krypton, Kr						
	77	$\beta^+ K$				
	78	0.35		-51.09	0.08	
	79	$I \beta^+ K$		-50.59	0.06	
	80	2.27		-54.06		
	81	$I K$				
	82	11.6		-56.18	0.06	
	83	11.5 I	$\frac{9}{2}$	-55.32	0.06	
	84	56.9		-57.40	0.6	
	85	$I \beta^-$		-55.92	0.08	
	86	17.4		-57.47	0.07	
	87	$\beta^- I_n$		-54.94	0.16	
	88	β^-				
	89	$\beta^- I_n$				
	90	β^-				
	91	β^-				
	92	β^-				
	93	β^-				
	94	β^-				
	95	β^-				
	96	β^-				
	97	(β^-)				
37. Rubidium, Rb						
	81	$\beta^+ K$				
	82	$I \beta^+ K$				
	83	K				
	84	$I \beta^- \beta^+ K$				
	85	72.2 I	$\frac{5}{2}$	-56.9	0.3	
	86	$I \beta^-$	2			
	87	27.8 β^-	$\frac{3}{2}$	-58.8	0.2	
		$4-6 \times 10^{10}$ yr				
	88	β^-				
	89	β^-				
	90	β^-				
	91	$I \beta^-$				
	92	β^-				
	93	β^-				
	94	β^-				
	95	β^-				
	97	β^-				
38. Strontium, Sr						
	81	β^+				
	82	K				
	83	β^+				
	84	0.5		-55.77	0.13	

Table of Nuclear Species (Continued)

Z	A	Stability	Spin	Mass Excess (Mev)	Error	$(W_n$ Mev)
	85	$I\ K$				
	86	9.9		−58.81	0.10	9.5*
	87	7.0 I	$\frac{9}{2}$	−58.88	0.07	8.4
	88	82.6		−61.38	0.1	11.2*
	89	β^-				
	90	β^-				
	91	β^-				
	92	β^-				
	93	β^-				
	94	β^-				
	97	β^-				
39. Yttrium, Y						
	82	β^+				
	83	β^+				
	84	$\beta^+\ K$				
	85	β^+				
	86	β^+				
	87	$I\ (\beta^+)\ K$				
	88	$I\ \beta^+\ K$				
	89	100 I	$\frac{1}{2}$	−61.26	0.10	
	90	β^-				
	91	$I\ \beta^-$				
	92	β^-				
	93	β^-				
	94	β^-				
	95	(β^-)				
	97	β^-				
40. Zirconium, Zr						
	86	K				
	87	$\beta^+\ K$				
	88	(K)				
	89	$I\ \beta^+$				
	90	51.5		−60.15	0.23	12.0
	91	11.2	$\frac{5}{2}$			7.2
	92	17.1				8.7
	93	β^-				
	94	17.4				
	95	β^-				
	96	2.8				
	97	β^-				
41. Niobium, Nb (Cb)						
	90	β^+				
	91	$I\ K$				
	92	β^-				
	93	100 I	$\frac{9}{2}$	−60.15	0.08	8.7
	94	$I\ \beta^-$				7.3

Table of Nuclear Species (Continued)

Z	A	Stability	Spin	Mass Excess (Mev)	Error	W_n (Mev)
	95	$I \beta^-$				
	96	β^-				
	97	$I \beta^-$				
	99	β^-				
42.	Molybdenum, Mo					
	90	β^+				
	91	$I \beta^+$				
	92	15.9				13.3
	93	$I K$				8.3
	94	9.1		−61.2	0.7	
	95	15.7	$5\!/\!2$			
	96	16.5		−59.6	0.4	
	97	9.4	$5\!/\!2$			7.1
	98	23.8		−59.5	0.4	
	99	β^-				
	100	9.6		−57.2	0.4	
	101	β^-				
	102	β^-				
	105	β^-				
43.	Technetium, Tc					
	92	$\beta^+ K$				
	93	$\beta^+ K$				
	94	$I \beta^+ K$				
	95	$I \beta^+ K$				
	96	$I K$				
	97	$I (K)$				
	98	(K)				
	99	$I \beta^-$	$9\!/\!2$			
	100	β^-				
	101	β^-				
	102	β^-				
	105	β^-				
44.	Ruthenium, Ru					
	95	$\beta^+ K$				
	96	5.9				
	97	K				
	98	1.91				
	99	12.70	$5\!/\!2$			
	100	12.69				
	101	17.01	$5\!/\!2$			
	102	31.52				
	103	β^-				
	104	18.67				
	105	β^-				

Table of Nuclear Species (Continued)

Z	A	Stability	Spin	Mass Excess (Mev)	Error	W_n (Mev)
	106	β^-				
	107	β^-				
45.	Rhodium, Rh					
	99	β^+				
	100	β^+ K				
	101	K				
	102	β^- β^+ (K)				
	103	100 I	½			9.4
	104	I β^-				6.8
	105	I β^-		−56.8	0.2	
	106	β^-		−55.3	0.3	
	107	β^-				
	109	β^-				
46.	Palladium, Pd					
	100	K				
	101	β^+ K				
	102	0.96		−58.2	0.1	
	103	K				
	104	10.97		−59.0	0.1	
	105	22.23 I	⅝	−57.4	0.2	
	106	27.33		−58.8	0.2	
	107	β^-				
	108	26.71		−57.7	0.1	
	109	I β^-				
	110	11.81		−56.2	0.1	
	111	I β^-				
	112	β^-				
	113	β^-				
47.	Silver, Ag					
	103	β^+				
	104	β^+				
	105	K				
	106	I β^+ K		−55.9	0.2	
	107	51.4 I	½	−57.1	0.2	
	108	β^-		−55.7	0.1	7.0
	109	48.6 I	½	−56.4	0.5	9
	110	I β^-		−54.4	0.2	
	111	I β^-		−55.02	0.14	
	112	β^-				
	113	β^-				
	114	β^-				
	115	β^-				
48.	Cadmium, Cd					
	104	β^+				
	105	β^+ K				

Table of Nuclear Species (Continued)

Z	A	Stability	Spin	Mass Excess (Mev)	Error	W_n (Mev)
	106	1.22		−56.1	0.1	
	107	$\beta^+ K$		−55.37	0.14	
	108	0.88		−57.2	0.1	
	109	K		−56.26	0.14	
	110	12.4		−57.2	0.1	
	111	12.8 I	½	−56.1	0.1	
	112	24.1		−57.0	0.2	
	113	12.3 I β^-	½	−55.3	0.1	6.6
	114	28.9		−55.9	0.1	
	115	I β^-		−54.10	0.11	
	116	7.6				
	117	I β^-				
	118	β^-				
49. Indium, In						
	107	K				
	108	K				
	109	$\beta^+ K$				
	110	I β^+		−53.26	0.13	
	111	K		−55.2	0.2	
	112	I $\beta^- \beta^+ K$		−54.2	0.2	
	113	4.2 I (K)	9⁄2	−55.5	0.1	
	114	I $\beta^- \beta^+ K$		−54.22	0.09	
	115	95.8 I β^- ∼ 6 × 10¹⁴ yr.	9⁄2	−55.5	0.1	9
	116	I β^-		−53.60	0.14	6.6
	117	I β^-		−53.64	0.14	
	118	β^-				
	119	β^-		−51.60	0.2	
50. Tin, Sn						
	108	K				
	111	$\beta^+ K$		−55.2	0.5	
	112	1.0				
	113	I $\beta^+ K$		−55.02	0.13	
	114	0.6		−56.4	0.6	
	115	0.3	½	−55.8	0.2	
	116	14.2		−56.5	0.1	
	117	7.6 I	½	−55.4	0.1	
	118	24.0		−56.1	0.2	9.1
	119	8.6 I	½	−54.8	0.1	6.6
	120	33.0		−55.3	0.1	
	121	I β^-		−53.12	0.14	6.2
	122	4.7		−53.5	0.2	
	123	I β^-		−51.2	0.2	
	124	6.0		−51.3	0.1	8.5
	125	I β^-				

Table of Nuclear Species (Continued)

Z	A	Stability	Spin	Mass Excess (Mev)	Error	W_n (Mev)
	126	β^-				
	127	β^-				
51. Antimony, Sb						
	116	β^+				
	117	K				
	118	$I \ \beta^+$				
	119	K				
	120	$(I) \ \beta^+ \ K$		-52.6	0.3	
	121	57.2	$\frac{5}{2}$	-53.4	0.2	9.2
	122	$I \ \beta^-$		-52.1	0.1	6.6
	123	42.8	$\frac{7}{2}$	-53.1	0.3	
	124	$I \ \beta^-$		-50.3	0.2	
	125	β^-		-50.8	0.3	
	126	β^-				
	127	β^-				
	129	β^-				
	131	β^-				
	132	β^-				
	133	β^-				
52. Tellurium, Te						
	118	K				
	119	K				
	120	0.09		-53.2	0.2	
	121	$I \ K$				
	122	2.5		-54.1	0.1	
	123	$0.9 \ I$	$\frac{1}{2}$	-52.4	0.4	
	124	4.6		-53.3	0.1	
	125	$7.0 \ I$	$\frac{1}{2}$	-51.6	0.3	
	126	18.7		-52.0	0.1	
	127	$I \ \beta^-$		-50.2	0.2	
	128	31.8		-49.8	0.1	
	129	$I \ \beta^-$				
	130	34.5		-48.0	0.1	
	131	$I \ \beta^-$		-46.5	0.4	
	132	β^-				
	133	$I \ \beta^-$				
	134	β^-				
	135	β^-				
53. Iodine, I						
	121	β^+				
	122	β^+				
	123	$(I) \ K$				
	124	$\beta^+ \ K$		-49.6	0.3	
	125	K		-51.5	0.3	
	126	$\beta^- \ \beta^+ \ K$		-50.16	0.13	

Table of Nuclear Species (Continued)

Z	A	Stability	Spin	Mass Excess (Mev)	Error	W_n (Mev)
	127	100	$\frac{5}{2}$	−50.4	0.1	
	128	$\beta^-\,K$		−49.70	0.10	
	129	β^-	$\frac{7}{2}$	−50.01	0.13	
	130	β^-		−48.22	0.10	
	131	β^-		−48.6	0.4	
	132	β^-				
	133	β^-				
	134	β^-				
	135	β^-				
	136	β^-				
	137	$\beta^-\,n$				
	138	β^-				
	139	β^-				
54.	Xenon, Xe					
	121	β^+				
	122	β^+				
	123	β^+				
	124	0.096		−50.5	0.1	
	125	K				
	126	0.090		−51.4	0.1	
	127	$I\,K$				
	128	1.92		−51.7	0.1	
	129	26.4 I	$\frac{1}{2}$	−50.3	0.2	
	130	4.08		−51.2	0.1	
	131	21.2 I	$\frac{3}{2}$	−49.6	0.4	
	132	26.9		−50.1	0.1	
	133	$I\,\beta^-$				
	134	10.4		−48.4	0.1	
	135	$I\,\beta^-$				
	136	8.87		−46.1	0.1	
	137	$\beta^-\,I_n$				
	138	β^-				
	139	β^-				
	140	β^-				
	141	β^-				
	143	β^-				
	144	β^-				
	145	β^-				
55.	Cesium, Cs					
	123	β^+				
	125	β^+				
	127	β^+				
	128	$\beta^+\,K$				
	129	K				
	130	?				

Table of Nuclear Species (Continued)

Z	A	Stability	Spin	Mass Excess (Mev)	Error	W_n (Mev)
	131	K	$\frac{5}{2}$			
	132	K				
	133	100 I	$\frac{7}{2}$			9.1
	134	$I\ \beta^-$	4			
	135	$I\ \beta^-$	$\frac{7}{2}$			
	136	β^-				
	137	β^-	$\frac{7}{2}$			
	138	β^-				
	139	β^-				
	140	β^-				
	141	β^-				
	142	β^-				
	143	β^-				
	144	β^-				
	145	β^-				
56.	Barium, Ba					
	127	β^+				
	128	K				
	129	β^+				
	130	0.10				
	131	K				
	132	0.10				
	133	$I\ K$				
	134	2.4				
	135	6.6 I	$\frac{3}{2}$			
	136	7.8		-47.7	0.9	
	137	11.3 I	$\frac{3}{2}$	-46.4	0.9	
	138	71.7		-46.7	0.8	
	139	β^-				5.2
	140	β^-				
	141	β^-				
	142	β^-				
	143	β^-				
	144	β^-				
	145	β^-				
57.	Lanthanum, La					
	131	β^+				
	132	β^+				
	133	$\beta^+\ K$				
	134	$\beta^+\ K$				
	135	K				
	136	$\beta^+\ K$				
	137	(K)				
	138	0.09 $I\ K\ \beta^-$ $(2 \times 10^{11}$ yr$)$				
	139	99.91	$\frac{7}{2}$			8.8

Table of Nuclear Species (Continued)

Z	A	Stability	Spin	Mass Excess (Mev)	Error	W_n (Mev)
	140	β^-				
	141	β^-				
	142	β^-				
	143	β^-				
	144	β^-				
	145	β^-				
58. Cerium, Ce						
	133	$\beta^+ K$				
	134	K				
	135	$(\beta^+) K$				
	136	0.19				
	137	K				
	138	0.25				
	139	K				
	140	88.5		-47.6	0.8	9.1*
	141	β^-				
	142	11.1		-43.1	0.8	7.2*
	143	β^-				
	144	β^-				
	145	β^-				
	146	β^-				
59. Praseodymium, Pr						
	137	β^+				
	138	$\beta^+ K$				
	139	$\beta^+ K$				
	140	$\beta^+ (K)$				
	141	100	$\frac{5}{2}$	-45.2	0.7	9.6
	142	β^-				
	143	β^-				
	144	β^-				
	145	β^-				
	146	β^-				
60. Neodymium, Nd						
	139	$\beta^+ K$				
	140	K				
	141	$\beta^+ K$				
	142	27.1				
	143	12.2	$\frac{7}{2}$			
	144	23.9 α				
		$\sim 3 \times 10^{15}$ yr		-41.0	0.7	
	145	8.3	$\frac{7}{2}$			
	146	17.2				
	147	β^-				
	148	5.7				
	149	β^-				

Table of Nuclear Species (Continued)

Z	A	Stability	Spin	Mass Excess (Mev)	Error	W_n (Mev)
	150	5.6		-29.2	0.7	7.4
	151	β^-				
61. Promethium, Pm						
	141	β^+				
	143	K				
	145	(K)				
	146	β^-				
	147	β^-				
	148	β^-				
	149	β^-				
	150	β^-				
	151	β^-				
62. Samarium, Sm						
	144	3.2				
	145	K				
	146	α				
	147	15.1 α	$(\tfrac{5}{2})$			
		1.25×10^{11} yr				
	148	11.3				
	149	13.8	$(\tfrac{5}{2})$			
	150	7.5				
	151	β^-				
	152	26.6				
	153	β^-				
	154	22.5				
	155	β^-				
	156	β^-				
63. Europium, Eu						
	145	K				
	147	K				
	148	K				
	149	K				
	150	β^+				
	151	47.8	$\tfrac{5}{2}$			
	152	$I\ \beta^-\ K$				
	153	52.2 I	$\tfrac{5}{2}$			
	154	β^-				
	155	β^-				
	156	β^-				
	157	β^-				
64. Gadolinium, Gd						
	148	α				
	149	K, α				
	150	α				
	151	K				

Table of Nuclear Species (Continued)

Z	A	Stability	Spin	Mass Excess (Mev)	Error	W_n (Mev)
	152	0.20				
	153	K				
	154	2.2				
	155	14.7				
	156	20.5				
	157	15.7				
	158	24.9				
	159	β^-				
	160	21.9				
	161	β^-				
65. Terbium, Tb						
	149	$K\ \alpha$				
	151	α				
	152	K				
	153	K				
	154	$\beta^+\ K$				
	155	K				
	156	$\beta^+\ K$				
	157	(K)				
	158	(β^+)				
	159	100	$\frac{3}{2}$			
	160	β^-				
	161	β^-				
66. Dysprosium, Dy						
	156	0.052				
	158	0.090				
	159	K				
	160	2.29 I				
	161	18.9	$(\frac{7}{2})$			
	162	25.5				
	163	25.0	$(\frac{7}{2})$			
	164	28.2				
	165	$I\ \beta^-$				
	166	β^-				
67. Holmium, Ho						
	160	$\beta^+\ K$				
	161	$(\beta^+)\ K$				
	162	$\beta^-\ K$				
	163	K				
	164	β^-				
	165	100	$\frac{7}{2}$			
	166	β^-				
68. Erbium, Er						
	160	K				
	161	K				

Table of Nuclear Species (Continued)

Z	A	Stability	Spin	Mass Excess (Mev)	Error	W_n (Mev)
	162	0.14				
	163	(β^+) (K)				
	164	1.6				
	165	K				
	166	33.4 I				
	167	22.9	$\frac{7}{2}$			
	168	27.1				
	169	β^-				
	170	14.9				
	171	β^-				
69.	Thulium, Tm					
	165	K				
	166	(β^-) β^+ K				
	167	K				
	168	(β^-) K				
	169	100 I	$\frac{1}{2}$			
	170	β^-				
	171	β^- I				
70.	Ytterbium, Yb					
	166	K				
	167	<0.002				
	168	0.14				
	169	K				
	170	3.0 I				
	171	14.3	$\frac{1}{2}$			
	172	21.8				
	173	16.1	$\frac{5}{2}$			
	174	31.8				
	175	β^-				
	176	12.7				
	177	β^-				
71.	Lutetium, Lu					
	170	K				
	171	(I) K				
	172	I β^+ K				
	173	K				
	174	β^- K				
	175	97.4	$\frac{7}{2}$			
	176	2.6 I β^- K 2.2×10^{10} yr			≥ 7	
	177	I β^-				
72.	Hafnium, Hf					
	170	β^+				
	171	K				
	172	K				

Table of Nuclear Species (Continued)

Z	A	Stability	Spin	Mass Excess (Mev)	Error	W_n (Mev)
	173	K				
	174	0.199				
	175	K				
	176	5.23 I		−7.2	3.0	
	177	18.55	½ or ¾			
	178	27.23		−6.0	1.2	
	179	13.73 I	½ or ¾			
	180	35.07 I		2.7	0.6	
	181	β^-				
73. Tantalum, Ta						
	176	K				
	177	K				
	178	$I \beta^+ K$				
	179	K				
	180	$\beta^- K$				
	181	100 I	⁷⁄₂	2.9	1.2	7.6
	182	$I \beta^-$				6.0
	183	β^-				
	184	β^-				
	185	β^-				
74. Wolfram, W						
	176	$\beta^+ K$				
	177	K				
	178	K				
	179	$I K$				
	180	0.14				
	181	K				
	182	26.4		3.1	1.0	
	183	14.4 I	½	5.5	1.2	
	184	30.6		4.8	1.0	
	185	$I \beta^-$				
	186	28.4				
	187	β^-				
	188	β^-				
75. Rhenium, Re						
	182	K				
	183	$(I) K$				
	184	$I K$				
	185	37.1	⁵⁄₂			
	186	$\beta^- K$				
	187	62.9 $\beta^- I$ $\sim 5 \times 10^{10}$ yr	⁵⁄₂			7.3*
	188	$\beta^- I$				
76. Osmium, Os						
	182	K				

Table of Nuclear Species (Continued)

Z	A	Stability	Spin	Mass Excess (Mev)	Error	W_n (Mev)
	183	K				
	184	0.02				
	185	K				
	186	1.6 I				
	187	1.6 I				
	188	13.3				
	189	16.1	½			
	190	26.4 I				
	191	β^- I				
	192	41.0				
	193	β^-				
	194	β^-				
77. Iridium, Ir						
	187	β^+ K				
	188	β^+ K				
	190	I β^+ (K)				
	191	38.5	3⁄2			
	192	I β^-				
	193	61.5 I	3⁄2			7.8*
	194	β^-				
78. Platinum, Pt						
	188	K				
	190	0.01 α ($\sim 5 \times 10^{11}$ yr)				
	191	K				
	192	0.8				
	193	K I				
	194	32.8		23.8	1.3	9.5
	195	33.7 I	½	24.4	0.7	6.1
	196	25.4		25.6	0.6	8.2
	197	β^- I				
	198	7.2				
	199	β^-				
79. Gold, Au						
	191	K				
	192	β^+ K				
	193	K				
	194	β^+ K				
	195	I K				
	196	I β^- K				
	197	100 I	3⁄2			7.9
	198	β^-				6.4
	199	β^-				
	200	β^-				
	201	β^-				
	203	β^-				

Table of Nuclear Species (Continued)

Z	A	Stability	Spin	Mass Excess (Mev)	Error	W_n (Mev)
80.	Mercury, Hg					
	193	$K\,I$				
	195	$K\,I$				
	196	0.15				
	197	$I\,K$				
	198	10.02				
	199	16.8 I	½			
	200	23.1				
	201	13.2	¾			6.4
	202	29.80				
	203	β^-				
	204	6.85				
	205	β^-				
81.	Thallium, Tl					
	198	K				
	199	K				
	200	K				
	201	K				
	202	K				
	203	29.5	½			8.8
	204	$\beta^-\,K$				6.5
	205	70.5	½			7.6
	206	β^-		37.9		6.2
	207 (AcC″)	β^-		40.0		
	208 (ThC″)	β^-		43.7		
	209	β^-		47.6		
	210 (RaC″)	β^-		52.4		
82.	Lead, Pb					
	198	$(\beta^+)\,(K)$				
	199	K				
	200	K				
	201	$I\,K$				
	203	K				
	204	1.5 I				
	205	$K > 10^{10}$ yr				
	206 (RaG)	23.6		36.2		8.2
	207 (AcD)	22.6 I	½	38.1		6.8
	208 (ThD)	52.3		38.7	1.4	7.3
	209	β^-		44.1		3.9
	210 (RaD)	β^-		46.4		
	211 (AcB)	β^-		51.8		
	212 (ThB)	β^-		54.8		
	214 (RaB)	β^-		62.7		
83.	Bismuth, Bi					
	198	$K\,\alpha$				

Table of Nuclear Species (Continued)

Z	A	Stability	Spin	Mass Excess (Mev)	Error	W_n (Mev)
	199	$K\ \alpha$				
	200	K				
	201	$(I)\ K$				
	202	K				
	203	K				
	204	K				
	205	K				
	206	K				
	207	K				
	208	(K)				
	209	100 α	$\frac{9}{2}$	43.4	1.4	7.4
		2×10^{17} yr				
	210 (RaE)	$I\ \beta^-\ \alpha$	(0)	46.4		4.1
	211 (AcC)	$\beta^-\ \alpha$		50.4		
	212 (ThC)	$\beta^-\ \alpha$				
	213	$\beta^-\ \alpha$		57.3		
	214 (RaC)	$\beta^-\ \alpha$		61.7		
	215	β^-				
84.	Polonium, Po					
	200	α				
	201	α				
	202	$K\ \alpha$				
	203	K				
	204	$K\ \alpha$				
	205	$K\ \alpha$				
	206	$K\ \alpha$				
	207	$K\ \alpha$				
	208	α				
	209	$K\ \alpha$		45.0		
	210 (RaF)	α		45.2		
	211 (AcC')	$I\ \alpha$		49.3		
	212 (ThC')	α		51.1		
	213	α		56.1		
	214 (RaC')	α		57.9		
	215 (AcA)	$(\beta^-)\ \alpha$		62.9		
	216 (ThA)	$\beta^-\ \alpha$		65.3		
	218 (RaA)	$\beta^-\ \alpha$		72.4		
85.	Astatine, At					
	204	$K\ (\alpha)$				
	205	$(K)\ (\alpha)$				
	206	K				
	207	$K\ \alpha$				
	208	$I\ K\ \alpha$				
	209	$K\ \alpha$				
	210	K				

Table of Nuclear Species (Continued)

Z	A	Stability	Spin	Mass Excess (Mev)	Error	W_n (Mev)
	211	$K\ \alpha$				
	212	α				
	214	α		58.9		
	215	α		62.2		
	216	α				
	217	α		68.1		
	218	$\beta^-\ \alpha$		72.0		
	219	$\beta^-\ \alpha$				
86.	Emanation, Em (Radon, Rn)					
	206	α				
	207	α				
	208	$K\ \alpha$				
	209	$K\ \alpha$				
	210	$K\ \alpha$				
	211	$K\ \alpha$				
	212	α				
	215	α				
	216	α		62.9		
	217	α		67.7		
	218	α		68.8		
	219 (An)	α		73.5		
	220 (Tn)	α		75.3		
	221	$\beta^-\ \alpha$				
	222 (Rn)	α		81.6		
87.	Francium, Fr					
	211	K				
	212	$K\ \alpha$				
	218	α		70.4		
	219	α		73.3		
	220	α		75.5		
	221	α		78.1		
	222	β^-				
	223 (AcK)	$\beta^-\ \alpha$		84.4		
88.	Radium, Ra					
	213	α				
	219	α				
	220	α		74.2		
	221	α		78.2		
	222	α		79.0		
	223 (AcX)	α		83.1		
	224 (ThX)	α		84.7		
	225	β^-		87.9		
	226 (Ra)	α		90.1		
	227	β^-				
	228 (MsTh$_1$)	β^-		96.9		
	229	(β^-)				

Table of Nuclear Species (Continued)

Z	A	Stability	Spin	Mass Excess (Mev)	Error	W_n (Mev)
89. Actinium, Ac						
	222	α		81.1		
	223	$K\ \alpha$		83.6		
	224	$K\ \alpha$		85.4		
	225	α		87.7		
	226	β^-				
	227 (Ac)	$\beta^-\ \alpha$	$\frac{3}{2}$	93.4		
	228 (MsTh₂)	$\beta^-\ (\alpha)$		96.4		
	229	β^-				
90. Thorium, Th						
	223	α				
	224	α		85.1		
	225	$K\ \alpha$		88.5		
	226	α		89.0		
	227 (RdAc)	α		93.2		
	228 (RdTh)	α		93.9		
	229	α		96.4		
	230 (Io)	α		98.4		
	231 (UY)	β^-		102.4		
	232 (Th)	100 $\alpha\ \beta^-$ 1.39×10^{10} yr		104.8		6.0
	233	β^-		107.4		4.9
	234 (UX₁)	β^-		109.5		
	235	β^-				
91. Protoactinium, Pa						
	226	α		91.8		
	227	$K\ \alpha$		93.8		
	228	$K\ \alpha$		95.2		
	229	$K\ \alpha$		97.0		
	230	$\beta^-\ K\ \alpha$		100.6		
	231 (Pa)	α	$\frac{3}{2}$	102.2		
	232	β^-		104.0		
	233	β^-		105.8		
	234 (UZ)(UX₂)	$\beta^-\ I$ (UX₂)		108.5		
	235	β^-				
	237	(β^-)				
92. Uranium, U						
	227	α				
	228	$K\ \alpha$		95.6		
	229	$K\ \alpha$		98.6		
	230	α		98.6		
	231	$K\ \alpha$				
	232	α		102.9		
	233	α	$\frac{5}{2}$	105.0		
	234 (UII)	0.0058 α 2.48×10^5 yr		106.9		

Table of Nuclear Species (Continued)

Z A	Stability	Spin	Mass Excess (Mev)	Error	W_n (Mev)
235 (AcU)	0.72 α	$\frac{5}{2}$	110.7		
	7.13 $\times$ 10^8 yr				
236	α				
	2.39 $\times$ 10^7 yr				
237	β^-		114.9		
238 (UI)	99.28 α		117.3		5.8
	4.51 $\times$ 10^9 yr				
239	β^-		121.7		4.6
240	β^-				
93. Neptunium, Np					
231	$K\ \alpha$		103.8		
232	K				
233	$K\ \alpha$				
234	K				
235	$K\ \alpha$				
236	$\beta^-\ K$				
237	$I\ \alpha$	$\frac{5}{2}$	114.2		
238	β^-		117.5		
239	β^-				
240	β^-				
241	β^-				
94. Plutonium, Pu					
232	$K\ \alpha$		105.9		
234	$K\ \alpha$		108.3		
235	$K\ \alpha$				
236	α		112.3		
237	K				
238	α		116.1		
239	$I\ \alpha$		119.7		
240	α				
241	$\beta^-\ \alpha$		123.3		
242	α				
243	β^-				
95. Americium, Am					
237	$K\ \alpha$				
238	K				
239	$K\ \alpha$		120.4		
240	K				
241	α				
242	$I\ \beta^-\ K\ \alpha$		126.5		
243	α				
244	β^-				
96. Curium, Cm					
238	$\alpha\ K$				
239	K				

Table of Nuclear Species (Continued)

Z	A	Stability	Spin	Mass Excess (Mev)	Error	W_n (Mev)
	240	$K\ \alpha$		122.4		
	241	K				
	242	α				
	243	α				
	244	α				
	(245)	α				
	246					
	247					
97.	Berkelium, Bk					
	243	$K\ \alpha$				
	244	K				
	245	$K\ \alpha$				
	246	K				
	249	$\beta^-\ (\alpha)$				
	250	β^-				
98.	Californium, Cf					
	244	$K\ \alpha$				
	246	α				
	247	K				
	248	α				
	249	α				
	250	α				
	251	(α)				
	252	α				
	253	β^-				
99.	Einsteinium, E					
	246	K				
	247	$K\ \alpha$				
	253	α				
	254	β^-				
	255					
100.	Fermium, Fm					
	(254)	α				
	(255)	α				
	256	α f				
101.	Mendelevium, Mv					
	(256)	K				

AUTHOR INDEX

SUBJECT INDEX